MILLER'S
Collectors Cars
PRICE GUIDE

MILLER'S
Collectors
Cars
PRICE GUIDE

1999-2000

Volume VIII

Consultant: Judith Miller

General Editor: Dave Selby

Foreword by
The Earl of March

MILLER'S COLLECTORS CARS PRICE GUIDE 1999–2000

Created and designed by
Miller's Publications
The Cellars, High Street
Tenterden, Kent TN30 6BN
Telephone: 01580 766411

Consultant: Judith Miller

General Editor: Dave Selby
Editorial and Production Co-ordinator: Sue Boyd
Editorial Assistants: Jo Wood, Nancy Charles
Designer: Kari Reeves
Advert Designer: Simon Cook
Advertising Executives: Jill Jackson, Melinda Williams
Production Assistants: Gillian Charles, Caroline Bugeja
Additional Photography: Ian Booth, Neill Bruce, Simon Clay, Goddard Picture Library,
David Gooley, Bruno Grégoire, Stewart Harvey,
Gordon Jolley, Alberto Martinez, Bob Masters,
David Merewether, Doug Mitchel, Robin Saker,
Marc Souvrain, Tom Wood (National Motor Museum), Werkfoto
Indexer: Hilary Bird

First published in Great Britain in 1998
by Miller's, a division of Mitchell Beazley,
imprints of Reed Consumer Books Limited
Michelin House, 81 Fulham Road, London SW3 6RB
and Auckland

A CIP catalogue record for this book is
available from the British Library

ISBN 1 84000 057 0

Illustrations and film output by CK Litho, Whitstable, Kent
and Perfect Image, Hurst Green, E. Sussex
Colour origination by Pica Colour Separation Overseas Pte. Ltd, Singapore
Printed and bound by Toppan Printing Co., (HK) Ltd, China

Front cover illustrations:

1948 Alfa Romeo 6C 2500 Super Sport. **Est £30,000–40,000** *Pou*
Nelson Piquet's 1986 Hungarian Grand Prix Williams-Honda helmet. **£7,000–7,500** *BKS*
1927 Bentley 3 Litre Speed Model. **£60,000–65,000** *BKS*
1955 Rolls-Royce Silver Cloud I. **£11,000–13,000** *COYS*
1950s Rolls-Royce bronze mascot. **£1,200–1,500** *COB*
1967 Porsche 910. **£200,000+** *COYS*

CONTENTS

ACKNOWLEDGEMENTS

The publishers would like to acknowledge the great assistance given by our consultants:

Chris Alford	Newland Cottage, Hassocks, West Sussex BN6 8NU
David Baldock	Tel: 01580 211326
Darren Banks	Race-Lit, Unit 6, Healey New Mills, Healey Road, Ossett, West Yorkshire WF5 8NF
Malcolm Barber	81 Westside, London SW4 9AY Tel: 0171 228 8000
Rex Cadman	The Old Rectory, 45 Sandwich Road, Ash, Nr Canterbury, Kent CT3 2AF
Martin Cannell	2 Argyle Road, Hesketh Park, Southport, Lancs PR9 9LH
Mike Clarke	Little Ramsden, Reading Street, Tenterden, Kent TN30 7HS
Tom Falconer	Claremont Corvette, Snodland, Kent ME6 5NA
Paul Foulkes-Halbard	Foulkes-Halbard of Filching, Filching Manor, Jevington Road, Wannock, Polegate, East Sussex BN26 5QA
Tony Gosnell	Tel: 01428 722933
David Hayhoe	Grand Prix Contact Club, 28 Pine Avenue, West Wickham, Kent BR4 OLW
Simon Johnson	Military Vehicle Trust, 7 Carter Fold, Mellor, Lancs BB2 7ER
Tim Schofield	Coys, 2–4 Queen's Gate Mews, London SW7 5QJ
Mike Smith	Chiltern House, Ashendon, Aylesbury, Bucks HP18 OHB
Mike Stallwood and Tim Fuggle	RR Motor Services Ltd, Bethersden, Ashford, Kent TN26 3DN
Toby Wilson	Sotheby's, 34–35 New Bond Street, London W1A 2AA Tel: 0171 293 5000

We would like to extend our thanks to all auction houses, their press offices, and dealers who have assisted us in the production of this book along with the organisers and press offices of the following events:

Beaulieu September Autojumble & Automart

Louis Vuitton Classic

Goodwood Festival of Speed

RAC British Grand Prix

Coys International Historic Festival

Beltring '98 – The War and Peace Show

Rétromobile, Paris

KEY TO ILLUSTRATIONS

Each illustration and descriptive caption is accompanied by a letter code. By referring to the following list of Auctioneers (denoted by *), Dealers (•), Clubs, Museums and Trusts (§), the source of any item may be immediately determined. Inclusion in this edition no way constitutes or implies a contract or binding offer on the part of any of our contributors to supply or sell the goods illustrated, or similar articles, at the prices stated. Advertisers in this year's directory are denoted by †.
  If you require a valuation, it is advisable to check whether the dealer or specialist will carry out this service and if there is a charge. Please mention Miller's when making an enquiry.
A valuation by telephone is not possible. Most dealers are willing to help you with your enquiry; however, they are very busy people and consideration of the above points would be welcomed.

AUS	§†	Austin A30-35 Owners Club, Barbara Scott (membership sec), 16 Dene View, Ashington, Northumberland NE63 8JT Tel: 01670 853347
BAm	§	British Ambulance Soc, 5 Cormorant Drive, Hythe, Hants SO45 3GG Tel: 01703 841999
BaW	•†	Barry Walker, Barley Leys Farm, Haselor Hill Temple, Grafton, Stratford-on-Avon, W. Midlands B49 6NH Tel: 01789 400181
BC	•†	Beaulieu Garage Ltd, Beaulieu, Hants SO42 7YE Tel: 01590 612999
BHM	•	Brands Hatch Morgans, Borough Green Grange, Maidstone, Kent TN15 8HA Tel: 01732 882017
BKS	*†	Brooks, 81 Westside, London, SW4 9AY Tel: 0171 228 8000
BLE	•†	Ivor Bleaney, PO Box 60, Salisbury, Wiltshire, SP5 2DH Tel: 01794 390895
BRIT	*†	British Car Auctions Ltd, Classic & Historic Automobile Division, Auction Centre, Blackbushe Airport, Blackwater, Camberley, Surrey GU17 9LG Tel: 01252 878555
C	*	Christies, 8 King Street, St James's, London SW1Y 6QT Tel: 0171 839 9060
Car	•†	Chris Alford Racing and Sportscars, Newland Cottage, Hassocks, Sussex BN6 8NU Tel: 01273 845966
CARS	•†	C.A.R.S. (Classic Automobilia & Regalia Specialists), 4-4a Chapel Terrace Mews, Kemp Town, Brighton, Sussex BN2 1HU Tel: 01273 601960
CC	•	Collectors Cars, Drakeshill, Birmingham Road, Kenilworth, Warwicks CV8 1PT Tel: 01926 857705
CGC	*	Cheffins Grain & Comins, 2 Clifton Road, Cambridge, Cambs CB2 4BW Tel: 01223 358721/213343
CLAR	§	Club Alpine Renault UK Ltd, 71 Bedford Avenue, Barnet, Herts EN5 2ES
CLH	§	Classic Hearse Register Tel: 01268 472313
COB	•	Cobwebs, 78 Northam Road, Southampton, Hampshire, SO14 0PB Tel: 01703 227458
COHN	•	Terry Cohn, Rotherwood Lodge, Jumps Road, Churt, Surrey GU10 2JZ Tel: 01252 795000
COR	•†	Claremont Corvette, Snodland, Kent ME6 5NA Tel: 01634 244444
COYS	*	Coys of Kensington, 2/4 Queens Gate Mews, London SW7 5QJ Tel: 0171 584 7444
CPUK	§	Club Peugeot UK, Pole Position, 2 Steeple Heights Drive, Biggin Hill, Westerham, Kent TN16 3UN
CRC	§	Craven Collection of Classic Motorcycles, Brockfield Villa, Stockton-on-the-Forest, Yorkshire YO3 9UE Tel: 01904 488461/400493

CTP	•†	Classic Trading Post, Longbarn, Lewes Road, Cross-in-Hand, Heathfield, East Sussex TN21 0TP Tel: 01435 863800
DB	•†	David Baldock, Kent Tel: 01580 211326
DDM	*	Dickinson Davy & Markham, Wrawby Street, Brigg, Humberside DN20 8JJ Tel: 01652 653666
DEV	•	Devonshire Motor Company, 3-5 Susans Road, Eastbourne, E. Sussex BN21 3HA Tel: 01323 411310
DHAM	•†	Duncan Hamilton & Co Ltd, PO Box 222, Hook, Basingstoke, Hants RG27 9YZ Tel: 01256 765000
DRJ	•	The Motorhouse, DS & RG Johnson, Thorton Hall, Thorton, Bucks MK17 0HB Tel: 01280 812280
EAE	•†	Eagle E-Types, Henry Pearman, Brookside Farm, Tinkers Lane, Hadlow Down, Sussex Tel: 01825 830966
EDVV	§	Enfield & District Veteran Vehicle Trust, Whitewebbs Museum, Whitewebbs Road, Enfield, Middlesex EN2 9HW Tel: 0181 367 1898
EPP	•	Epping Motor Company, 558 High Road, Ilford, Essex IG3 8EQ Tel: 0181 590 3103
ESM	*†	East Sussex Minors, The Workshop, Bearhurst Farm, Stonegate, Sussex TN5 7DU Tel: 01580 200203
FCV	•	Forge Classic & Vintage Vehicles, Ashford Road, St Michaels, Kent Tel: 01580 766446
FHD	•†	F. H. Douglass, 1a South Ealing Road, Ealing, London W5 4OT Tel: 0181 567 0570
FHF	•	Foulkes-Halbard of Filching, Filching Manor, Filching, Wannock, Polegate, Sussex BN26 5QA Tel: 01323 487838
FOS	•†	Foskers, U5 Brands Hatch Circuit, Scratchers Lane, Fawkham, Kent DA3 8NG Tel: 01474 874777
FYC	§	Ford Y&C Model Register, Bob Wilkinson, Castle Farm, Main St, Pollington, Goole, Humberside DN14 0DJ Tel: 01405 860836
GAZE	*	Thomas Wm Gaze & Son, 10 Market Hill, Diss, Norfolk IP22 3JZ Tel: 01379 651931
GPCC	§	Grand Prix Contact Club, David Hayhoe, 43 New Barn Lane, Bridgewood, Uckfield, East Sussex TN22 5EL Tel: 01825 764918
GPT	•†	Grand Prix Top Gear, The Old Mill, Mill End, Standon, Herts SG11 1LR Tel: 01279 843999
H&H	*†	H & H Classic Auctions Ltd, Whitegate Farm, Hatton Lane, Hatton, Warrington, Cheshire WA4 4BZ Tel: 01925 730630
HOLL	*	Dreweatt Neate Holloways, 49 Parsons Street, Banbury, Oxon OX16 8PF Tel: 01295 253197

IMPS § Invicta Military Vehicle Preservation Society, 58 Ladds Way, Swanley, Kent BR8 8HW
Tel: 01322 408738

JUN •† Junktion, The Old Railway Station, New Bolingbroke, Boston, Lincolnshire PE22 7LB
Tel: 01205 480068

LE •† Laurence Edscer, Flat B Semple Mews, Semple House, Gardeners Lane, Romsey, Hants SO51 6AD
Tel: 01703 814665

LF * Lambert & Foster, 77 Commercial Road, Paddock Wood, Kent TN12 6DR
Tel: 01892 832325

LOM •† Lombarda Sport Ltd, 2 Railway Mews, Notting Hill, London W10 6HN
Tel: 0171 792 9773

MEE • Nicholas Mee & Company Ltd, 36-38 Queensgate Place Mews, London SW7 5BQ
Tel: 0171 581 0088

Mot • Motospot, North Kilworth, Nr Lutterworth, Leicestershire LE17 6EP
Tel: 01455 552548/0850 450269

MPG • MotorPost Gallery, 5 Shadwell Park Court, Leeds, Yorkshire LS17 8TS
Tel: 0113 225 3525

MSMP• Mike Smith Motoring Past, Chiltern House, Ashendon, Aylesbury, Bucks HP18 0HB Tel: 01296 651283

MUN •† Munich Legends Ltd, The Ashdown Garage, Chelwood Gate, East Sussex RH17 7DE Tel: 01825 740456

MVT § Military Vehicle Trust, 7 Carter Fold, Mellor, Lancs BB2 7ER
Tel: 01254 812894

NCC § Naylor Car Club, Airedale Garage, Hollins Hill, Shipley, York BD17 7QN

NMV § Norfolk Military Vehicle Group, Fakenham Road Stanhoe, King's Lynn, Norfolk PE31 8PX
Tel: 01485 518052

NTMV§ North Thames Military Vehicle Preservation Society, 22 Victoria Avenue, Grays, Essex RM16 2RP

P(E) * Phillips, Alphin Brook Road, Alphington, Exeter, Devon EX2 8TH
Tel: 01392 439025

PA *† Parkes Auctions Ltd, 2/4 Station Road, Swavesey, Cambs CB4 5QJ
Tel: 01954 232332

PALM * Palm Springs Exotic Car Auctions, 602 East Sunny Dunes Road, Palm Springs, California 92264 USA
Tel: 760 320 3290

PC Private Collection

PMB •† Pooks Motor Bookshop, Fowke Street, Rothley, Leicestershire LE7 7PJ
Tel: 0116 237 6222

Pou * Poulain Le Fur Commissaires Priseurs Associes, 20 rue de Provence, 75009 Paris, France
Tel: 01 42 46 81 81

PORT • Portfield Sports & Classics Ltd, Quarry Lane, Chichester, W. Sussex PO19 2NX
Tel: 01243 528500

PPH • Period Picnic Hampers
Tel: 0115 937 2934

RAC § Royal Automobile Club, PO Box 700, Bristol, Glos BS99 1RB
Tel: 01454 208000

RCC •† Real Car Co, Snowdonia Business Park, Coed y Parc, Bethesda, Gwynedd LL57 4YS
Tel: 01248 602649

RRM • RR Motor Services Ltd, Bethersden, Ashford, Kent TN26 3DN
Tel: 01233 820219

S * Sotheby's, 34-35 New Bond Street, London W1A 2AA
Tel: 0171 293 5000

SJR •† Simon J. Robinson (1982) Ltd, Ketton Garage, Durham Road, Coatham, Munderville, Darlington, Co Durham DL1 3LX
Tel: 01325 311232

SLM * Sloan's Auctioneers, Miami Gallery, 8861 NW 18th Terrace, Suite 100, Miami, Florida 33171, USA
Tel: 305 592-2575

SVV • Smallbone Vintage Vehicles, 116/118 Raddlebarn Road, Selly Oak, Birmingham, West Midlands B29 6HQ
Tel: 0121 472 7139

SW • Spinning Wheel Garage, Sheffield Road, Sheepbridge, Chesterfield, Derbyshire S41 9EH
Tel: 01246 451772

SWO * G. E. Sworder & Sons, 14 Cambridge Road, Stansted Mountfitchet, Essex CM24 8BZ
Tel: 01279 817778

TALA • Talacrest, 74 Station Road, Egham, Surrey TW20 9LF
Tel: 01784 439797

TAR/ Tar • Tarrant Antiques, Lorraine, 23 Market Place, Ringwood, Hampshire, BH24 1BL
Tel: 01425 461123

TAY * Taylors, Honiton Galleries, 205 High Street, Honiton, Devon EX14 8LF
Tel: 01404 42404

THOR •† Thoroughbred Cars Tel: 0181 501 2727

TPM • T. P. Motors, Unit 5, Moatway Industrial Estate, Barwell, Leicester LE9 8EY
Tel: 01455 846302

TPS • Trevor's Pump Shop, 2 Cement Cottages Station Road, Rainham, Kent ME8 7UF
Tel: 01634 361231

TRJ § Trojan Owners' Club, Troylands, St Johns, Earlswood Common, Redhill, Surrey RH1 6QF
Tel: 01737 763643

TSh * Thimbleby & Shorland, 31 Great Knollys Street, Reading, Berkshire RG1 7HU
Tel: 01734 508611

UMC •† Unicorn Motor Company, Brian R. Chant, M.I.M.I., Station Road, Stalbridge, Dorset DT10 2RH
Tel: 01963 363353

VIC •† Vicarys of Battle Ltd, 32 High St, Battle, Sussex TN33 0EH
Tel: 01424 772425

VIN • Vintage & Sports Car Garage Ltd, 47 West Street, Harrietsham, Kent ME17 1HX
Tel: 01622 859570

WILM •† Wilmington Classic Cars, Lewes Road, Wilmington, Polegate, East Sussex BN26 5JE
Tel: 01323 486136

If you would like to contribute photographs towards the next edition of *Miller's Collectors Cars Price Guide*, please contact this office by the end of January 1999. Tel: 01580 766411.

HOW TO USE THIS BOOK

I t is our aim to make the guide easy to use. Marques are listed alphabetically and then chronologically. Commercial Vehicles, Children's Cars, Replica Vehicles, Restoration Projects, Racing & Rallying and Military Vehicles are located after the marques, towards the end of the book. In the Automobilia section objects are grouped alphabetically by type. If you cannot find what you are looking for please consult the index which starts on page 348.

---

48 AUSTIN-HEALEY

1954 Austin-Healey 100/4, 4 cylinders, 2660cc, thoroughly overhauled, new wiring loom, exterior chrome renovated, new chrome wire wheels, interior, hood and tonneau cover completely re-trimmed.
£15,000–17,000 *COYS*

1959 Austin-Healey Sprite MkI, 4 cylinders, 948cc, extensive restoration, sills replaced, floorpan overhauled, full respray, chrome replated, steering overhauled, new rear springs, new brake cylinders, shoes and copper pipes, rebuilt radiator and new wiring loom, interior completely re-trimmed, new black fabric hood, perspex sidescreens replaced.
£8,750–9,750 *ADT*

Caption
provides a brief description of the vehicle or item, and could include comments on its history, mileage, any restoration work carried out and current condition.

Miller's Starter Marque

Starter Austin-Healeys: *Austin Healey Sprite MkI 'Frog-eye'; Austin-Healey Sprite MkII–V.*

• Few cars have a cuter face than the cheeky little Austin-Healey Sprite MkI that everyone knows as the 'Frog-eye'. Truth be told, it's not very fast. A contemporary road test in *The Motor* quoted a leisurely 0–60mph time of 20.5 seconds. Acceleration petered out altogether at 84mph. But what it lacked in outright pace it more than made up for with true agility and genuine sporting feel.

• It's a viable restore-while-you-drive car, with basic readily available mechanicals – mostly Austin A35 with a bit of Morris Minor. Many of the same virtues apply to the Sprite MkII–V, which is identical to the MG Midget in all but minor detail. With both makes to choose from the Midget and Sprite MkII–V were made in far larger numbers than the 'Frog-eye' and are that much more affordable and readily available.

Austin Milestones

1866: Herbert Austin born 8 November.
1905: Austin Motor Company founded.
1914: Austin became public company.
1975: British Leyland nationalised.
1980: British Leyland reorganises with Austin-badged cars produced under Austin-Rover Group banner.
1986: 5,000,000th Mini was produced 19 February.
1987: Austin name disappears from remaining models and company name shortened to the Rover Group. The end of Austin.

Source Code
refers to the 'Key to Illustrations' on page 10 which lists the details of where the item was photographed, and whether a dealer or auction house. Advertisers are also indicated on this page.

Miller's Starter Marque
refers to selected marques that offer affordable, reliable and interesting classic motoring.

Information Box
covers relevant information on marques, designers, racing drivers and special events.

1957 Austin-Healey 100/6 BN4,
6 cylinders, 2639cc, 4 speed gearbox with overdrive, bare metal respray, converted to right-hand drive, chrome and wire wheels and interior refurbished.
£12,500–14,000 *H&H*

1963 Austin-Healey 3000 MkIIA, converted to right-hand drive, imported, very good restored condition, including new wheels and tyres, new hood and new tonneau.
£15,000–17,000 *H&H*

AUSTIN-HEALEY Model	ENGINE cc/cyl	DATES	CONDITION		
			1	2	3
100 BN 1/2	2660/4	1953-56	£20,000	£14,000	£8,000
100/6, BN4/BN6	2639/6	1956-59	£18,000	£13,500	£8,000
3000 Mk I	2912/6	1959-61	£20,000	£13,000	£8,500
3000 Mk II	2912/6	1961-62	£22,000	£15,000	£9,000
3000 Mk III	2912/6	1964-68	£24,000	£17,000	£11,000
Sprite Mk I	948/4	1958-61	£7,000	£6,000	£3,000
Sprite Mk II	948/4	1961-64	£4,000	£3,000	£2,000
Sprite Mk III	1098/4	1964-66	£4,500	£3,000	£1,500
Sprite Mk IV	1275/4	1966-71	£5,000	£3,000	£1,500

Price Boxes
give the value of a particular model, dependent on condition and are compiled by our team of experts, car clubs and private collectors.
Condition 1 refers to a vehicle in top class condition but not *concours d'élégance* standard, either fully restored or in very good original condition.
Condition 2 refers to a good, clean roadworthy vehicle, both mechanically and bodily sound.
Condition 3 refers to a runner, but in need of attention, probably to both bodywork and mechanics. It must have a current MOT.
Restoration projects are vehicles that fail to make the Condition 3 grading.

Price Guide
these are worked out by a team of trade and auction house experts, and are based on actual prices realised. Remember that Miller's is a PRICE GUIDE not a PRICE LIST and prices are affected by many variables such as location, condition, desirability and so on. Don't forget that if you are selling it is quite likely you will be offered less than the price range. Price ranges for items sold at auction include the buyer's premium.

FOREWORD

Motor racing has been a part of my family history since 1931 when my grandfather won the famous Brooklands Double 12 race in his MG. Five years later he held a private hill climb competition for the Lancia Car Club in Goodwood Park, using the same piece of road that we now use for the Festival of Speed. My grandfather was an apprentice with Bentley and went on to design and style bodywork for both Riley and AC cars.

As President of the British Automobile Racing Club I am very pleased to see the club so closely involved with not only the Festival of Speed but also the Goodwood Motor Circuit revival. These two events form the backbone of historic motor racing at Goodwood and I am pleased to say that the public's enthusiasm for classic cars and motorcycles continues to grow. The return of racing to the Goodwood Circuit will be truly a magical step back in time and I hope will satisfy the demands of the most knowledgeable spectator.

Miller's Collectors Cars Price Guide has done much to help both professional and amateur classic and vintage car enthusiasts. The guide is undoubtedly an essential addition to the bookshelves of those who want to know more about the history and value of the world's great cars.

March.

STATE OF THE MARKET

Most dealers report less activity and lower sales this year than in the latter half of last year, and yet the same period has witnessed some of the most successful car auctions of the 1990s. The situation is, perhaps, underlined by the fact that when long-time dealer David Howard decided to retire to France, he called in a regional firm of auctioneers to dispose of his remaining stock.

It is a measure of the underlying strength of the market, however, that a number of setbacks experienced by the classic car movement have not diminished the enthusiasm of buyers or the prices they are prepared to pay at auction. The uncertainty concerning the future over the phasing out of leaded petrol in the year 2000 has been compounded by high interest rates, which has made money more expensive in Britain and the pound sterling strong against foreign currencies.

We have also seen the phasing out, in the last budget, of the rolling date for exemption from VED (Vehicle Excise Duty) for classic vehicles, and only vehicles manufactured prior to January 1, 1973 are now eligible for this concession under the 'Historic' category. The strong pound means that fewer foreign buyers have participated in British auctions, but there have still been enough of them to ensure a strong defensive home market. Additives being introduced by the oil companies look like solving the petrol problem, and enthusiasts are busy lobbying their MPs about VED.

The sale at the Goodwood Festival of Speed held by Brooks each year concentrates mainly on sporting machinery with a Bentley 4½ litre Vanden Plas supercharged tourer realising £397,500, the highest price for the year so far, being sold to Rolls-Royce Motor Cars of Crewe. This auction generated over £2 million. Sotheby's at Althorp held an auction devoted to Rolls-Royce and Bentley motor cars, with a 1920 Rolls-Royce Silver Ghost dual cowl Phæton by Park Ward achieving £98,850, and later in the year a 1911 Silver Ghost by Barker sold for £496,500 in London.

Christie's achieved £441,500 for a 1956 Maserati 300S in unrestored condition (rumoured to have been Fangio's car), and £56,500 for a 1970 Mercedes-Benz 280SE cabriolet, among other excellent prices. Coys were at Silverstone with a sale total approaching £4 million. The 1964 Ferrari LM250 (ex-Scuderia Filipinetti) achieved £353,775, and an Alfa Romeo 8C 2600 Corsa made £300,000. More modest classics also did well – a 1957 Jaguar XK140 (admittedly ex-Mike Hawthorn) achieving £46,463, and a 1957 BMW 507 Spyder £97,868.

Brooks made two forays into Germany, one at the Nürburgring Oldtimer Grand Prix where they established an auction record with the ex-Gerhard Berger Italian Grand Prix-winning 1988 Ferrari F1 87/88C single-seater at £199,217. Other prices included £124,125 for the ex-Scuderia Brescia Corsa Ford GT40.

The first built 1963 Aston Martin DB5 convertible by Touring sold for £58,558. Brooks also established a regular venue at the Mercedes-Benz Museum at Stuttgart, selling Mercedes, Benz and related material.

Sotheby's Geneva sold the Mimram Collection (the family that took over Lamborghini), with most cars selling. Highest price in this collection was for the 1969 Lamborghini Miura SV Iota (the only Lamborghini) which sold for £123,190, a 1966 AC Cobra 427 MkIII making £112,890, and £249,574 was paid for a 1933 Rolls-Royce Phantom II town car by Brewster and £99,780 for a 1931 Minerva Type AL convertible limousine by Rollston.

Another 'first' was Brooks' joint venture in Paris with French auctioneers Etude Tajan, a £1 million auction where highlights included a Bugatti type 35 at £155,880 and £75,050 for a 1920 Voisin boat-tailed sports. Brooks held a series of sales in conjunction with the Earl's Court Motor Show in October, where good prices included £89,500 for a 1960 Ferrari 250GT, £86,200 for a 3 litre short chassis boat-tailed two-seater sports and £31,625 for a 1955 Jaguar XK140 with left-hand drive. The £38,900 paid for a 1948 Jaguar 3½ litre drophead was almost back to 1980s prices.

In Australia two Edwardian Benz cars (ex-works) and a 1912 Prince Henry Vauxhall saw international bidding at Brooks Goodman, realising £81,000, £56,000 and £87,550 respectively, all going to European collectors.

Coys 'True Greats' at Islington, London, last November produced prices of £225,260 for a 1926 Mercedes-Benz 630K torpedo tourer, and £202,900 for both a 1965 Ford GT40 MkI and a 1967 Porsche 910 racer and (inexplicably) £100,100 for a 1930 Bentley 4½ litre by Vanden Plas missing engine, gearbox, doors, radiator and much else! More recently, their Chiswick House, London, sale this May produced many prices of £70,000 and above, including a 1931 Bentley 4½ litre tourer (£97,860), a 1935 Lagonda M45 tourer (£72,165), with over £100,000 paid for a 1937 Delahaye 135M Competition.

Interest in Formula 1 memorabilia and collectables appears to be growing with Brooks, Sotheby's and Christie's specialising in this sector. The last sale in the auction season saw Brooks in London take the auction record for the year when a 1956 Maserati 250F GP single-seater achieved £500,000, lifting the market which had otherwise appeared to have been faltering slightly.

Clearly there is still plenty of confidence in the market, and while post-war classics are still relatively cheap, good-quality cars in all stratas command top money, and the money is there. With signs that the recession in Europe is easing, the future looks bright, with British auction houses prominent in the international marketplace.

Malcolm Barber

FUEL FOR THOUGHT

Like it or not, there's one burning issue that classic car enthusiasts the world over will have to address on the road ahead to the millennium and beyond. Come the year 2000 leaded fuel will be withdrawn throughout most of Europe. However, this does not mean, as some pessimists fear, that our cherished old cars will become mere static museum exhibits, unusable and immobile artefacts of a bygone industrial age. That's the good news, but without a doubt the worldwide hobby will have to adapt to flourish into the 21st century.

The practical reality for most enthusiasts lies with fuel additives, lead replacement petrol or converting cylinder heads to run on unleaded fuel. But there's no need to panic. Many older American cars, with big, lazy, low-revving engines seem well able to ingest unleaded fuel. We should also be thankful to enthusiasts who are prepared to experiment with unleaded fuel on our behalf. I recently learned of an enthusiast who has run an unmodified 1969 Triumph Herald on unleaded fuel for five years, clocking up a five-figure mileage with no reported problems. It certainly seems to be the case that some cars, as long as they are not subjected to sustained high revs or heavy-footed acceleration, are able to live with unleaded fuel.

With additives we have to keep a watching brief as test results emerge, but some of the best advice I've heard comes from the MG Owners' Club. They say there's no need to panic and immediately lay out on an unleaded cylinder-head conversion as a knee-jerk reaction. Instead they recommend that, when normal wear and tear warrants a cylinder-head overhaul, that should be the time to invest in a cylinder-head conversion.
Other good news is that unleaded cylinder heads from reputable suppliers are becoming more widely available. Depending on how much you 'do-it-yourself' the costs can be as little as £200 or £300, and that's quite a modest outlay to make your classic future-proof.

Increasingly too, classified 'For Sale' adverts are detailing unleaded conversions as a positive selling point. Although our hobby is steeped in nostalgia it's good to see that so many enthusiasts are moving with the times.

Taxing Issues

Many British enthusiasts rejoiced when, in 1996, cars over 25 years old were given exemption from paying the annual road-fund licence or vehicle excise duty. Although I appreciated the saving, which amounts to £150 a year, I feared that once classic car owners had been differentiated as a separate group of road users it might allow the possibility of being discriminated against and having our use of old cars restricted. Thankfully, for the time being at least, no real threat has materialised, but this curious piece of legislation has become curiouser still,

by the replacement of the rolling 25-year tax-exempt qualification with a fixed cut-off date of January 1, 1973.

There are countless numbers of cars – the Triumph Stag, TR6, MGB, MG Midget and P6 Rover to name just a few – that bridge the cut-off date, yet it seems a strange anomaly that, for example, a Triumph Spitfire registered before the end of 1972 should pay no road tax, while an identically specified Spitfire registered days later in 1973 should pay full road tax.

Some observers feared that this would create a classic car underclass, with popular budget classics registered from 1973 onwards being devalued. So far, this doesn't seem to have happened and it's a positive sign for the health of the hobby that even owners of modest classic cars, perhaps worth only two or three years' road tax, value their enjoyment of old cars more than a £150 year tax-break.

Auction Advice

In 1997 well over 6,000 classic cars were offered by UK auction houses; that's well over 1,000 up on the year before. What has also become clear is that more and more enthusiasts are considering buying at auction. With that in mind here are a few tips to help you buy at auction.
* If you have time, visit an auction before you go to one to buy – just to soak up the atmosphere and study the etiquette.
* Decide what you're after and research the particular make, model and specification you want – and of course, how much it's worth.
* If the car you're after is coming up at auction tell the auction house you are interested and ask them what they know about it – someone at the auction house may well have driven it. Study the documentation, making sure the records of work relate to that car and not the vendor's Lada.
* If you like what you find you should register to bid and you'll then be given a numbered paddle with which to bid (there's none of this covert winking at classic car auctions).
* Take into account the buyer's premium. Some auction houses charge 5 per cent of the hammer prices; occasionally it's even 0 per cent; and at others its 15 per cent of the hammer price up to £30,000 and 10 per cent for additional sums. VAT is payable on the premium. Thus, to a hammer price of £1,000 a 15 per cent premium would add £150, then £26.25 VAT (17.5 per cent of £150) for a total of £1,176.25.
* Arrange cleared funds. If you do not settle in time, usually 24 hours, you may start to incur storage costs.
* If you want to drive the car away remember to make preliminary insurance arrangements; otherwise, most auction houses can recommend a transport company.

Dave Selby

ABARTH

l. **1956 Fiat Abarth 750 Coupé Viotti,** 747cc, 4 cylinders, excellent condition, full restoration in 1996, engine rebuilt to produce a claimed 70bhp. **£14,500–17,000** *COYS*

Carlo Abarth was especially pleased with Viotti's design, which was shown at the 1956 Geneva Salon, and planned full scale-production for the car. This car is the only example completed, so while most Abarths are rare, this one is unique.

AC

1928 AC 12-35hp Acedes Two-Seater, 6 cylinder, single overhead camshaft, 1438cc, 40bhp at 4,000rpm, 3-speed manual gearbox in unit with rear axle, 2 litre AC block fitted with original engine internals, original bodywork, in need of minor attention. **£8,000–9,000** *C*

The light six came in both 1500cc and 2 litre sizes, and the company was quickly accepted as the source of well-finished and lively medium-priced automobiles. The slender two-seater open tourer, with wide bench seat matched by a right-hand gear lever, offering a spacious double dickey seat, was particularly successful – whether as the Aceca with wind-up windows or in simpler Royal or Acedes variants with removable celluloid sidescreens. Very few 12hp AC sixes were built, and not many have survived.

1937 AC 16/70 Two-Door Four-Seater Tourer, triple-carburettor sports engine rebuilt in 1991, sound chassis, coachwork generally good, interior worn but serviceable, recently rewired, 1,000 miles covered since June 1992. **£30,000–34,000** *BKS*

The famous John Weller-designed 1991cc, overhead camshaft six entered production in 1922, later helping to secure the marque's place in motoring history when, in 1926, a 2 litre AC became the first British car to win the Monte Carlo Rally. ACs of the 1930s were offered in a wide variety of body styles, this being a fine example of the marque's most desirable option, the four-seater tourer.

1957 AC Ace Bristol, 6 cylinder, 2 litre engine, left-hand drive, fully restored, new knock-off wire wheels. **£35,000–40,000** *S*

l. **1952 AC 2 litre Saloon,** full mechanical and body restoration. **£7,000–8,000** *BC*

AC Model	ENGINE cc/cyl	DATES	CONDITION 1	2	3
Sociable	636/1	1907-12	£10,500	£9,000	£4,500
12/24 (Anzani)	1498/4	1919-27	£14,000	£11,500	£7,500
16/40	1991/6	1920-28	£18,000	£15,000	£11,000
16/60 Drophead/Saloon	1991/6	1937-40	£24,000	£21,000	£15,500
16/70 Sports Tourer	1991/6	1937-40	£35,000	£26,000	£18,000
16/80 Competition 2 Seater	1991/6	1937-40	£55,000	£45,000	£35,000

l. **1958 AC Ace Bristol Two-Seater Sports,**
100D 2 litre engine, 4-speed gearbox with
overdrive, front disc brakes, left-hand drive,
3 previous owners, major restoration in 1992,
with relatively little mileage since.
£37,000–40,000 *BKS*

*The AC Ace made its debut at Earl's Court in
1953. Initially offered with AC's own 2 litre
engine, a unit that traced its ancestry back to
vintage days, the exciting new car was soon to be
offered as the Ace Bristol, equipped with Bristol's
BMW-inspired 2 litre engine, developing 105bhp.*

1959 AC Ace Bristol Two-Door Roadster, 6 cylinder, 2 litre engine, left-hand drive, current owner
since 1981, having covered a mere 620 miles, restored in the 1970s, with a £3,700 engine rebuild in 1978.
£25,000–30,000 *BKS*

*The success of Cliff Davis's Tojeiro sports racer prompted AC Cars to put the design into production in
1954 as the Ace. The pretty Ferrari 166-inspired Barchetta bodywork was retained, as was the ladder-
frame chassis and all-independent suspension, but the power unit was AC's own venerable, 2 litre, long-
stroke six. With a modest 80bhp (later 100bhp) on tap, it endowed the Ace with respectable, if not
outstanding, performance. From 1956 onwards, the more powerful (up to 130bhp) Bristol 6-cylinder engine
was available, and in this form the car could touch 121mph.*

1960 AC Ace 1991cc, 6 cylinder, disc brakes all-
round, one of only 6 fitted with the lightweight
close-ratio gearbox, original HMV radio, vehicle's
history known since new, bodywork restored in
1987, original maroon leather upholstery, all
instrumentation believed to be correct.
£26,000–29,000 *BRIT*

1961 AC Greyhound Coupé, 1971cc, 6 cylinders,
one of only 80 produced.
£7,350–8,350 *H&H*

AC Model	ENGINE cc/cyl	DATES	CONDITION 1	2	3
2 litre	1991/6	1947-55	£6,000	£4,000	£1,000
Buckland	1991/6	1949-54	£8,500	£5,500	£2,500
Ace	1991/6	1953-63	£30,000	£25,000	£18,000
Ace Bristol	1971/6	1954-63	£42,000	£30,000	£25,000
Ace 2.6	1553/6	1961-62	£38,000	£32,000	£29,000
Aceca	1991/6	1954-63	£24,000	£17,000	£12,000
Aceca Bristol	1971/6	1956-63	£28,000	£21,000	£16,000
Greyhound Bristol	1971/6	1961-63	£16,000	£13,000	£8,000
Cobra Mk II 289	4735/8	1963-64	£90,000	£80,000	£70,000
Cobra Mk III 427	6998/8	1965-67	£125,000	£100,000	£90,000
Cobra Mk IV	5340/8	1987-	£55,000	£40,000	£32,000
428 Frua	7014/8	1967-73	£19,000	£15,000	£12,000
428 Frua Convertible	7014/8	1967-73	£25,000	£20,000	£16,000
3000 ME	2994/6	1976-84	£15,000	£10,000	£8,000

Racing history for Cobra will put the price to over £100,000–120,000.

AC 427 and 428

Body styles: Two-seat convertible and two-seat fastback coupé.
Construction: Tubular-steel backbone chassis with separate all-steel body.
Engine: Ford V8, 6997cc or 7016cc, both overhead valve.
Power output: 425bhp at 6,000rpm (427); 345bhp at 4,600rpm (428).
Transmission: Ford four-speed manual or three-speed automatic; Salisbury rear axle with limited-slip differential.
Suspension: Double wishbones and combined coil spring/telescopic damper units front and rear.
Brakes: Servo-assisted Girling discs front and rear.
Top speed: 139.3mph (auto).
0–60mph: 5.9 seconds (auto).
0–100mph: 14.5 seconds (auto).
Average fuel consumption: 12–15mpg.
Production: 80 – 51 convertibles and 29 fastbacks.
The refined bruiser known as the AC 427 and 428 was born of a combination of British engineering, American Ford V8 power and Italian design, courtesy of Frua, who penned the sharply elegant convertible and fastback bodies to clothe the Cobra's simple, but rugged, and sure-footed chassis. The convertible was first seen at the London Motor Show in October 1965; the first fixed-head car – the fastback – was ready in time for the Geneva show, in March 1966. A few early cars had the ferocious 6997cc Cobra V8 (427cu in, hence the model name). The remainder were 428 models with the tamer 7016cc (428cu in) 345bhp Ford V8.

Production was beset by problems from the start. The first cars were not offered for sale until 1967; and as late as March 1969, only 50 had been built, for despite its monumental performance, the 428 fell between two stools. It cost significantly less than pure-bred Italian exotics like Ferraris and Maseratis, but considerably more than British contemporaries like the Aston Martin DB6 and Jensen Interceptor. Small-scale production continued into the 1970s, but its days were numbered, and it was finally killed off by the oil crisis of October 1973; the last 428 was built soon after and was sold during 1974.

1968 AC Cobra 427, 6997cc, V8 engine.
£120,000–130,000 *EPP*

Only 510 cars were made from 1965–69. 400bhp engines were standard, although some street legal versions have been tuned to 490bhp.

1982 AC 3000 ME, 3000cc.
£8,500–9,500 *H&H*

This car belonged to Mr Andrew Hurlock, Managing Director of AC Cars. When manufacture switched to Scotland, the car was used as a development vehicle for the proposed Mk2, a project undertaken in conjunction with Alfa Romeo. Many modifications were made to overcome the problems associated with the Mk1.

1994 AC Cobra MkIV, 5 litre, Ford V8 engine, only 3,700 recorded miles, described as being in 'as new' condition.
£47,000–50,000 *BKS*

The Cobra MkIV was a continuation of the original AC/Shelby Cobra, manufactured under a licence that granted Autokraft Ltd the exclusive right to use the AC name and logo on its products. It was assembled using the original body buck over which AC Cobra panels were formed in the 1960s to ensure total authenticity.

ALEXIS

l. **1958 Alexis GT,** 1.5 litre, BMC B-series engine in MGA tune, Buckler frame, Rochdale GT body with Kamm tail, Series I Lotus Eleven suspension, contemporary racing history.
£3,750–4,250 *BKS*

ALFA ROMEO

One of the most charismatic names in the
motoring pantheon, the Milanese company
Alfa Romeo began life in 1910 as ALFA –
Anonima Lombardo Fabbrica Automibili –
and became Alfa Romeo when industrialist
Nicolo Romeo took control in 1915. During the
1920s, Alfa Romeo produced some exquisite
sporting machines and dominated Grand Prix
racing for a decade, before being overwhelmed
by the might of the Mercedes and Auto Union
teams in the mid-1930s. After 1945, Alfas
became more accessible, and many models
from the 1960s onwards have been
tagged 'poor man's Ferrari'. Since 1987,
Alfa Romeo has been part of Fiat.

1929 Alfa Romeo 6C 1500, 6 cylinder, 1487cc,
open sports tourer by James Young.
£30,000–35,000 *COYS*

*This second series car is probably the most original
example in the world, having had the same owner
since new. It has never needed major restoration and
remains in a superb state.*

**1938 Alfa Romeo 6C 2300B 'Corto'
Spider,** replacement body (a copy of the
original, which was removed in the 1950s),
fully restored, finished in midnight blue
with cream side panels, new blue hide
interior, rebuilt engine and gearbox.
£100,000–115,000 *S*

*The 6C 2300 engine appeared in 1934 and
was to an entirely new overhead camshaft
design. The following year, the 2300B
appeared with independent torsion bar
suspension and was offered in 'Lungo'
(long), 'Corto' (short) and 'Pescara' form.*

1950 Alfa Romeo 6C 2500 Super Sport *'Villa d'Este'*,
coachwork by Touring, transmission described as 'good',
and all other aspects 'very good'.
£42,000–45,000 *BKS*

*The 6C 2500 was one of the last designs that the great Vittorio
Jano essayed for Alfa Romeo, and it was also the last of the
bespoke Alfa Romeos. Introduced in 1939, it came in various
types, the Super Sport being the short-wheelbase version, which
was more than 300lb lighter than the saloons. All 6C 2500
models were exceptional performers for their time. The double
overhead camshaft engine produced 110bhp, which gave
100+mph on the road. Production continued until 1952, but
only 474 examples of the Super Sport were made, and the 'Villa
d'Este' is probably the most desirable. It was named after one of
Italy's most celebrated hotels, which used to host a renowned
concours d'élégance. When a 6C 2500 SS with a special body by
Touring won the event, it was decided to make a limited run for
select clients. In 1988, this car was acquired by the Dutch
National Motor Museum, which completed its restoration.*

r. **1959 Alfa Romeo
Giulietta Sprint,**
4 cylinders, double
overhead camshafts,
capable of 102.5mph.
£6,000–7,000 *Pou*

ALFA ROMEO Model	ENGINE cc/cyl	DATES	CONDITION 1	2	3
24HP	4084/4	1910-11	£25,000	£16,000	£12,000
12HP	2413/4	1910-11	£18,000	£11,000	£8,000
40-60	6028/4	1913-15	£32,000	£24,000	£14,000
RL	2916/6	1921-22	£30,000	£24,000	£14,000
RM	1944/4	1924-25	£28,000	£17,000	£13,000
6C 1500	1487/6	1927-28	£50,000*	£20,000+	£10,000+
6C 1750	1752/6	1923-33	£100,000+	£80,000+	-
6C 1900	1917/6	1933	£18,000	£15,000	£12,000
6C 2300	2309/6	1934	£22,000	£18,000	£15,000
6C 2500 SS Cabriolet/Spider	2443/6	1939-45	£100,000	£50,000	£40,000
6C 2500 SS Coupé	2443/6	1939-45	£60,000	£40,000	£30,000
8C 2300 Monza/Short Chassis	2300/8	1931-34	£1,000,000+	£400,000+	£200,000
8C 2900	2900/8	1935-39	£1,000,000+	£500,000+	£300,000

Value is very dependent on sporting history, body style and engine type.
*The high price on this model is dependent on whether it is 1500 supercharged/twin overhead cam.

1965 Alfa Romeo Giulia 1300 Ti Four-Door Saloon, left-hand drive, subject to comprehensive no-expense-spared restoration in 1995, fitted with race-prepared engine, close-ratio gearbox, lowered suspension, plumbed-in extinguisher, roll cage and racing seats.
£9,000–10,000 *BKS*

The suffix denotes the high-performance version of this classic Italian sports saloon.

1967 Alfa Romeo 1600 Duetto Spider, body by Pininfarina, 1570cc, 4 cylinders.
£14,000–16,000 *LOM*

Miller's Starter Marque

Alfa Romeos: *1750 and 2000 GTV; 1300 Junior Spider, 1600 Duetto Spider, 1750 and 2000 Spider Veloce; 1300 and 1600 GT Junior; Alfasud ti and Sprint.*

- Responsive, eager and sweet twin-cam engines, finely balanced chassis, nimble handling and delightful looks are just some of the characteristic traits of classic Alfas from the mid-1960s onwards. They are also eminently affordable. For the kind of money that would buy you an MGB or Triumph TR, you could be a little more adventurous and acquire an engaging Alfa Romeo sporting saloon or convertible.

- The bad news is that the unfortunate reputation Alfas of the 1960s and 1970s earned for rusting was deserved. Even that has an advantage, however, because the suspicion still lingers and helps keep prices comparatively low. In fact, most Alfas from that period will have had major surgery at least once, so you should be able to find one with plenty of metal. Even so, take a magnet along. Classic Alfa owners – or Alfisti as they prefer to call themselves – have a saying: 'You pay for the engineering and the engine, but the body comes free'.

- Bear in mind, too, that maintenance costs are likely to be higher than for an MG or Triumph TR.

r. **1968 Alfa Romeo Duetto Spider,** 1570cc, 4 cylinders, original right-hand drive, sound bodywork, good paintwork, new carpet, unmarked upholstery, twin-cam engine, chassis, tyres, transmission and gearbox described as excellent, 40,000 recorded miles.
£8,750–9,750 *S*

1969 Alfa Romeo 1750 Spider Veloce, 1779cc, 4 cylinders in-line, twin overhead camshaft, 5-speed manual gearbox, 4-wheel disc brakes, restored at a cost of about £15,000, body comprehensively stripped, rebuilt and repainted, all-new upholstery, carpets, door panels and trim added as required, new black double-duck hood with hood cover fitted, engine totally dismantled and rebuilt as necessary, brakes and suspension stripped and rebuilt with a new brake servo fitted at the same time.
£14,000–15,000 *C*

ALFA ROMEO Model	ENGINE cc/cyl	DATES	CONDITION 1	2	3
2000 Spider	1974/4	1958-61	£15,000	£9,000	£3,000
2600 Sprint	2584/6	1962-66	£11,000	£7,500	£4,000
2600 Spider	2584/6	1962-65	£14,000	£12,000	£5,000
Giulietta Sprint	1290/4	1955-62	£10,000	£7,000	£4,000
Giulietta Spider	1290/4	1956-62	£11,000	£6,000	£4,500
Giulia Saloon	1570/4	1962-72	£5,000	£3,000	£1,500
Giulia Sprint (rhd)	1570/4	1962-68	£10,500	£6,000	£2,000
Giulia Spider (rhd)	1570/4	1962-65	£11,000	£8,000	£5,000
Giulia SS	1570/4	1962-66	£16,000	£13,000	£10,000
GT 1300 Junior	1290/4	1966-77	£7,000	£5,500	£3,000
Giulia Sprint GT (105)	1570/4	1962-68	£7,500	£5,000	£3,000
1600GT Junior	1570/4	1972-75	£7,000	£4,000	£2,000
1750/2000 Berlina	1779/ 1962/4	1967-77	£4,000	£2,500	£1,500
1750GTV	1779/4	1967-72	£9,000	£7,000	£3,000
2000GTV	1962/4	1971-77	£8,000	£5,500	£3,000
1600/1750 (Duetto)	1570/ 1779/4	1966-67	£10,000	£7,500	£5,000
1750/2000 Spider (Kamm)	1779/ 1962/4	1967-78	£9,000	£6,000	£4,000
Montreal	2593/8	1970-77	£10,000	£8,000	£5,000
Junior Zagato 1300	1290/4	1968-74	£10,000	£7,000	£4,000
Junior Zagato 1600	1570/4	1968-74	£11,000	£8,000	£5,000
Alfetta GT/GTV (chrome)	1962/4	1972-86	£4,000	£2,500	£1,000
Alfasud	1186/ 1490/4	1972-83	£2,000	£1,000	£500
Alfasud ti	1186/ 1490/4	1974-81	£2,500	£1,200	£900
Alfasud Sprint	1284/ 1490/4	1976-85	£3,000	£2,000	£1,000
GTV6	2492/6	1981-	£4,000	£2,500	£1,000

1962 Alfa Romeo 2600 Sprint, 2584cc, 6 cylinders, 145bhp at 5,900rpm.
£6,000–7,000 *Pou*

1964 Alfa Romeo 2600 Spider, 2584cc, 6 cylinders, one of only a 100 or so right-hand drive models.
£13,000–15,000 *LOM*

l. **1960 Alfa Romeo 2000 Saloon,** 1975cc, 4 cylinders, 105bhp at 5,700rpm, recently resprayed.
£1,500–2,000 *Pou*

The Berlina 2000 replaced the celebrated 1900 and remained in production from 1958 to 1961.

r. **1960 Alfa Romeo 2000 Spider,** 1974cc, 4 cylinders.
£15,000–16,000 *LOM*

1973 Alfa Romeo Montreal,
2593cc, V8, 200bhp at 6,500rpm,
4-wheel disc brakes.
£9,000–10,000 *Pou*

r. **1974 Alfa Romeo Montreal,** 2600cc,
V8 engine, one of only 103 right-hand
drive made.
£17,000–19,000 *LOM*

1967/8 Alfa Romeo Giulia GTC, very rare,
only 99 right-hand drive models made by
Bertone and Touring.
£17,000–20,000 *LOM*

1978 Alfa Romeo 2.0 Kamm Tail Spider,
body by Pininfarina, 1962cc, 4 cylinders, 132bhp.
£12,000–14,000 *LOM*

l. **1978 Alfa Romeo
2000 Spider Veloce,**
4 cylinders, 132bhp,
2 owners, bodywork
restored in 1991, new
mohair hood, good
condition in most
respects, very good
bodywork and interior.
£6,500–8,000 *BKS*

*Wind tunnel testing
resulted in the 2000
sporting a drag-reducing
Kamm tail, while other
improvements included
bigger brakes and a
limited-slip differential.*

1971 Alfa Romeo Giulia 1300 Super,
1290cc, 4 cylinders, 89bhp at 6,000rpm,
4-wheel disc brakes.
£3,000–3,300 *Pou*

1970 Alfa Romeo Giulia GT 1300 Junior,
1290cc, 4 cylinders, 89bhp at 6,000rpm, 4-wheel
disc brakes, 186 miles recorded since new engine
and clutch fitted.
£5,000–6,000 *Pou*

1972 Alfa Romeo Montreal, 2499cc, V8, recent work to the brakes, steering, wheel bearings and gear linkage, amounting to over £1,000, 57,168 recorded miles, which are believed genuine.
£4,500–6,000 *COYS*

Alfa Romeo's stylish Montreal was first shown at the World Expo in Montreal in 1967. Originally intended as only a show car, based on the existing Giulia GTV floorpan, it created such positive reaction that the possibility of putting it into production was investigated. At the 1970 Geneva Motor Show, a production version was displayed. Installed in the engine bay was Alfa's classic V8 quad-cam racing engine, mated to a 5-speed ZF gearbox. With 200bhp, performance was brisk: near 140mph maximum speed and 0–60mph reached in 7.6 seconds. Unfortunately, timing was not good, the energy crisis of the mid-70s effectively ensuring the car's premature demise. However, production continued in limited numbers until 1977, by which time only 3,925 examples had been built.

1983 Alfa Romeo GTV 6, 2492cc, 60° V6, 160bhp, new paint, reupholstered, air conditioning, exceptional condition.
£4,000–5,000 *Pou*

1982 Alfa Romeo Alfasud, professionally resprayed at a cost of £880 in 1994, when a new front wing and replacement rear arches were also fitted, excellent condition.
£600–800 *PA*

r. **1984 Alfa Romeo 2.0 MkIII Spider,** 1962cc, 4 cylinders.
£8,000–9,000 *LOM*

l. **1991 Alfa Romeo SZ,** coachwork by Zagato, quad-cam 60° V6, 210bhp, 0-60mph in under 7.0 seconds, 1,865 miles in the hands of original owner.
£26,500–29,500 *BKS*

Launched at the 1989 Geneva Salon, the SZ entered production that autumn and was limited to an edition of 1,000 left-hand drive coupés, all finished in red with tan leather upholstery. Despite its bluff nose, with a battery of six small Carello lights, the wedge-shaped SZ had an outstandingly low drag coefficient of just 0.3 and exceptional straight-line stability, even at speeds in excess of 140mph.

ALLARD

At the age of 19, in 1929, Sydney Herbert Allard was already racing three-wheeled Morgans and selling cars at his family's south London Ford dealership. In the 1930s, he became a major force in trials and hillclimbs, and by 1936 he had built his first Allard special, based on a Ford V8 chassis with lightweight bodywork that included bits of a Bugatti Type 57. Further specials followed and developed into the big, 'hairy-chested' sports cars that were the company's staple offerings, all of which were produced in limited numbers. Sydney Allard drove his own creations to win the 1949 British Hillclimb Championship and the 1952 Monte Carlo Rally.

1950 Allard J2 Competition Two-Seater, 5.4 litre, pushrod overhead valve Cadillac V8 engine, 160bhp at 3,500rpm, single downdraught carburettor, 3-speed manual gearbox with special close ratios and synchromesh, independent front suspension by divided axle with coil springs, de Dion rear with coil springs, hydraulically operated Alfin drum brakes all-round, left-hand drive.
£67,500–75,000 *C*

The Allard J2 has been described as 'the finest sports motorcycle on four wheels'; when it was combined with the mighty Cadillac V8, there was little that could outrun it on the racing circuits, as Sydney Allard demonstrated when he took third place and class victory at Le Mans in 1950. The Allard-designed chassis frame was particularly rigid, and the body was built of aluminium. About 90 J2 two-seaters were built in 1950–51, the majority tuned and destined for competition. Few classic cars in history have a more detailed history than this one: with a present mileage of 9,346 miles, it has been kept and maintained in close to ideal conditions throughout its life.

r. **1952 Allard P2 Safari Eight-Seater Estate Car,** 5.4 litre, Cadillac V8 engine, pushrod overhead valves, 160/200bhp at 5,800rpm, 3-speed manual synchromesh gearbox, independent front suspension by divided axle, de Dion rear, vertical coil springs all-round, subject of a lengthy and exhaustive restoration with only limited use since, period radio and Rimbellisher wheel trims, 93,399 recorded miles.
£21,000–24,000 *C*

A large car of commanding presence on the road, the Safari demands attention wherever it goes.

1950 Allard P-Type Two-Door Saloon, 3.6 litre, Ford V8 engine, 85bhp at 3,800rpm, 3-speed manual gearbox, transverse leaf-spring suspension to divided front and live rear axle, hydraulically operated drum brakes all-round, right-hand drive, 2-door light alloy body on wooden frame, good original leather upholstery, well-preserved head lining, unrestored but tidy engine bay, sound condition.
£6,000–8,000 *C*

The P-Type's performance potential was underlined when Sydney Allard, navigated by Tom Lush, won the 1952 Monte Carlo Rally outright in exceptionally severe winter conditions. Altogether, 800 P saloons were built, making it the most popular of all Allards.

1955 Allard J2R Sports Racing Car, 4.7 litre, Ford V8 engine, pushrod overhead valves, 260bhp at 5,800rpm, single 4-choke carburettor, 3-speed manual synchromesh gearbox, independent front suspension by divided axle, de Dion rear, coil springs all-round, hydraulically operated drum brakes all-round (inboard at rear).
£67,500–75,000 *C*

Very few J2Rs were built, possibly only five or 10. This particular J2R appeared in 1955 and may be the last one. The original 270bhp Cadillac engine has been replaced with one of the 'small block' 289cu in V8 power units evolved from the Ford Fairlane V8 in the early 1960s by Carroll Shelby to power the AC Cobra.

ALLARD Model	ENGINE cc/cyl	DATES	CONDITION 1	2	3
K/K2/L/M/M2X	3622/8	1947-54	£18,500+	£12,000	£8,000
K3	var/8	1953-54	£24,000	£15,000	£11,000
P1	3622/8	1949-52	£19,500	£13,000	£8,000
P2	3622/8	1952-54	£22,000	£18,000	£11,500
J2/J2X	var/8	1950-54	£60,000+	£50,000	£35,000
Palm Beach	1508/4, 2262/6	1952-55	£12,000	£10,000	£5,500
Palm Beach II	2252/ 3442/6	1956-60	£25,000+	£20,000	£11,000

ALVIS

l. **c1934 Alvis Speed 25,** 3571cc, 6 cylinders, good condition, but lacking an interior, offered as a virtually completed restoration project requiring finishing.
£15,500–18,500 *COYS*

The Alvis 3.5 litre was announced in October 1935 and formed the basis of the company's finest cars: the Speed 25 and the 4.3 litre. The Speed 25s engine was a 3571cc straight-six that produced 106bhp at 3,800rpm. Even when fitted with a standard sports saloon body, it was capable of 95mph and 0–50mph in 11 seconds.

1934 Alvis Crested Eagle Sports Saloon, coachwork by Charlesworth, 2511cc, 19.8bhp, extensive history from 1949 to date, restored in 1989, recent new radiator, brakes and engine overhaul.
£15,000–17,000 *Mot*

1947 Alvis TA14 Mulliner Saloon, retrimmed to original, poor paintwork, good running condition.
£5,500–6,500 *UMC*

1948 Alvis TA14 Saloon, 1892cc, 4 cylinders, 4-speed manual gearbox, bodywork in good condition, interior in good order, finished in red with a grey headlining, new red carpet, all electrical equipment operational.
£6,000–7,000 *H&H*

1951 Alvis TA21 Drophead, 2993cc, 6 cylinders, 2 owners, completely restored by Red Triangle at a cost of over £40,000, superb condition, fully history.
£17,500–20,000 *PA*

ALVIS Model	ENGINE cc/cyl	DATES	CONDITION 1	2	3
12/50	1496/4	1923-32	£20,000	£13,000	£7,000
Silver Eagle	2148	1929-37	£16,000	£12,000	£8,000
Silver Eagle DHC	2148	1929-37	£18,000	£13,000	£9,000
12/60	1645/4	1931-32	£15,000	£10,000	£7,000
Speed 20 (tourer)	2511/6	1932-36	£35,000	£28,000	£18,000
Speed 20 (closed)	2511/6	1932-36	£22,000	£15,000	£11,000
Crested Eagle	3571/6	1933-39	£10,000	£7,000	£4,000
Firefly (tourer)	1496/4	1932-34	£12,000	£10,000	£6,000
Firefly (closed)	1496/6	1932-34	£7,000	£5,000	£4,000
Firebird (tourer)	1842/4	1934-39	£13,000	£10,000	£6,000
Firebird (closed)	1842/4	1934-39	£7,000	£5,000	£4,000
Speed 25 (tourer)	3571/6	1936-40	£38,500	£30,000	£20,000
Speed 25 (closed)	3571/6	1936-40	£23,000	£17,000	£12,000
3.5 litre	3571/6	1935-36	£35,000	£25,000	£18,000
4.3 litre	4387/6	1936-40	£44,000	£30,000	£22,000
Silver Crest	2362/6	1936-40	£14,000	£10,000	£7,000
TA	3571/6	1936-39	£18,000	£12,000	£8,000
12/70	1842/4	1937-40	£10,000	£8,000	£6,000

ALVIS Model	ENGINE cc/cyl	DATES	CONDITION 1	2	3
TA14	1892/4	1946-50	£9,500	£8,000	£4,500
TA14 DHC	1892/4	1946-50	£14,000	£12,000	£5,000
TB14 Roadster	1892/4	1949-50	£15,000	£10,000	£8,000
TB21 Roadster	2993/6	1951	£16,000	£10,000	£7,000
TA21/TC21	2993/6	1950-55	£12,000	£9,000	£5,000
TA21/TC21 DHC	2993/6	1950-55	£17,000	£13,000	£10,000
TC21/100 Grey Lady	2993/6	1953-56	£13,000	£11,000	£5,000
TC21/100 DHC	2993/6	1954-56	£19,000	£15,000	£9,000
TD21	2993/6	1956-62	£11,000	£8,000	£6,000
TD21 DHC	2993/6	1956-62	£22,000	£16,000	£10,000
TE21	2993/6	1963-67	£15,000	£10,000	£8,000
TE21 DHC	2993/6	1963-67	£25,000	£16,000	£12,000
TF21	2993/6	1966-67	£16,000	£12,000	£9,500
TF21 DHC	2993/6	1966-67	£28,000	£17,000	£13,000

1961 Alvis TD21 Series I Saloon, 3 litre, 4-speed manual gearbox, wire wheels, period radio and spotlamps, history, very sound, well maintained. **£8,250–9,250** *UMC*

ARMSTRONG-SIDDELEY

1933 Armstrong-Siddeley 12hp Saloon, 1400cc, 6 cylinders, pre-selector 4-speed gearbox, restored in the late 1980s to an excellent standard. **£5,250–6,250** *H&H*

1965 Alvis TE21 Drophead Coupé, 2993cc, 6 cylinders, very good order bodily and mechanically, resprayed in 1990, lined hood renewed in 1991 along with a new stainless steel exhaust system. **£13,000–15,000** *BRIT*

The TE and TF series were distinguishable from the earlier models by their then fashionable stacked headlamps. With coachwork by Park Ward, these motor cars were both elegant and luxurious. The price for such exclusivity, however, was high, for the model was almost twice as expensive as the contemporary Jaguar MkII saloon. Built between 1964 and 1967, with a total production of 458 vehicles, these cars are now sought after; only 106 were built in drophead form.

1953 Armstrong-Siddeley Whitley Saloon, 2309cc, 6 cylinders, 18hp, bare metal respray in 1987, fitted with optional synchromesh gearbox. **£2,750–3,500** *BRIT*

ARMSTRONG-SIDDELEY Model	ENGINE cc/cyl	DATES	CONDITION 1	2	3
Hurricane	1991/6	1945-53	£10,000	£7,000	£4,000
Typhoon	1991/6	1946-50	£7,000	£3,000	£2,000
Lancaster/Whitley	1991/ 2306/6	1945-53	£8,500	£6,500	£3,500
Sapphire 234/236	2290/4 2309/6	1955-58	£7,500	£5,000	£3,000
Sapphire 346	3440/6	1953-58	£9,000	£5,000	£3,000
Star Sapphire	3990/6	1958-60	£10,000	£7,000	£4,000

ASTON MARTIN

The impact and allure of Aston Martin is far beyond the small numbers built. The company's first prototype was made in 1914, the second completed in 1919 with limited production commencing in 1922. Since then production has always remained limited and it was not until 1984 that the 10,000th Aston Martin, a V8 model, was built. For much of its life, until Ford took control in 1987, Aston Martin's existence has been precarious. It first went bankrupt in 1925; then in 1947 industrialist David Brown took over, heralding the era of the glamourous DB – or

David Brown – Astons. In many ways these were the glory years with racing successes capped by a 1959 Le Mans win for Carrol Shelby and Roy Salvadori in a DBR1. On the road the DB4, 5 and 6 models were the stuff of dreams – literally – with a DB4 costing approximately two E-type Jaguars. Yet the company still struggled financially. In 1972 David Brown gave up the struggle – losses were reckoned at £1 million a year – and after several changes of ownership the company's future became secure when Ford took over in 1987.

1938 Aston Martin 15/98 2 litre, 1950cc, 4 cylinders, originally bodied as a long-chassis Bertelli Saloon, purchased derelict and transformed into a 4-seater open tourer in 1996 after a 4-year rebuild, engine rebuilt at a cost of £6,500, only 500 miles covered since.
£11,000–13,000 *COYS*

The 15/98 was designed as a sporting tourer that would have a wider appeal than a high-performance sports car. The result was essentially a detuned Speed Model with wet rather than dry sump lubrication. Performance was impressive, the 98bhp motor providing an 85mph maximum speed and 0–50mph acceleration in around 13 seconds.

1952 Aston Martin DB2 Saloon, 2580cc, 6 cylinders, double overhead camshaft, 125bhp at 5,000rpm, 4-speed manual gearbox, complete body up restoration begun in 1989 to return the car to original show condition, over £42,000 spent since, engine to Vantage specification.
£33,000–37,000 *C*

1949 Aston Martin DB1 Two-Door Cabriolet, 1970cc, 4 cylinders, overhead valve engine, 115bhp, one of only 15 built, good condition throughout, no known modifications from the factory specification.
£30,000–35,000 *BKS*

The 2.6 litre twin-cam engine had been designed under the guidance of the legendary W. O. Bentley. It was a superb design that remained the mainstay of all Aston Martins until the arrival of a new V8 in late 1969.

ASTON MARTIN Model	ENGINE cc/cyl	DATES	CONDITION 1	2	3
Lionel Martin Cars	1486/4	1921-25	£26,000	£18,000	£16,000
International	1486/4	1927-32	£36,000	£20,000	£16,000
Le Mans	1486/4	1932-33	£52,000	£38,000	£32,000
Mk II	1486/4	1934-36	£40,000	£30,000	£25,000
Ulster	1486/4	1934-36	£80,000+	£50,000	-
2 litre	1950/4	1936-40	£30,000	£20,000	£12,000

Value is dependent upon racing history, originality and completeness.
Add 40% if a competition winner or works team car.

1955 Aston Martin DB2/4 Two-Door Sports Coupé, 3 litre, 140bhp, restored, gearbox and rear axle inspected on reassembling the car, which otherwise has been totally rebuilt.
£26,000–29,000 *BKS*

1958 Aston Martin DB MkIII Saloon, left-hand drive, restored, fitted with later Aston Martin engine, very good overall condition.
£29,000–34,000 *S*

l. **1961 Aston Martin DB4 Series II,** 3670cc, 6 cylinders, excellent restored condition, documented history.
£35,000–38,000 *MEE*

l. **1961 Aston Martin DB4 Series III Sports Saloon,** 3670cc, double overhead camshaft, 6 cylinder engine, right-hand drive, green metallic paintwork with matching interior trim and leather upholstery, manual transmission, comprehensive history file and servicing records, unrestored, good condition.
£28,000–30,000 *BKS*

When the DB4 was introduced in 1958, it was the most powerful and fastest British production car, and its aerodynamic styling by Touring of Milan looked sensational. The all-aluminium bodywork, was built to Touring's Superleggera principles, mounted on a trellis of small-diameter tubes welded together.

ASTON MARTIN Model	ENGINE cc/cyl	DATES	CONDITION 1	2	3
DB1	1970/4	1948-50	£30,000	£20,000	£16,000
DB2	2580/6	1950-53	£30,000+	£18,000	£14,000
DB2 Conv	2580/6	1951-53	£35,000+	£28,000+	£17,000
DB2/4 Mk I/II	2580/ 2922/6	1953-57	£30,000	£18,000	£14,000
DB2/4 Mk II Conv	2580/ 2922/6	1953-57	£40,000	£25,000	£15,000
DB2/4 Mk III	2580/ 2922/6	1957-59	£40,000	£22,000	£15,000
DB2/4 Mk III Conv	2580/ 2922/6	1957-59	£38,000+	£26,000	£20,000
DB Mk III Conv	2922/6	1957-59	£46,000	£28,000	£20,000
DB Mk III	2922/6	1957-59	£35,000	£22,000	£18,000
DB4	3670/6	1959-63	£35,000	£22,000	£16,000
DB4 Conv	3670/6	1961-63	£60,000	£35,000	-
DB4 GT	3670/6	1961-63	£100,000+	£80,000	-
DB5	3995/6	1964-65	£35,000	£26,000	£20,000
DB5 Conv	3995/6	1964-65	£48,000+	£38,000	-
DB6	3995/6	1965-69	£30,000	£20,000	£16,000
DB6 Mk I auto	3995/6	1965-69	£28,000	£18,000	£14,000
DB6 Mk I Volante	3995/6	1965-71	£45,000+	£32,000	£28,000
DB6 Mk II Volante	3995/6	1969-70	£50,000+	£40,000	£30,000
DBS	3995/6	1967-72	£14,000	£15,000	£9,000
AM Vantage	5340/8	1977-78	£20,000	£15,000	£10,000
V8 Vantage Oscar India	5340/8	1978-82	£30,000+	£25,000	£20,000
V8 Volante	5340/8	2978-82	£40,000+	£30,000	£25,000

1963 Aston Martin DB5 Convertible, 4 litre, 282bhp, left-hand drive, never restored, poor paintwork, bodywork in good original condition with no rust, interior average condition, in most other respects in very good condition. £59,000–64,000 *BKS*

1967 Aston Martin DB6 Vantage, 325bhp, manual gearbox, power steering, documented history, superb restored condition. £48,000–52,000 *MEE*

1965 Aston Martin DB5, 3995cc, 6 cylinders, chassis restored between 1985 and 1990, engine has undergone major work, 5-speed ZF gearbox, 3,000 miles completed since steering bushes replaced. £18,500–22,000 *BRIT*

The Aston Martin DB5 was tested by Autocar *in September 1963. Performance figures of 0–60mph in 8.1 seconds and a top speed of 142.6mph were recorded. In all, 1,021 DB5s were built, of which 123 were convertibles and 12 were shooting brakes. Production came to an end in September 1965.*

Did You Know?

- The DB6 may ooze pure-bred Bulldog Britishness, but the styling is an evolution of the Touring of Milan-designed DB4.
- Prince Charles owns a DB6 Volante.
- At top speeds, the upturned tail of the DB6 was said to reduce aerodynamic lift by half.
- Six DB6 estates were built by coachbuilder Harold Radford.

l. **1969 Aston Martin DB6 Volante,** automatic gearbox, power steering, complete service history, only 30,000 miles from new, outstanding original condition. £65,000–75,000 *MEE*

Aston Martin DB6 (1965–71)

Engine: 3995cc, straight-six, double overhead camshaft.
Power output: 282–325bhp.
Transmission: ZF five-speed manual or Borg-Warner automatic.
Brakes: Four-wheel discs.
Top speed: 148+mph.
0–60mph: 6.1–6.7 seconds.
0–100mph: 15 seconds.
Production: 1,753.
Price in 1967: £5,084 for Vantage saloon.
Prices today: Saloon, £20,000–40,000; Volante (convertible), £35,000–65,000.

If James Bond had ever hung up his Walther PPK and settled down with wife and kids, the DB6 with its characteristic upturned Kamm tail would have been the Aston for him. With 4 proper seats, the option of automatic transmission and power steering, it was almost practical.
Of the classic DB series, which began with the DB4 in 1958, the DB6 was also the fastest. However, in the eyes of some enthusiasts, it is a little softer and less outrightly sporting than its forebears. Consequently, the DB6, although the most civilised of the classic DB saloons, is the least prized and most affordable.

1970 Aston Martin DB6 MkII, 3995cc, 6 cylinders, engine rebuilt, low mileage covered since, engine bay detailing, bare metal respray, new wire wheels, new Wilton carpets, new head lining, fitted with Koni shock absorbers all-round and SU carburettors instead of the Brico fuel injection system.
£28,000–32,000 *COYS*

In August 1969, the DB6 was announced in MkII guise. Visually, it differed from the MkI in having flared wheel arches and the wider wheels of the concurrent DBS, but mechanically it remained the same, albeit with power steering as standard. Production of the DB6 MkII ended in November 1970.

1970 Aston Martin DBS Vantage, 4 litre, 6 cylinders engine, twin-cam, manual gearbox, 44,000 recorded miles.
£12,500–14,000 *S*

l. **1979 Aston Martin V8 Volante,** 5340cc, 8 cylinders, £8,000 spent on restoration, inner and outer sills replaced, paintwork renovated, mechanical parts completely stripped, worn components renewed, Vantage front spoiler added, very good condition.
£37,000–40,000 *COYS*

AUBURN

1931 Auburn 8-98A Cabriolet, 8 cylinder in-line Lycoming side valve engine, 268cu in, 98hp at 3,400rpm, 3-speed manual gearbox, semi-elliptic leaf-sprung suspension front and rear, 4-wheel drum brakes, 10 year restoration, has received a great number of awards.
£31,000–35,000 *C*

Auburn was started in 1903 by Frank and Morris Eckhart of Auburn, Indiana. As the automobile business grew and began to involve large operations, most of the smaller companies were overwhelmed, but Auburn trudged on. They were one of only a few companies to experience increased sales during the Depression because they had more dealerships. Eventually, however, Auburn's size caught up with them. In 1925, E. L. Cord became Auburn's general manager and set out to save the company. He gave the cars much needed style. Cord started the policy of changing body styles every few years to maintain sales. In 1925, he introduced the 8-63 and 8-88 models into the range designed by James Crawford, utilizing the Lycoming straight-eight engine. This model proved very successful and continued until 1930, when the effects of the Depression really began to take hold. Consequently, Auburn decided to sell just one model and introduced the 8-98.

AUSTIN

In 1905, Herbert Austin left the fledgling Wolseley company to set up the Austin Motor Company at Longbridge, on the outskirts of Birmingham, and by 1914 the young company, guided by the legendary hard-working Austin, had become Britain's biggest car manufacturer. For his company's contribution to the war effort Herbert Austin was knighted in 1917 and in 1922 made another mark with the incredible Austin 7. Austin became the first Baron Austin of Longbridge in 1936, but died in 1941. The company he founded merged with rival Morris in 1952 to form the British Motor Corporation and thereafter the product lines converged until, eventually, the Austin name disappeared in 1987. The legacy of Austin is a wide variety of affordable classics from the original Austin 7 and Austin 7 Mini of 1959, the humble A30 and A35, to a broad range of family saloons and the occasional odd-ball such as the charming Austin Metropolitan and the glamourous US-influenced A90 Atlantic.

1912 Austin 10/12, 4 cylinders, excellent original condition, unrestored, VCC dated.
£23,000–25,000   *SVV*

1931 Austin 7 Box Saloon, 747cc, 4 cylinders, restored, retrimmed, later 4-speed gearbox.
£4,000–4,500   *UMC*

1931 Austin Chummy, 747cc, reconditioned engine, finished in maroon and black.
£4,250–4,750   *VIN*

AUSTIN Model	ENGINE cc/cyl	DATES	CONDITION 1	2	3
25/30	4900/4	1906	£35,000	£25,000	£20,000
20/4	3600/4	1919-29	£20,000	£12,000	£6,000
12	1661/4	1922-26	£8,000	£5,000	£2,000
7/Chummy	747/4	1924-39	£7,000	£5,000	£2,500
7 Coachbuilt/Nippy/Opal etc	747/4	1924-39	£10,000	£9,000	£7,000
12/4	1861/4	1927-35	£5,500	£5,000	£2,000
16	2249/6	1928-36	£9,000	£7,000	£4,000
20/6	3400/6	1928-38	£12,500	£10,000	£8,000
12/6	1496/6	1932-37	£6,000	£4,000	£1,500
12/4	1535/4	1933-39	£5,000	£3,500	£1,500
10 and 10/4	1125/4	1932-47	£4,000	£3,000	£1,000
10 and 10/4 Conv	1125/4	1933-47	£5,000	£3,500	£1,000
18	2510/6	1934-39	£8,000	£5,000	£3,000
14	1711/6	1937-39	£6,000	£4,000	£2,000
Big Seven	900/4	1938-39	£4,000	£2,500	£1,500
8	900/4	1939-47	£3,000	£2,000	£1,000
28	4016/6	1939	£6,000	£4,000	£2,000

Prices for early Austin models are dependent on body style, landaulette, tourer, etc.

Austin 7 (1922–39)

Engine: Water-cooled, 4 cylinders, 747.5cc.
Power output: 13–23bhp.
Transmission: Three-speed manual; four-speed from 1933.
Top speed: 45+mph.
Price in 1923: £165.

The diminutive Austin 7 may have been the car Sir Herbert Austin didn't want to make, but it revived his company's fortunes when near bankruptcy, and introduced motoring in miniature to first-time car owners all over the world. As the short-lived boom after WWI turned into depression, Sir Herbert was forced to consider a small, cheap car to match the shrinking pockets of his customers, and when he showed his wife the first Austin 7, he is reported to have said, 'There, that's what we have got to come to.'

Austin envisioned the buyer of the car as being 'the man who, at present, can only afford a motorcycle and side-car combination and yet has the ambition to become a motorist.' His hunch was right: the diminutive Austin 7 was acclaimed as a 'scaled-down motor car, rather than scaled-up motorcycling', and eventually sold more than 375,000. Today, its cheeky charm will still raise a chuckle, even if you're stuck behind one teetering along a country lane.

1933 Austin 7 Box Saloon, 747cc, 4 cylinders, very good condition.
£3,500–4,000 *CC*

1933 Austin 7 Special, 747cc, 4 cylinders, restoration recently completed, panelled in aluminium and finished in French Racing blue, engine rebuilt, all mechanical components good, remote gearchange linkage, all-new tyres, exhaust and interior trim in blue leathercloth.
£3,000–3,500 *BRIT*

Such was the popularity of the Austin 7 that as the model grew old and its value diminished, enthusiasts of modest means acquired tired examples and stripped them down to be rebodied in a sporting fashion.

1935 Austin 7 Opal Two-Seater Tourer, 747cc, 4 cylinder, kept in South Africa since new, repatriated in 1994 and subsequently stored, finished in blue and black, sound condition, engine recently overhauled, new clutch linings, export-model 18in wheels and four-blade cooling fan, retrimmed blue vinyl interior.
£3,350–3,750 *BRIT*

By 1935, despite the fact that the Austin 7 had been in production for 13 years, it was still selling in vast numbers, the lowest priced model in the Austin catalogue for that year being the Opal two-seat tourer, priced at 100 guineas (£105). Whereas the rest of the Austin range had adopted the cowled radiator style for 1935, the Opal retained its chrome radiator until 1936.

Did You Know?

- The Austin 7 was made under licence in several countries: by Nissan in Japan; as the Rosengart in France; as the Bantam in the USA; and as the Dixi in Germany. The Dixi was the first motor car assembled by BMW, and it's a poignant irony that what was once Austin now belongs to BMW.
- The Austin 7 will fit on a full-size billiard table – because the original plans for the Austin 7 were drawn up on a billiard table at Herbert Austin's home, Lickey Grange.

1935 Austin 7 Nippy, 747cc, 4 cylinders, in good order throughout mechanically, engine fitted with 4-branch exhaust manifold and SU carburettor, electrical system in good order, black vinyl hood with hood cover, full tonneau, reupholstered seats. **£5,500–6,000** *BRIT*

First introduced in 1933 as the Type 65, this sports model became known as the Nippy. The specification included a modified front axle and underslung rear springs, together with a tuned engine developing 21bhp.

1934 Austin 10/4 Saloon, 1141cc, 4 cylinder, 4-speed manual gearbox, fair to good condition throughout, no MOT. **£2,500–3,000** *H&H*

1938 Austin 10 Cambridge Saloon, first owned by Winston Churchill. **£60,000–70,000** *S*

Austin of England provided Winston Churchill with arguably his most famous wartime transport, in the form of a standard 10 Cambridge saloon. The black, four-door version was registered, with Winston Churchill's signature in the log book as first owner, on 3 June 1938. The car remained in his ownership until 1950. It was put up for sale, in good repair, at Sotheby's in October 1967 and acquired by the Sixth Marquess of Bath, long interested in establishing a Churchill collection at his Wiltshire estate.

Miller's Starter Marque

Starter Austins: *Austin 7; A55/60 Cambridge; A90/95/99/105/110 Westminster; Metropolitan; A30/35/40; 1100 and 1300.*

- Although, in general, post-war Austin models were quite populous, not all are in plentiful supply. Those listed above have been blessed with a good survival rate, spares and club support, and normally possess those Austin virtues of sturdiness and dependability.

- From the pre-war period, the Austin 7 offers a viable entry to vintage-style motoring and the friendly competition of The Vintage Sportscar Club. Over 290,000 were made between 1922 and 1939, making them still plentiful today. They are affordable, too, and tremendous fun.

- One of the most engaging Austins of the post-war era is the cute Austin/Nash Metropolitan, which came in a choice of dazzling ice-cream colours – red, yellow and turquoise over white. Initially, the Metropolitan, was built by Austin for the American Nash company as a 'sub-compact', or two-thirds scale 'Yank tank'. It was available in the UK from 1957.

1932 Austin Two-Door Tourer, 3133cc, 4 cylinders, dickey seat, good original order, garage stored since 1991. **£5,000–5,500** *S*

Products of the Austin Motor Company of Longbridge represented around a quarter of total British output of private cars in the late 1920s and during the following decade, when a choice of over 50 models was available. For a time, the company was the largest domestic manufacturer of motor cars. The Heavy Four met the demand for a moderate sized car offering good performance at an economic price.

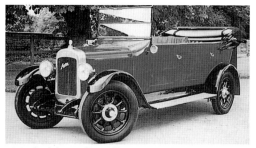

1927 Austin 20 Open Tourer, 4 cylinders, rebodied shortly after the war by Caffyns, restored a few years ago, generally good condition, running well.
£12,000–13,000 *BKS*

1935 Austin 16 Five-Seater Saloon, 2249cc, 6 cylinder side valve engine, very good condition.
£7,500–8,500 *CC*

| Cross Reference |
| For Austin Mini see Mini |

l. **1936 Austin Ascot Saloon,** 1775cc, 4 cylinders, 4-speed manual gearbox, current MOT, 87,000 miles recorded and believed to be genuine, restored in 1985, hardly used since.
£4,250–4,750 *H&H*

1936 Austin 12/6, sound condition.
£3,400–3,900 *CC*

1933 Austin 12/6 Harley Saloon, 1496cc, 6 cylinders, good condition, reconditioned engine, well maintained, retrimmed in leathercloth.
£6,000–7,000 *UMC*

r. **1938 Austin Mayfair Limousine,** 3400cc, 6 cylinders, extensively rebuilt in the 1980s, on long-term display at Longleat, has seen little recent use.
£10,000–11,000 *S*

The long-wheelbase Austin 20 Mayfair, at the top end of the Longbridge range, was introduced in 1936.

l. **1948 Austin A125 Sheerline**, 3993cc, 6 cylinders, left-hand drive, sound coachwork, fair original interior, good overall condition.
£3,000–3,500 *BRIT*

1951–56 Austin A30, 803cc, good condition.
£1,500–2,000 *AUS*

1957–59 Austin A35, 948cc, good condition.
£2,000–2,500 *AUS*

r. **1955 Austin A30 Saloon,** 803cc, 45,000 miles from new, detailed history.
£2,200–2,600 *H&H*

Austin A30/A35 (1951–59)

Body styles: Two- and four-door saloon, Countryman estate, van and pick-up.
Engine: OHV four-cylinder, 803cc (A30); 948cc (A35).
Power output: 28bhp at 4,500rpm (A30); 34bhp at 5,100 rpm (A35).
Transmission: Four-speed manual.
Brakes: Hydro-mechanical drums.
Top speed: 65mph (A30); 75mph (A35).
0–60mph: 38 seconds (A30); 29 seconds ((A35).
Fuel consumption: 35–45mpg.
Production: 576,672.
Price in 1951: £529.

When the Austin A30 appeared in 1951, the peanut-shaped four-seater was intended to rival the Morris Minor, launched in 1948. But shortly after the baby Austin appeared, the two rival companies merged under the BMC banner. Even though it was a moderate success, the Austin was rather overshadowed by the million-selling Minor. Nevertheless, the A30 was a pert and capable economy package. It was the first Austin to feature unitary construction, initially being equipped with a peppy 803cc overhead-valve engine, the first of the famous A-series engines that went on to power the Mini and Metro. In 1956, the A30 was updated to become the A35. Externally, it featured a larger rear window and other detail changes, but underneath had a 948cc engine that considerably improved performance. Saloon production ended in 1959 with the arrival of the Mini, but A35 vans continued to be built until 1968.

**1956 Austin
A30,** 803cc.
£1,000–1,200 *CGC*

1957 Austin Metropolitan Saloon, 1489cc,
4 cylinders, good overall condition.
£1,200–1,600 *Pou*

r. **1957 Austin A35
Pick-up,** 948cc, one
of only about 60
known to exist.
£3,000–4,000 *AUS*

*Fewer than 500 A35
Pick-ups were made,
and they rarely come
up for sale.*

1960/61 Austin A40 Farina Saloon MkI,
full history, sound original condition.
£900–1,150 *UMC*

1960 Austin A40, 948cc, 4 cylinders, Town and
Country tyres all-round, auxiliary lamps, competed
successfully in the 1995 Monte Carlo Challenge.
£1,000–1,300 *BRIT* .

*The Farina-designed Austin A40 replaced the A35 in
1958. Despite its new look, the mechanical components
were as before, as was the Austin dependability.*

1959 Austin DS7 Princess IV Saloon,
coachwork by Vanden Plas, BMC 4 litre engine,
General Motors Hydramatic transmission, stored
in a heated building for 15 years, has undergone
a major £5,000 overhaul, including new brakes,
exhaust and steering.
£5,500–6,500 *BKS*

*Commenting on the new Vanden Plas Princess IV
announced for the 1956 Earl's Court Show, The
Autocar wrote: 'The new Princess allies high power,
effortless cruising, easy and accurate control, good
looks and the finest in coachwork and comfort. All
these are to be purchased at around half the cost of
the most expensive cars in this category, so that its
power to compete and indeed make a real impact
on this specialised market is apparent.'*

1963 Austin Cambridge A60 Deluxe Saloon,
1622cc, manual transmission, original condition,
13,000 miles, original tyres, spare unused, red
leather interior preserved in excellent condition
by leopard skin-patterned seat covers.
£2,500–2,750 *BKS*

*After Pinin Farina's successful redesign of the A40,
Austin's larger cars duly received attention from
the Italian coachbuilders. The first of these – the
Austin Cambridge A55 MkII – appeared in 1959.
Also badged as a Morris, MG, Riley and Wolseley,
the newcomer had new bodywork sporting
controversial tail fins. The Cambridge was
revamped for 1962 as the A60 with revised styling
– out went the fins.*

1968 Austin Princess 1300, 1275cc, 4 cylinders,
Bordeaux metallic finish, wood and leather-
trimmed interior, well maintained, good condition.
£3,750–4,250 *Pou*

1972 Austin 1300, 18,000 warranted miles, one
owner from new, tool kit complete and unused.
£600–800 *PA*

AUSTIN Model	ENGINE cc/cyl	DATES	CONDITION 1	2	3
16	2199/4	1945-49	£3,000	£2,000	£1,000
A40 Devon	1200/4	1947-52	£2,000	£1,200	£750
A40 Sports	1200/4	1950-53	£6,000	£4,000	£2,000
A40 Somerset	1200/4	1952-54	£2,000	£1,500	£750
A40 Somerset DHC	1200/4	1954	£5,000	£4,000	£2,500
A40 Dorset 2 door	1200/4	1947-48	£2,000	£1,500	£1,000
A70 Hampshire	2199/4	1948-50	£2,000	£1,500	£1,000
A70 Hereford	2199/4	1950-54	£2,000	£1,500	£1,000
A90 Atlantic DHC	2660/4	1949-52	£8,000	£6,000	£4,000
A90 Atlantic	2660/4	1949-52	£6,000	£4,000	£3,000
A40/A50 Cambridge	1200/4	1954-57	£1,200	£750	£500
A55 Mk I Cambridge	1489/4	1957-59	£1,000	£750	£500
A55 Mk II	1489/4	1959-61	£1,000	£750	£500
A60 Cambridge	1622/4	1961-69	£1,000	£750	£500
A90/95 Westminster	2639/6	1954-59	£2,000	£1,500	£750
A99 Westminster	2912/6	1959-61	£1,500	£1,000	£500
A105 Westminster	2639/6	1956-59	£2,000	£1,500	£750
A110 Mk I/II	2912/6	1961-68	£2,000	£1,500	£750
Nash Metropolitan	1489/4	1957-61	£2,500	£1,500	£750
Nash Metropolitan DHC	1489/4	1957-61	£4,000	£3,000	£1,500
A30	803/4	1952-56	£1,000	£500	-
A30 Countryman	803/4	1954-56	£1,500	£1,000	-
A35	948/4	1956-59	£1,000	£500	-
A35 Countryman	948/4	1956-62	£1,500	£1,000	-
A40 Farina Mk I	948/4	1958-62	£1,250	£750	£200
A40 Mk I Countryman	948/4	1959-62	£1,500	£1,000	£400
A40 Farina Mk II	1098/4	1962-67	£1,000	£750	-
A40 Mk II Countryman	1098/4	1962-67	£1,200	£750	£300
1100	1098/4	1963-73	£1,000	£750	-
1300 Mk I/II	1275/4	1967-74	£750	£500	-
1300GT	1275/4	1969-74	£1,250	£1,000	£750
1800/2200	1800/2200/4	1964-75	£1,500	£900	£600
3 litre	2912/6	1968-71	£3,000	£1,500	£500

AUSTIN-HEALEY

Donald Mitchell Healey, born in Cornwall in 1898, could well have become a motor-racing hero in his own right. From 1930 to 1934 he raced for the small British firm of Invicta, winning the Monte Carlo outright in an S-type Invicta in 1931. Yet instead of chasing laurels as a racing driver he chose to pursue a career as an automotive engineer, working before WWII for Riley and Triumph. Then, from 1946 to 1954 producing his own Healey sporting motor cars, but always in limited numbers. In 1952, his career took a dramatic turn when he unveiled his latest design, the Healey 100, at the Earl's Court Motor Show in London. He had already contracted to use an Austin engine in this new sports car and such was the public response that Austin agreed to manufacture the whole car to give birth to the Austin-Healey marque. Although continually updated the basic design lasted until 1968.

1954 Austin-Healey 100, 3-speed with overdrive gearbox, one of the minority of BN1s built in right-hand drive form, restored in 1988/89, £7,500 spent since, full engine rebuild in 1996.
£14,000–16,000   *BKS*

1955 Austin-Healey 100/4, 2660cc, 4 cylinders, new Dunlop tyres, braking system and carburettors overhauled, underside treated with Hammerite, sills and box sections injected with Waxoyl, 33,827 miles.
£23,000–26,000   *BRIT*

l. **1957 Austin-Healey 100/6**, 2639cc, unrestored, factory works specification.
£17,000–18,000   *THOR*

1956 Austin-Healey 100M, 2660cc, 4 cylinders, restored c1990, left-hand drive.
£18,500–22,500   *BKS*

The short-lived BN2, introduced at the 1955 London Motor Show and destined for production during the succeeding model year, was only available in uprated form as the 100M, equipped with Le Mans kit engine improvements as standard. These raised maximum power to 110bhp without loss of flexibility, and increased top speed to 109mph. Only 640 100Ms were produced, making the model one of the rarest and most desirable of Healeys.

r. **1959 Austin-Healey 100/6**, 2639cc, imported from Texas in 1989, completely restored in 1990, converted to right-hand drive, over £14,000 spent on restoration, has won various cups and trophies since.
£15,500–18,000   *H&H*

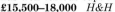

Austin-Healey 3000 (1959–68)

Engine: 2912cc overhead-valve straight-six.
Body styles: Two-seater roadster, 2+2 roadster, 2+2 convertible.
Power output: 3000 MkI, 124bhp at 4,600rpm; 3000 MkII, 132bhp at 4,750rpm; 3000 MkIII, 150bhp at 5,250rpm.
Transmission: Four-speed manual with overdrive.
Brakes: Front discs; rear drum.
Top speed: 110–120mph.
0–60mph: 9.5–10.8 seconds.
Production: 42,926 (all 3000 models).

What to watch: Rust can turn Healey heaven into a nightmare. A lot have been imported to the UK from the US, so make sure your right-hand-drive car didn't start life as a left-hooker. If it did, pay less. Triple-carburettor 3000 MkIIs are tricky to set up.
Austin-Healey fact: As US safety and emissions rules began to stranlge the Austin-Healey, Donald Healey considered widening the

body to accommodate the Rolls-Royce 4 litre engine. Only 3 prototypes were built before the project was scuppered.

Donald Healey had a vision of an affordable, true 100mph sports car that would fill a gap in the American market between the Jaguar XK120 and the cheap and cheerful MG T-Series. The Austin-Healey 100 fitted the bill perfectly and, in fact, about 80 per cent of all production went Stateside. The original Austin-Healey 100/4 became the 100/6 in 1956 when it received a 2639cc six-cylinder engine. Then, in 1959, this was bored out to 2912cc and rounded up to give the model name Austin-Healey 3000. For most, the 3000 rates as the definitive 'Big Healey'. Faster and more refined than earlier versions, it had front disc brakes and, later, even wind-up windows, but it was still spartan enough to appeal to died-in-the-wool sports car enthusiasts.

1959 Austin-Healey 100/6, 2639cc, left-hand drive, restored to show standard.
£13,000–15,000 *Mot*

1959 Austin-Healey 3000 MkI, 4-speed manual gearbox with overdrive, left-hand drive, new clutch, gearbox rebuilt, new half wiring loom, fuel pump, starter motor, water pump, front exhaust and dampers, fully resprayed.
£9,500–11,000 *H&H*

1957 Austin-Healey 100/6, 2639cc, 6 cylinders, excellent condition.
£16,000–20,000 *FCV*

AUSTIN HEALEY Model	ENGINE cc/cyl	DATES	CONDITION 1	2	3
100 BN 1/2	2660/4	1953-56	£20,000	£14,000	£8,000
100/6, BN4/BN6	2639/6	1956-59	£18,000	£13,500	£8,000
3000 Mk I	2912/6	1959-61	£20,000	£13,000	£8,500
3000 Mk II	2912/6	1961-62	£22,000	£15,000	£9,000
3000 Mk IIA	2912/6	1962-64	£23,000	£15,000	£11,000
3000 Mk III	2912/6	1964-68	£24,000	£17,000	£11,000
Sprite Mk I	948/4	1958-61	£7,000	£6,000	£3,000
Sprite Mk II	948/4	1961-64	£4,000	£3,000	£2,000
Sprite Mk III	1098/4	1964-66	£4,500	£3,000	£1,500
Sprite Mk IV	1275/4	1966-71	£5,000	£3,000	£1,500

l. **1959 Austin-Healey 3000 MkI,** 2912cc. **£10,500–12,000** *H&H*

1960 Austin-Healey 3000 MkI, BT7 2+2 version, left-hand drive, overdrive transmission, restored to highest standard, chassis and bodyshell stripped to bare metal, latter renovated using original Austin-Healey panels, full mechanical overhaul, new wiring loom, interior trim, carpets, glass and chrome.
£15,250–17,500 *BKS*

A development of the preceding 100/6 rather than a genuinely new model, the Austin-Healey 3000 was launched in March 1959. The two cars looked virtually identical; under the skin was the same separate ladder-type chassis and independent front/live rear axle suspension. However, improvements to the 3000 included a slightly enlarged (to 2912cc) version of the C-series six-cylinder engine and Girling disc brakes up front. Breathing through twin SU carburettors, the revised power unit produced 124bhp at 4,600rpm. Top speed – with optional hardtop fitted – was increased to 114mph, with 0–60mph in around 11 seconds.

1961 Austin-Healey 3000 MkII, 124bhp at 4,600rpm, right-hand drive, one owner from new, restored between 1991 and 1993 at a cost of £100,000.
£23,000–27,000 *BKS*

Unveiled in March 1961, the MkII version with restyled grille and bonnet intake was the last 3000 available as a two-seater.

1966 Austin-Healey 3000 MkIII Phase 2, left-hand drive, totally stripped to bare metal, chassis rebuilt, complete body restoration, new floor, sills and outriggers, all mechanical components overhauled or rebuilt, all electrical components replaced or rebuilt, new wiring loom, completely retrimmed, new carpets, plated fittings either brand new or rechromed, new stainless steel exhaust, concours condition.
£19,000–22,000 *PA*

1963 Austin-Healey 3000 MkIIA 2+2, 2912cc, right-hand drive, 5,000 miles since complete restoration at a cost of £25,000.
£14,500–16,000 *PA*

1966 Austin-Healey 3000 MkIII, right-hand drive, full body and trim restoration in 1996, excellent condition throughout.
£19,500–22,000 *BKS*

The Austin-Healey 3000 MkIII, with the more powerful 148bhp engine, appeared in the spring of 1964, to be followed later that year by the Phase 2 version. The latter featured revised rear suspension to eliminate axle tramp. The most obvious new development, though, was the improved interior's walnut-veneered dashboard. Although more luxurious, the 3000's performance remained formidable: top speed was 121mph and the 0–60mph time dipped below 10 seconds. By the time production ended in December 1967, over 16,000 Phase 2 3000s – the car's most popular variant – had been built.

Miller's Starter Marque

Starter Austin-Healeys: *Austin-Healey Sprite MkI 'Frog-eye'; Austin-Healey Sprite II–V.*

- The Donald Healey Motor Company and Austin had forged close links in the early 1950s with their co-operative venture, the Austin-Healey 100. In 1958, its little brother, the Sprite, was born, a small spartan sports car designed down to a price and based on the engine and running gear of the Austin A35 saloon, with a bit of Morris Minor too. The A35 saloon was perfectly adequate, admirable even, but the sports car that borrowed so many components from it was different altogether. Curvaceous and captivating, nimble and peppy, it belied its stock origins. It was affordable too, yet the 'Frog-eye' really was a sports car and had a sweet raspberry exhaust note to prove it.

- In 1961 the 'Frog-eye' was reclothed in the more conventional skin of the MG Midget; the Sprite versions endured until 1971, while the Midget soldiered on until 1979.

- All Austin-Healey Sprites are viable restore-while-you-drive cars with readily available parts and a strong club and specialist network.

1958 Austin-Healey Sprite MkI, 948cc, British Racing green with matching interior, wire wheels, restored.
£9,000–10,000 *BC*

1959 Austin-Healey Sprite MkI, 948cc, 4 cylinder pushrod overhead valve engine, twin SU carburettors, 42.5bhp at 5,000rpm, 4-speed manual gearbox, wishbone and coil spring independent front suspension, live rear axle with quarter-elliptic leaf springs, hydraulically operated drum brakes all-round, right-hand drive, low mileage, comprehensively restored between 1990 and 1994 at a total cost of £10,500 (including basic cost of the car), engine modified to accept lead-free petrol, 34,994 miles.
£9,000–10,000   *C*

Austin Healey Sprite MkI (1958–61)

Body Style: Two-seater roadster.
Construction: Unitary body/chassis.
Engine: BMC A-Series 948cc, four cylinder, overhead valve.
Power Output: 43bhp at 5,200rpm.
Transmission: Four-speed manual, synchromesh on top three ratios.
Suspension: Front: independent, coil springs and wishbones. Rear: quarter-elliptic leaf springs, rigid axle.
Brakes: Hydraulic, drums all-round.
Top Speed: 84mph.
0–60mph: 20.5 seconds.
Average Fuel Consumption: 35–45mpg.
Production: 38,999.
Price in 1958: £668 17s.

1960 Austin-Healey Sprite MkI, 948cc, 4 cylinder, totally rebuilt to original specification, all major components fully reconditioned, new stainless steel exhaust system fitted.
£7,000–8,000   *BRIT*

1968 Austin-Healey Sprite MkIV, 1275cc, wire wheels, totally restored, £14,000 spent (including the original purchase and £3,500 respray), 23,000 miles from new.
£4,500–5,000   *H&H*

AUTOVIA

The short-lived Autovia was conceived from Victor Riley's desire to produce a luxury car, and in 1935 he began to examine the potential of the project. For practical assistance, Riley turned to C. M. Van Eugen, who had spent his working life with Daimler and Lea-Francis. He became entirely responsible for this make, the intention being to enter the Rolls-Royce 25/30 market. Van Eugen designed a new 2829cc V8 engine based on the Riley block, and this was fitted into a very low chassis.

1939 Autovia Special Two-Seater, 2849cc, original V8 engine, 4 SU carburettors, tubular exhaust manifolds, 4-speed pre-selector gearbox. totally rebuilt on a short chassis with an aluminium body on an ash frame.
£9,500–11,000   *H&H*

This particular example was the penultimate Autovia made.

BARRE

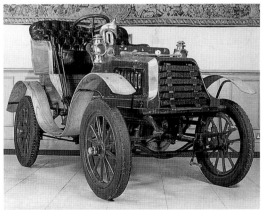

1903 Barré Type Y Two-Seater, 699cc, De Dion Bouton single-cylinder engine with automatic inlet valve, cone clutch, 3-speed and reverse gearbox, semi-elliptic front and rear suspension, rear wheel and transmission brakes, right-hand drive, not running, but all components present.
£18,000–20,000   *C*

Despite the Barré body plates, dashboard plate and a gearbox lid that proclaim 'Barré Constructeurs, Niort', this car is pure Lacoste et Battmann with its De Dion Bouton engine. Although the bodywork may not be original, it has been on the tubular chassis for a long time and is of the correct style for a Barré of this type and age.

The French firm of Barré started in the early 1890s as cycle makers and at the turn of the century added motor cars to their output. Like many manufacturers of that time, Barré were assemblers of motor cars, buying in components, and ceased trading in 1930.

BEAN

1924 Bean 11.9 Saloon, 1796cc, 4 cylinders, restored, all nickel-plated fittings in fine order.
£10,500–12,500 *BRIT*

This 11.9 saloon is reputed by the Bean Car Club to be the sole survivor of the model with saloon coachwork. The V-screened body is typical of the period and is of fine appearance in blue and black. It is fitted with an interior partition and is believed to have been built for a funeral director as a following car.

BEDFORD

1919 Bedford Buick 'H' Series 27.3hp Grosvenor Empress Coupé, 4 litre, 6 cylinder valve-in-head engine, 3-speed gearbox, restored in the 1960s.
£8,500–10,000 *BKS*

The Bedford Motor Co (1907) marketed this American-style car as their own, but in fact it was an imported Buick chassis with British coachwork. This particular example has been rallied in Ireland and used in film and TV work.

BENTLEY

After working as a railway engineer and enjoying his recreation as an enthusiastic motorcyclist, Walter Owen Bentley set up his first commercial automotive venture in 1912, when he took over an agency selling three makes of French car just off London's Baker Street. During WWI, he worked on aero-engines and in 1919 founded Bentley Motors. The first 3 litre prototype took to the road in 1920, production getting under way at Cricklewood in north-west London in 1922. Two years later, a 3 Litre won at Le Mans, and a sporting legend was created with further Le Mans victories in 1927, 1928, 1929 and 1930. Yet Bentley's formidable racing reputation wasn't enough to keep the company in the black, and it fell into receivership in 1931, to be taken over by Rolls-Royce in 1933. These refined Derby-built Rolls-Royce-designed Bentleys became known as 'the silent sports cars', and many were graced with supremely elegant bodies. After WWII production resumed at Crewe. The MkVI Bentley of 1946 represented a turning point as the first Rolls-Bentley product to be offered with an off-the-shelf factory body, although special bodies were still available. By 1955 the standard-bodied Bentley S-series was little more than a Rolls-Royce with a Bentley radiator. However, in the 1980s, Bentley began to emerge from the shadows of Rolls-Royce and regain its true sporting identity. In today's market S-Series and T-Series Bentleys can often be slightly cheaper than their Rolls-Royce counterparts.

1921 Bentley 3 Litre Four-Seater Tourer, later Speed Model engine, recently overhauled twin 'sloper' SU carburettors and magneto, A-type close-ratio gearbox, desirable 9ft 9½in short-wheelbase chassis, all original running gear with the exception of 4-wheel brakes fitted by the Bentley factory in 1925, rebodied in replica Vanden Plas tourer style.
£60,000–65,000 *BKS*

From 1919 to 1931 total Bentley production was just 3,024 cars.

1924 Bentley 3 Litre Red Label Speed Model Open Tourer, 2996cc, 4 cylinders, lightweight 4-seater Vanden Plas type open coachwork, short chassis.
£60,000–70,000 *COYS*

1924 Bentley 3 Litre Speed Model Four-Seater Tourer, coachwork by Vanden Plas (originally fitted to a 1925 Speed Model owned by Sir Henry Birkin), well restored, finished in British racing green with green and black upholstery.
£48,000–53,000 *BKS*

W. O. Bentley proudly displayed the new four-cylinder, 3 litre car bearing his own name at the 1919 Olympia Motor Exhibition. In only mildly developed form, this was the model that would become a legend in motor racing history and which, with its leather-strapped bonnet, classic radiator design and British racing green livery, has become the archetypal vintage sports car. By 1924, an investment of £925 brought delivery of the Speed Model 3 litre (or Red Label, as it is popularly known) with the A-type close-ratio gearbox and 90mph performance. The short-wheelbase (9ft 9½in) and twin SU 'sloper' carburettors significantly enhanced the performance in comparison with the standard model and, when fitted with Vanden Plas tourer coachwork, it could be considered the ultimate specification.

1926 Bentley 3 Litre Boat-Tail Two-Seater, one of only 7 fitted with boat-tailed sports coachwork by Surbico (Surbiton Coach & Motor Works), very original.
£86,000–106,000 *BKS*

The '100mph' model, normally distinguished by a unique design of inverse tapered 'Supersports' radiator and bulkhead (as fitted to this car), was the rarest of all the production 3 litre Bentleys. It was inspired by Dr Dudley Benjafield's racing successes at Brooklands in 1924–25 with his 'No. 2' two-seater, built on a standard chassis cut down to a 9ft wheelbase. A high (3.53:1) final drive ratio made the guaranteed 100mph just attainable. The first of these high-performance chassis was delivered in March 1925, and production continued until the summer of 1926. Only 18 '100mph' Bentleys were built.

1930 Bentley Speed Six, Le Mans replica, Green Label short chassis, fully race prepared, excellent condition.
£220,000–250,000 *FHF*

l. **1926 Bentley 3 Litre Red Label Speed Model,** short chassis, Vanden Plas body.
£75,000–95,000 *FHF*

BENTLEY Model	ENGINE cc/cyl	DATES	CONDITION 1	2	3
3 litre	2996/4	1920-27	£100,000	£75,000	£50,000
Speed Six	6597/6	1926-32	£400,000	£250,000	£160,000
4.5 litre	4398/4	1927-31	£175,000	£125,000	£80,000
4.5 litre Supercharged	4398/4	1929-32	£600,000+	£300,000	£200,000
8 litre	7983/6	1930-32	£350,000	£250,000	£100,000
3.5 litre Saloon & DHC	3699/6	1934-37	£70,000	£30,000	£15,000
4.25 litre Saloon & DHC	4257/6	1937-39	£70,000	£35,000	£20,000
Mark V	4257/6	1939-41	£45,000	£25,000	£20,000

Prices are very dependent on engine type, chassis length, matching chassis and engine numbers, body style and original extras like supercharger, gearbox ratio, racing history and originality.

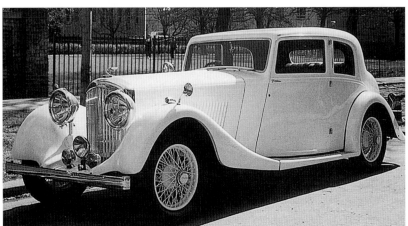

l. **1935 Bentley 3½ Litre Two-Door Coupé,** rare 2-door coupé bodywork by Park Ward, sunroof, rear-mounted spare, complete chassis-up restoration, resprayed in white during 1995/96, reupholstered tan interior, instruments, wood trims and brightwork all in very good condition, electrical equipment rewired, only 2,000 miles covered since engine rebuild.
£29,000–33,000 *S*

1934 Bentley 3½ Litre Three-Position Drophead Coupé, coachwork by Hooper, early A-series car, 105bhp, top speed in excess of 90mph, no-expense-spared restoration, meticulous mechanical rebuild, new cylinder head allowing the use of lead-free fuel, Bentley Drivers' Club overdrive unit, over £150,000 recently spent, concours condition.
£97,000–107,000 *S*

The 3½ litre was notably the first of the so-called 'Derby Bentleys', and when introduced in 1933 it was publicised as 'The Silent Sportscar'. This particular example was the first drophead coupé built by Hooper on a Derby Bentley chassis. Recently, it gained a First in Class award at the Rolls-Royce Enthusiasts' Club annual meeting at Althorp, together with the Hooper Trophy.

1936 Bentley 4¼ Litre Tourer, 4-seater body in the style of the American coachbuilder Brewster, restored mechanically, excellent condition.
£36,000–40,000 *BKS*

The 4¼ litre Bentley was the last of the 'Rolls-Bentley' sporting cars built in the 1930s. Although by the time it appeared, W. O. Bentley himself had left the company to head design at Lagonda, the overall package followed the principles he had laid down. The Rolls-Bentleys were fast, had excellent handling, and were reliable and practical. Prince Bira even took his 3½ litre Bentley on to the track at Le Mans during night-time practice and was quicker than some competitors in bespoke sports-racers. The 4¼ litre model of 1936 had more power, and one fitted with a Park Ward saloon body lapped Brooklands at 96mph to the 90mph of the 3½ litre car.

1937 Bentley 4¼ Litre Pillarless Sports Saloon, coachwork by Vanden Plas, 4257cc, restored in 1992 at a cost in excess of £60,000.
£29,000–33,000 *H&H*

1947 Bentley MkVI Special Tourer, 4257cc, 6 cylinders, 4-speed right-hand gearbox, 4-door open coachwork, rear-mounted fuel tank, cast aluminium foot-steps, full weather equipment, finished in British racing green, black upholstery, engine rebuilt in 1989, good condition.
£17,000–19,000 *S*

1947 Bentley MkVI Razor Edged Sports Saloon, coachwork by James Young Ltd, original specification, gearbox replaced in 1989, original radio, tool kit, handbook, stored for a number of years, requires recommissioning.
£6,000–8,000 *BKS*

1949 Bentley MkVI Sports Saloon, coachwork by H. J. Mulliner.
£18,500–22,500 *FHF*

1949 Bentley MkVI Standard Steel Saloon, 4257cc, 6 cylinders, manual gearbox, sunroof, resprayed 14 years ago in sand and sable, beige interior, Smith's eight-day clock, recently overhauled ignition, fuel, exhaust, clutch and brake systems, good general condition.
£12,700–14,000 *S*

The Bentley MkVI, announced in 1946, was a development of the short-lived MkV, curtailed by WWII. It was powered by a six-cylinder F-head engine, using overhead inlet and side exhaust valves to increase valve area, coupled to a four-speed right-hand gearbox. Standard steel bodywork was available from the makers. Over 5,200 examples of the MkVI were made before the introduction of the R-Type in 1952.

1951 Bentley MkVI Standard Steel Saloon, black paintwork, brown leather, woodwork and chrome in excellent condition, 101,000 miles from new, history.
£20,000–22,500 *RCC*

1952 Bentley R-Type Four-Door Saloon, right-hand drive, 1,864 miles covered since 1989, engine maintains good oil pressure, gearbox synchros good, regularly maintained, repainted 10 years ago, retrimmed in beige leather, rear picnic tables.
£10,000–13,000 *BKS*

A much needed improvement to the standard steel bodywork of the Bentley MkVI arrived in mid-1952 in the shape of an enlarged boot together with associated changes to the rear wings and suspension. This new model became known as the R-Type Bentley.

l. **1954 Bentley R-Type Saloon,** extensively restored, bare metal respray, chromework renewed, woodwork repolished, front seats reupholstered, all other leather trim renovated, new head lining, sunroof felt, boot carpet and leather wing piping, mechanically overhauled, new fuel pump, water pump, rear shock absorbers, brake linings, exhaust and tyres.
£16,000–18,000 *S*

BENTLEY Model	ENGINE cc/cyl	DATES	CONDITION		
			1	2	3
Abbreviations: HJM = H J Mulliner; PW = Park Ward; M/PW = Mulliner/Park Ward					
Mk VI Standard Steel	4257/ 4566/6	1946-52	£16,000	£11,000	£6,000
Mk VI Coachbuilt	4257/ 4566/6	1946-52	£25,000	£20,000	£12,000
Mk VI Coachbuilt DHC	4566/6	1946-52	£40,000+	£30,000	£20,000
R Type Standard Steel	4566/6	1952-55	£12,000	£10,000	£7,000
R Type Coachbuilt	4566/6	1952-55	£25,000	£20,000	£15,000
R Type Coachbuilt DHC	4566/ 4887/6	1952-55	£50,000	£35,000	£25,000
R Type Cont (HJM)	4887/6	1952-55	£80,000+	£40,000	£29,000
S1 Standard Steel	4887/6	1955-59	£15,000	£12,000	£7,000
S1 Cont 2 door (PW)	4877/6	1955-59	£30,000	£25,000	£20,000
S1 Cont Drophead	4877/6	1955-59	£80,000+	£75,000	£50,000
S1 Cont F'back (HJM)	4877/6	1955-58	£50,000	£35,000	£25,000
S2 Standard Steel	6230/8	1959-62	£15,000	£9,000	£6,000
S2 Cont 2 door (HJM)	6230/8	1959-62	£60,000	£40,000	£30,000
S2 Flying Spur (HJM)	6230/8	1959-62	£45,000	£33,000	£22,000
S2 Conv (PW)	6230/8	1959-62	£60,000	£50,000	£35,000
S3 Standard Steel	6230/8	1962-65	£16,000	£11,000	£9,000
S3 Cont/Flying Spur	6230/8	1962-65	£45,000	£30,000	£25,000
S3 2 door (M/PW)	6230/8	1962-65	£30,000	£25,000	£18,000
S3 Conv (modern conversion - only made one original)	6230/8	1962-65	£40,000	£28,000	£20,000
T1	6230/6, 6750/8	1965-77	£10,000	£8,000	£4,000
T1 2 door (M/PW)	6230/6, 6750/8	1965-70	£15,000	£12,000	£9,000
T1 Drophead (M/PW)	6230/6, 6750/8	1965-70	£30,000	£20,000	£12,000

1956 Bentley S1 Continental, coachwork by Park Ward.
£25,000–30,000 *BLE*

1954 Bentley R-Type Sports Saloon, coachwork by Bentley Motors, fully restored in 1990, engine runs well, automatic transmission and electrical equipment in working order, copies of maker's build sheets provided, good overall condition.
£8,500–10,000 *S*

The R-Type Bentley, introduced in 1952, was claimed to be the world's fastest production saloon. In all, 2,320 were built before production ceased in 1955.

r. **1957 Bentley S1 Saloon,** 4887cc, 6 cylinder, 4-speed automatic transmission, blue coachwork and beige leather interior in good condition.
£7,500–9,000 *H&H*

1956 Bentley S1 Saloon, 3250cc, 4-door, no power steering, needs some repairs.
£7,000–9,000 *VIC*

1957 Bentley S1 Continental Two-Door Saloon, coachwork by H. J. Mulliner, right-hand drive, well presented.
£38,000–43,000 *BKS*

1958 Bentley S1 Continental Flying Spur, 4887cc, very good condition throughout, under 60,000 miles, many original bills and receipts.
£27,000–30,000 *H&H*

This car featured in the television series The New Statesman, *being driven by its star, Rick Mayall.*

1959 Bentley S2, 6230cc, V8 engine, generally in good order, factory-fitted air conditioning, repainted approximately 12 years ago.
£9,500–11,000 *COYS*

The Rolls-Royce Silver Cloud and Bentley S-Series were announced in April 1956. Power was provided by the 4887cc straight-six engine of the Bentley R-Type Continental, producing an estimated 158bhp which, via the 4-speed automatic transmission, allowed a top speed of 100mph. The 110mph Silver Cloud II / S2 models of 1959 used Rolls's new light-alloy V8 engine, but otherwise differed only in having long-life chassis lubrication, standard power steering, increased front braking effect, a reduction in rear roll stiffness, a new ventilation system and a revised fascia.

l. **1959 Bentley S1 Standard Steel Saloon,** late specification, power steering, high-compression engine, electric windows, recent bare metal respray in metallic Steel Blue and Shell Grey, blue/grey leather interior, new chromework, refinished wood.
£18,000–22,000 *RCC*

1960 Bentley S2 Standard Steel Saloon, 6230cc, V8, electric windows, high-frequency horns with muting switch, fog lamps, split bench front seat, good original condition with all correct fittings, converted to right-hand drive, stored for a number of years, requires minor restoration and reconditioning.
£5,000–7,000 *S*

l. **1961 Bentley S2 Continental Drophead Coupé,** coachwork by Park Ward, 6230cc, V8, automatic transmission, 4-seater, electrically-operated hood, restored.
£58,000–68,000 *BKS*

This car was a true grand tourer, offering effortless 100mph performance. With a price tag of £8,226 in 1960, Park Ward's drophead coupé ranked third in the 'most expensive car' league at the Earl's Court Show that year.

1962 Bentley S2 Continental Two-Door Sports Saloon, coachwork by H. J. Mulliner, 6230cc, V8, maintained to a high standard, repainted in dark blue, upholstered in light beige leather, beige carpets, veneered fascias and cappings throughout, new tyres, map reading lights front and rear, 'occasional stool' cushions for fitting over the bumpers.
£31,000–34,000 *BKS*

Bentley's S2 series of cars, built alongside the Silver Cloud II at Crewe, represented a dramatic step forward for the company, being the first of the post-war models to adopt the 90° V8 engine in place of the 4.8 litre six of the S1. Engine capacity was increased significantly to 6230cc, ensuring adequate power and a sustainable top speed of around 115mph. Although slightly heavier than its predecessor, the S2 boasted a creditable 0–60mph time of 11.5 seconds. In Continental form, it was offered with a choice of coachwork by H. J. Mulliner, Park Ward or James Young. From a total S2 production run of 1,865 cars, no less than 388 were Continentals.

1962 Bentley S3 Continental Drophead Coupé, 6230cc, V8, twin SU carburettors, approximately 220bhp at 4,000rpm, 4-speed automatic transmission, wishbone and coil spring independent front suspension, live rear axle with semi-elliptic leaf spring suspension, hydro-mechanical drum brakes with servo assistance, power-assisted cam-and-roller steering, right-hand drive, completely restored, minor paintwork imperfections, hood, interior leatherwork, carpets and polished cappings in excellent condition.
£33,000–38,000 *C*

The first Bentley Continental appeared in 1952, and remained Bentley's flagship, the original Mulliner fastback being joined in 1954 by a light alloy drophead coupé from Park Ward. With the introduction of the S2 in 1952, the Continental gained Rolls-Royce's promising 6.3 litre V8 engine. The final version was the S3 of 1962. This had massive drum brakes, boosted by a gearbox-driven servo, and was powered by a modestly uprated version of the V8. The drophead's power-operated top was as shapely as any fixed-head coupé. Lowered, the hood disappeared into a well behind the rear seats to create an elegant open four-seater. For all that, its maximum speed was close to 120mph. Only 312 S3 Continentals were built.

1963 Bentley S3 Four-Door Saloon, 6.2 litre, V8, well maintained, some service history and bills.
£14,000–16,000 *BKS*

l. **1964 Bentley S3 Two-Door Saloon,** coachwork by H. J. Mulliner, Park Ward, 6230cc, V8, brakes overhauled, new exhaust, astral blue, would benefit from a respray, sills and underside good, grey leather upholstery in good condition, slight wear on driver's seat, new blue carpets, full-length Webasto sunroof.
£13,000–17,000 *BRIT*

1964 Bentley S3 Continental Two-Door Saloon, 6230cc, V8, Hydramatic 4-speed transmission, power steering, repainted in dark blue, interior trimmed in grey, good overall condition.
£17,500–22,500 *S*

1972 Bentley Corniche Convertible, black, fog lamps, shaded Sundym windscreen, black leather interior, in original order.
£30,000–35,000 *S*

This car was first owned by the Hon Alan Clark, MP, former Conservative minister and author of the best selling Diaries.

1973 Bentley T1 Saloon, 6750cc, V8, emerald green, coachwork and underside good throughout, mechanically good, transmission overhauled, black Everflex roof, beige leather upholstery.
£6,500–8,000 *BRIT*

r. **1979 Bentley T2 Saloon,** 6750cc, V8, new tyres, exhaust and brakes overhauled, 65,790 miles.
£7,500–9,000 *H&H*

1985 Bentley Mulsanne, 6750cc, V8, 3-speed automatic transmission, 47,500 recorded miles, good condition.
£14,000–16,000 *COYS*

1987 Bentley Turbo R, dark Oyster paintwork, Mushroom interior, twin headlight conversion, 72,000 recorded miles, full service history.
£24,000–26,000 *VIC*

1991 Bentley Turbo R Four-Door Saloon,
left-hand drive, black paintwork, black leather interior trim and carpets, built to US specification, active-ride suspension, 21,000 miles.
£35,000–38,000 *BKS*

A new range of Rolls-Royce and Bentley cars was launched in 1980, based on the Shadow II and T2 Series running gear and floorpan, but larger, wider and lower than those two models. Evoking the glorious Bentley days at Le Mans, the new Bentley was named the Mulsanne. In 1982, the Mulsanne Turbo was unveiled at the Geneva Salon. This employed a Garrett turbocharger to boost the 6750cc V8 engine's power output by almost 50 per cent and the top speed to 135mph. In 1985, the Turbo R was announced, being a development of the Mulsanne Turbo, but with firmer suspension, front air dam and stylish new aluminium road wheels.

1992 Bentley Continental R, left-hand drive, chromed radiator shell, regularly maintained, updated to improve comfort and performance, engine upgraded with fuel injection and turbo boost modifications, large-bore exhaust system, 34,000 miles.
£85,000–95,000 *S*

BIZZARRINI

In Italian sports car history, the name Giotto Bizzarrini is legendary. Starting out as a designer at Alfa Romeo in his early twenties, Bizzarrini moved on to Ferrari, where he became the project manager for the all-conquering 250 GTO. In 1962, he set up his own firm, Prototipi Bizzarrini Srl, in Livorno to concentrate on freelance design, and created the magnificent quad-camshaft V12 engine for Ferruccio Lamborghini's new company. Collaboration with Renzo Rivolta led to the Iso A3L Grifo GT Coupé, which was introduced in prototype form at the Turin Motor Show in November 1963, alongside Bizzarrini's own model, known as the Iso A3C Competition Coupé. Both cars were styled by Giorgio Giugiaro, the gifted Bertone designer, and were powered by tuned Corvette 327 V8 engines. The variant was produced under Bizzarrini's own name from 1965, and estimates of production suggest no more than 100 Bizzarrinis were built, but one source records a total of 149 cars. The company ceased trading in 1969.

1968 Bizzarrini GT Strada 5300 Berlinetta, 5354cc, V8, 4 Weber 45 DCOE 12 carburettors, Holley cylinder heads, left-hand drive, orange bodywork, black interior, replacement headlight lenses required, restored in 1989/90.
£57,500–67,500 *S*

The GT Strada 5300, named after the Italian word for 'street', followed by the approximate displacement of its 365bhp Chevrolet V8 engine, was constructed on an Iso chassis with bodywork by BBM of Modena, from the Bertone design. The hand assembled Bizzarrini presented an extremely low profile and, with a 4-speed, all-synchromesh Muncie manual gearbox, 4-wheel servo-assisted disc brakes and De Dion back axle, top speed exceeded 145mph. It achieved a class win at Le Mans in its debut year.

1966 Bizzarrini 5300 GT Strada, 5354cc, V8, 350bhp at 5,300rpm, body stripped and resprayed, gearbox and rear axle rebuilt, electrics overhauled, new headlights, new cooling fans, engine rebuilt, aluminium fuel tanks overhauled and pressure tested, new fuel, coolant and oil lines, new Koni shock absorbers, overhauled front suspension, history, excellent condition.
£95,000–105,000 *Pou*

BMW

Bayerische Flugzeug Werke, as the company was originally called, was founded in 1916 to make aero engines, becoming Bayerische Motoren Werke in 1922 with the commencement of motorcycle production. Cars followed in 1928 with the Dixi, an Austin 7 built under licence. The first true BMW, the 800cc four-cylinder 3/20 appeared in 1932 followed by a range of fine touring and sports cars. The pinnacle of the company's pre-war achievements was the lithe two litre 328 which, fitted with a beautiful streamlined body, won the 1940 Mille Miglia. The 328 undoubtedly had a strong influence on the shape of William Lyons' Jaguar XK120.

After the war BMW survived the nationalisation of its Eisenach factory, by then in East Germany, and several financial crises. The V8-engined 507 roadster – aimed at the Yankee dollar – was beautiful, but extortionately over-priced. The Isetta microcars (covered in our microcars section) brought salvation at first, then threatened oblivion as sales slumped in the late 1950s. The turn-around came in 1961 with the launch of the neat Michelotti-styled 1500 and 1800 models, which helped create BMW's modern reputation for superbly built prestige cars. It's amazing that strong hints of the original Michelotti designs remain even in today's accomplished BMWs.

l. **1935 BMW 315/1 Roadster,** 1.5 litre, synchromesh gearbox, twin-tube chassis, independent front suspension, fitted with additional petrol tank for long-range touring, completely restored, new top, new black leather interior, aluminium coachwork finished in black, original owner's manual, parts manual and spares list, excellent condition.
£35,000–40,000 *BKS*

Only 221 examples of this model were built, making it one of the rarest of BMWs.

BMW Model	ENGINE cc/cyl	DATES	CONDITION 1	2	3
Dixi	747/4	1927-32	£7,000	£3,000	£2,000
303	1175/6	1934-36	£11,000	£8,000	£5,000
309	843/4	1933-34	£6,000	£4,000	£2,000
315	1490/6	1935-36	£9,000	£7,000	£5,000
319	1911/6	1935-37	£10,000	£9,000	£6,000
326	1971/6	1936-37	£12,000	£10,000	£8,000
320 series	1971/6	1937-38	£12,000	£10,000	£8,000
327/328	1971/6	1937-40	£30,000+	£18,000	£10,000
328	1971/6	1937-40	£60,000+	-	-

1938 BMW 327 Cabriolet, coachwork by Reutter, 1971cc, 6 cylinders, twin carburettors, restored in 1988/89, engine and transmission rebuilt, new springs, largely original blue leather interior, repainted in blue 4 years ago, only 4,000 miles covered since restoration.
£28,000–32,000 *BKS*

The BMW 327 was one of the outstanding sports tourers of its day. Introduced in 1938, it was still being sold (as an EMW) as late as 1955 and, of course, it was one of the contributing elements of the original Bristol design. This particular example was delivered to the German Embassy in London in 1938 for the use of the then ambassador, Joachim von Ribbentrop. Upon his promotion, the car appears to have been inherited by the new ambassador, although its wartime history is not known. However, its post-war history is documented, with only three private owners during the last 40 years.

1940 BMW 327 Sports Two-Door Cabriolet, 1971cc, 6 cylinder in-line overhead valve engine, 55bhp, weight saving tubular chassis, left-hand drive, totally restored in 1997, interior refurbished to a high standard, one of only a few cabriolets to have survived.
£34,000–38,000 *S*

1971 BMW 2002 Tii Saloon, 1990cc, 130bhp, 4-speed manual gearbox, seats retrimmed in black hide, new carpets and head lining, gearbox rebuilt, new cylinder head, fuel injection system overhauled, 29,800 miles.
£2,250–2,750 *H&H*

BMW 507 (1956–59)

Body style: Two-seater roadster.
Construction: Box-section and tubular steel chassis; aluminium body.
Engine: All-aluminium 3168cc V8, two valves per cylinder.
Power output: 150bhp at 5,000rpm; some later cars 160bhp at 5,600rpm.
Transmission: Four-speed manual.
Suspension: Front: unequal-length wishbones,

torsion bars and telescopic dampers. Rear: live axle, torsion bars.
Brakes: Drums front and rear; front discs and rear drums on later cars.
Top speed: 125mph; 135–140mph with optional 3.42:1 final drive.
0–60mph: 9 seconds.
Average fuel consumption: 18mpg.
Production: 252/3, most left-hand drive.

BMW 507

Whoever would have thought BMW of the mid-1950s would have unveiled something as voluptuously beautiful as the 507. The company had a fine pre-war heritage that culminated in the crisp 328, but they didn't resume car production until 1952 with the curvy, but slightly plump, six-cylinder 501 saloon. The 502 was similarly styled. Then, at the Frankfurt show of late 1955, they exhibited two stunners, both designed by Count Albrecht Goertz, who worked for Studebaker before setting up a styling studio in New York. The 503 was merely beautiful. The 507 was more, much more – a delicious fantasy made real, not flashy, but dramatic, with a noble poise and powerful presence. Mercedes had already unveiled its

300SL in 1954, and the 507 was BMW's riposte. The company's finances were precarious and it was hoped that this stunning roadster would straighten them out, winning sales in the lucrative US market. The 507 even had the Americans' favourite engine configuration, a V8. But BMW's hopes for its boulevard beauty were a fantasy, too. For its exotic looks and 125mph performance were more than matched by an orbital price. Production, which had been largely by hand, ended in March 1959 after only 252 – some say 253 – had been built. In fact, the 507 took BMW to the brink of financial oblivion, yet if that had been the last BMW, it would have been a beautiful way to die. Instead, a humble bubble car helped them bounce back.

1957 BMW 507, 3.2 litre, V8, twin carburettors, 150bhp at 5,000rpm, 124mph maximum speed, 0–60mph in a little under 9.0 seconds, aluminium body over a steel frame, maintained to a very high standard, original and unrestored.
£98,000–112,000   *COYS*

BMW introduced the 507 at the 1955 Frankfurt Show. The beautiful two-seater roadster had been styled by Count Albrecht Goertz, who dispensed with BMW's traditional radiator grille. When production of the exclusive 507 ended in 1963, only 253 examples had been built.

Cross Reference
For BMW Isettas see Microcars section

1973 BMW 2002 Cabriolet, 1990cc, 4 cylinders, completely restored 5 years ago, in good order throughout.
£5,000–5,500   *BRIT*

1973 BMW 3.0 CSi, 3 litre engine, all original, restored, concours condition.
£6,000–10,000   *MUN*

1975 BMW 2002 Coupé, 1998cc, 4 cylinders 100bhp, 4-speed manual gearbox with overdrive, right-hand drive, new clutch and exhaust, 55,000 recorded miles, service history.
£2,500–3,000 *H&H*

1974 BMW 3.0 CSL, 3003cc, 4-speed gearbox with overdrive, Alpina alloy wheels, 90,000 recorded miles, good condition throughout, paintwork and upholstery in very good condition.
£4,500–5,000 *H&H*

This rare 3.0CSL ('L' stands for lightweight) is number 451 of only 500 that were manufactured.

1975 BMW 1602 Two-Door Saloon, 1573cc, 4 cylinders, full service history, 60,300 recorded miles.
£3,800–4,200 *S*

1979 BMW 320 Cabriolet, 1990cc, 6 cylinders, new tyres and exhaust, new fully lined dark blue cloth hood, new front wings 4 years ago, 76,000 miles, in good serviceable order.
£2,000–2,500 *BRIT*

Miller's Starter Marque

Starter BMWs: *1502, 1602, 2002, 2002 Touring.*

- The '02-series two-door saloons were launched in Germany in 1968. When they arrived in Britain in 1971, they were not particularly cheap: the 2002 model was £120 more than a Rover P6 2000, and only £170 less than a MkII 3.4 Jaguar, yet on the BMW there was neither a piece of polished wood nor hide trim in sight. Instead, the '02 models rewarded sporting drivers with their spirited performance and pert handling. They are easy to live with and generally robust, with good availability of reasonably priced spares.

- **Performance:** All, except the 1502, are good for 100mph, while the fuel-injected 2002 Tii offers a sizzling 0–60mph time of 8.2 seconds and a 118mph top speed. This and the twin-carb 2002 Ti are the best buys in performance terms, but many will have been mistreated by boy racers. The 1602, plain 2002 and 1502 make sensible down-market alternatives.

- **Rust:** Particular points to watch include the jacking points, which can fall out and leave the sills to rot from the inside. Look in the boot, too. Generally though, rust problems are no worse than any steel monocoque saloon.

- **Engines:** BMW engines are famed for their smooth, reliable performance and, if looked after, are good for more than 80,000 miles. On starting from cold, listen for rattling from the top end, which indicates camshaft/follower wear. The engines need an oil change every 5,000 miles, so look for documentation that confirms regular maintenance.

- All in all, the '02 Beemers are quite straightforward, but there are a couple of more exotic options. Cabriolets are undoubtedly desirable, but have some nasty rust-traps, particularly behind the rear seat where the hood is stowed. If you're not careful, Cabriolet restoration costs could spiral beyond reach.

- Likewise, the rare 2002 Turbo is an enthusiast's car rather than an every-day user. For a start, only 51 were sold in the UK. If you can find one, you'll get performance – and shattering bills to match.

BMW Model	ENGINE cc/cyl	DATES	CONDITION 1	2	3
501	2077/6	1952-56	£9,000	£7,000	£3,500
501 V8/502	2580,				
	3168/8	1955-63	£8,000	£5,000	£3,000
503	3168/8	1956-59	£25,000	£20,000	£15,000
507	3168/8	1956-59	£100,000	£70,000	£50,000
Isetta (4 wheels)	247/1	1955-62	£6,000	£3,000	£1,200
Isetta (3 wheels)	298/1	1958-64	£6,500	£2,500	£1,500
Isetta 600	585/2	1958-59	£2,000	£1,000	£500
1500/1800/2000	var/4	1962-68	£1,800	£800	£500
2000CS	1990/4	1966-69	£5,500	£4,000	£1,500
1500/1600/1602	1499/				
	1573/4	1966-75	£2,500	£1,500	£800
1600 Cabriolet	1573/4	1967-71	£6,000	£4,500	£2,000
2800CS	2788/6	1968-71	£5,000	£4,000	£1,500
1602	1990/4	1968-74	£3,000	£1,500	£1,000
2002	1990/4	1968-74	£3,000	£2,000	£1,000
2002 Tii	1990/4	1971-75	£4,500	£2,500	£1,200
2002 Touring	1990/4	1971-74	£3,500	£2,000	£1,000
2002 Cabriolet	1990/4	1971-75	£5,000	£3,000	£2,500
2002 Turbo	1990/4	1973-74	£10,000	£6,000	£4,000
3.0 CSa/CSi	2986/6	1972-75	£8,000	£6,000	£4,000
3.0 CSL	3003/				
	3153/6	1972-75	£16,000	£10,000	£7,500
MI	3500/6	1978-85	£70,000	£50,000	£35,000
633/635 CS/CSI	3210/3453/6	1976-85	£7,000	£3,000	£2,000
M535i	3453/6	1979-81	£4,500	£3,000	£2,500

1981 BMW M1 Two-Door Coupé, 3.5 litre, 6 cylinder, well maintained, history, 20,500 recorded miles, excellent condition.
£42,000–46,000 *BKS*

A proposed silhouette formula for production-based cars triggered the M1 project in the mid-1970s. Development was contracted first to Lamborghini, then to Giorgetto Giugiaro's Ital Design, although almost all cars were built in Germany. Giugiaro's compact glassfibre coupé bodywork was wrapped around a multi-tubular space-frame chassis, while a twin-cam, four-valves-per-cylinder version of BMW's 3.5 litre six, driving via a five-speed ZF transaxle, provided the power. First shown in 1978, the road-going M1 offered 277bhp and a top speed of 161mph. Only intended as a limited-edition model, the M1 ceased production after 456 examples had been built.

1986 BMW M635CSi Two-Door Coupé, 3.5 litre, 6 cylinders, new alloy wheels in 1994, new front wings in 1995, electric sunroof and seats, air conditioning, rear screen blind, metallic finish, Pearl leather interior, one of only 2 UK-market M635s with this finish, 114,320 warranted miles, well maintained, excellent condition apart from slight cracking of the driver's seat piping.
£10,000–11,000 *BKS*

The brainchild of BMW's Motorsport department, the M635CSi debuted in 1984. Its engine was a development of the M1 coupé's 3.5 litre, 24 valve, six, producing 286bhp. The increased power necessitated chassis improvements that included altered weight distribution, revised suspension, bigger brakes and a limited-slip differential. This example is one of two M635s that shared the BMW stand at the 1986 London Motor Show, and it was owned by BMW until 1987.

1985 BMW M635CSi, 3.5 litre, 6 cylinders, excellent condition.
£9,000–14,000 *MUN*

1984 BMW Alpina B9 3.5, 3430cc, 6 cylinders, automatic transmission, optional aerodynamic aids, air conditioning, electric sunroof and windows, black leather interior, sports exhaust.
£4,250–4,750 *COYS*

As the basis for its top conversion, German tuner Alpina chose the 528i, replacing its 184bhp, 2788cc engine with the 3430cc six from BMW's 635CSi/735i models. This was modified to increase output to 245bhp, providing 0–60mph and 0–100mph times of 6.8 and 16.9 seconds respectively, and a top speed of 153mph, which made the BMW Alpina the fastest production four-door saloon in the world at the time. The chassis was modified in keeping with performance. Body options included a large front air dam and rubber boot spoiler that helped reduce drag and front end lift. Inside the B9 3.5, bucket seats were standard, as were a high-quality stereo, tinted glass and electric mirrors. It made an impressive £23,000 package.

BRISTOL

Few car companies seem more quintessentially British than Bristol, yet their fine cars, which are still made today, are truly international. When wartime military contracts dried up, the Bristol Aeroplane Company decided to move into automobile manufacturing with the aim of building a 'high-speed luxury motor car for the connoisseur, a powerful, elegant model . . .' The first cars appeared in 1947, using a six-cylinder engine that was closely derived from a pre-war BMW unit. The grille of the 400 and subsequent models even retained the BMW hallmark of a double-kidney opening. Over the years, the Italian firms of Touring, Pininfarina and Zagato have all contributed to the styling, while in 1962 Bristol adopted American power in the form of Chrysler V8 engines.

1990 BMW Z1, 3500cc, red, one owner, 40,000 miles.
£18,000–22,000 *VIC*

A concept car first shown in 1986, the Z1 sports revived the 'internal skeleton' method of construction, by which moulded plastic panels clothed the galvanised steel frame and were braced by a moulded composite floor. Unusually, the doors dropped into the body sides to provide access. Production began slowly in 1988 at the rate of six cars per day, finishing in 1991 after 8,000 cars had been built.

1949 Bristol 400, 1971cc, 6 cylinders, light metallic blue, tan leather upholstery, very good condition.
£13,000–15,000 *COYS*

In 1946, the Bristol Aeroplane Company began building motor cars as well as aircraft, the result being the Bristol 400, a light and efficient car with an aerodynamic alloy body that allowed four to travel in comfort. Power was provided by the company's own version of the BMW 328 engine, a highly efficient 2 litre six with hemispherical combustion chambers and a complex 18-pushrod system to operate the valves. It produced 80bhp at 4,200rpm and drove through a four-speed gearbox, propelling the Bristol 400 to a top speed of 95mph. This was matched by good handling and cornering qualities.

BRISTOL Model	ENGINE cc/cyl	DATES	CONDITION 1	2	3
400	1971/6	1947-50	£18,000	£14,000	£8,000
401	1971/6	1949-53	£18,000	£14,000	£8,000
402	1971/6	1949-50	£22,000	£19,000	£12,000
403	1971/6	1953-55	£20,000	£14,000	£10,000
404 Coupé	1971/6	1953-57	£22,000	£15,000	£12,000
405	1971/6	1954-58	£17,000	£13,000	£10,000
405 Drophead	1971/6	1954-56	£25,000	£22,000	£18,000
406	2216/6	1958-61	£15,000	£11,000	£8,000
407	5130/8	1962-63	£15,000	£8,000	£6,000
408	5130/8	1964-65	£14,000	£10,000	£8,000
409	5211/8	1966-67	£14,000	£11,000	£7,000
410	5211/8	1969	£14,000	£10,000	£6,000
411 Mk 1-3	6277/8	1970-73	£16,000	£11,000	£8,000
411 Mk 4-5	6556/8	1974-76	£12,500	£9,500	£7,000
412	5900/ 6556/8	1975-82	£15,000	£9,000	£6,000
603	5211/ 5900/8	1976-82	£12,000	£8,000	£5,000

1949 Bristol 401 Cabriolet, 1971cc, 6 cylinders, rare Farina alloy-bodied example, recently restored at a cost of £35,000, maintained and stored to a high standard.
£27,500–35,000 *COYS*

In the autumn of 1949, Bristol launched the 401 model, which incorporated a host of detail improvements over the outgoing 400 and soon proved itself in competition. This particular example is one of the rare Farina-bodied 401s, six of which were commissioned, although only five are known to exist.

l. **1955 Bristol 403,** 2 litre, 6 cylinders, original triple downdraught Solex carburettors, right-hand drive, Becker Grand Prix radio, engine completely rebuilt 10 years ago.
£15,000–18,000 *BKS*

The 403, launched in 1953, was a refinement of the 401 with major mechanical improvements, including a reprofiled camshaft that increased power to a healthy 100bhp, giving greater response at low and medium speeds.

l. **1954 Bristol 404 Two-Door Coupé,** 2 litre, 6 cylinders, 105bhp, engine and running gear overhauled in 1968, bare metal respray in 1972, stored 1973-82, new brake servo in 1995, well maintained mechanically and cosmetically, well documented history.
£17,000–20,000 *BKS*

1963 Bristol 407 Two-Door Saloon, 5130cc, V8, maroon with grey leather upholstery, one of 88 407s produced, 121,000 miles, good condition.
£6,000–8,000 *BKS*

Bristol's line of V8-engined luxurious sports saloons began in 1961 with the Chrylser-powered 407, although it closely resembled the previous 406. The latter's BMW-based six-cylinder engine had been effectively outgrown by its increasingly weighty coachwork, but with 250bhp and a top speed of 125mph, the 407 re-established the Bristol as a true high-performance car. The 406's four-wheel disc brakes were retained for its successor, which came with Chrysler's Torqueflite automatic transmission as standard and coil-sprung front suspension in place of the previous transverse-leaf set up.

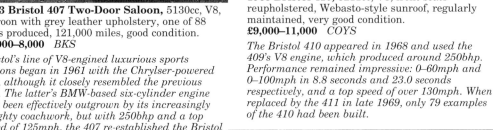

1968 Bristol 410, 5211cc, V8, front seats reupholstered, Webasto-style sunroof, regularly maintained, very good condition.
£9,000–11,000 *COYS*

The Bristol 410 appeared in 1968 and used the 409's V8 engine, which produced around 250bhp. Performance remained impressive: 0–60mph and 0–100mph in 8.8 seconds and 23.0 seconds respectively, and a top speed of over 130mph. When replaced by the 411 in late 1969, only 79 examples of the 410 had been built.

r. **1964 Bristol 408,** 5730cc, very good condition throughout.
£9,000–10,000 *H&H*

BRITANNIA

c1958 Britannia GT, Ford Zephyr 2.6 litre engine, has not run since 1985.
£2,000–2,500 *BKS*

This is the prototype Brittania, which has an aluminium body from which the moulds were taken for the fibreglass bodies of the five subsequent cars.

c1958 Britannia GT, chassis in good condition, wire wheels, glassfibre bodyshell, no engine, transmission, instruments or seats, needs restoring.
£350–450 *BKS*

This was the first left-hand drive model.

BSA

l. **1933 BSA 10hp Four-Door Saloon,** 1185cc, 4 cylinder, side valve engine, 4-speed pre-selector gearbox, Daimler fluid flywheel, opening windscreen, sliding roof, leather upholstery, restored some years ago, requires cosmetic attention.
£2,000–3,000 *BKS*

The Birmingham Small Arms Company, better known for their manufacture of motorcycles, offered a sturdy 10hp car for the 1934 season and exhibited no less than six body styles at Olympia in 1933.

1963 AC Ace RuddSpeed, 6 cylinders, 2553cc, race-prepared Ford engine, 240bhp, solid billet crank, Carillo rods, forged pistons, triple Weber carburettors, close-ratio Moss gearbox, disc brakes, restored to concours condition. **£55,000–60,000** *COYS*

Only 36 examples of this car were produced.

1932 Alfa Romeo 6C 1750 Gran Sport Spyder, 1750cc, completely restored, excellent condition throughout. **£260,000+** *S*

1935 Alfa Romeo 8C 2300 Corsa Spyder, short chassis, excellent restored condition. **£800,000+** *COYS*

1962 Alfa Romeo Giulietta SZ2 Coda Tronca, 1290cc double overhead camshaft engine, 5-speed gearbox, 100bhp, restored, good all-round condition.
£38,000–45,000 *BKS*

This was one of the first Coda Tronca machines. It was driven by Foitek & Ricci at Le Mans in 1962, but retired with clutch problems after 23 hours.

l. **1965 Alfa Romeo Giulia Spider,** 4-cylinder in-line engine, double overhead camshafts, 1600cc, 129bhp at 6,500rpm, 5-speed manual gearbox, left-hand drive, engine rebuilt, restored, good condition.
£12,000–14,000 *C*

Only 90 Spider Veloces were made between 1964 and 1965, this example being one of the last before Alfa Romeo discontinued the model.
This car was originally supplied to California and imported 10 years ago.

r. **1964 Alfa Romeo Giulia Sprint Special,** 4-cylinder in-line engine, 1570cc, 112bhp at 6,500rpm, very good condition.
£14,000–17,000 *Pou*

This car was styled by Bertone, along similar lines to the smaller 1290cc Giulietta.

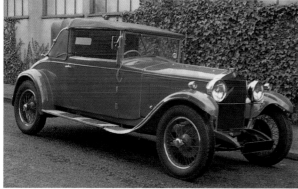

l. **1929 Alfa Romeo 6C Tourer,** coachwork by James Young, 6 cylinders, short-stroke, 1487cc overhead camshaft engine, 4-speed gearbox, shaft drive to rear wheels, mohair-lined hood, wind-down windows, electric starter, full electric lights, luggage boot, good condition.
£24,500–27,500 *S*

Alfa Romeo engines were frequently developed by engineers with racing experience – notable among them were Guiseppe Merosi and Vittorio Jano. A chassis for the 1½ litre model was on exhibition at the 1925 London Motor Show and series production started in 1927. Jano's six-cylinder engined cars achieved pre-eminence in the sports car arena 1927–30.

r. **1974 Alfa Romeo Montreal,** 2593cc, V8 engine, 5-speed gearbox, 200bhp, 137mph, good condition.
£8,500–9,000 *EPP*

The Montreal was first seen in Canada in 1967, hence the name. Just under 4,000 were produced from 1970 to 1977, and only approximately 100 with right-hand drive.

l. **1953 Alvis TA21 Tickford Drophead Coupé,** 2 owners, very good condition.
£13,500–15,000 *UMC*
The TA21 marked Alvis's first use of hydraulic brakes. The 2993cc six-cylinder engine could propel the car to 90+mph in later twin-carburettor form.

r. **1955 Alvis TC108G Cabriolet,** 3 litres, floor panels replaced, original interior trim, good overall condition.
£21,000–26,000 *S*
This is the first TC108G produced. Exhibited at the Geneva Salon of 1956 in Coupé form, it was subsequently returned to Graber for conversion to its current drophead coupé form.

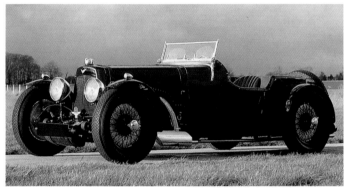

l. **1933 Aston Martin Le Mans Short Chassis Two-Seater Sports,** 4 cylinders, single overhead camshaft engine, 1495cc, 70bhp at 5,000rpm, 4-speed close-ratio gearbox, light Ulster-type front wings, hood and full tonneau cover, set of spare tyres, right-hand drive, good condition.
£57,500–65,000 *C*
The beautifully made, compact 1500cc sports models were built largely regardless of cost, and were formidable contenders in their class in many classic races of the time.

r. **1955 Aston Martin DB2/4 MkI Vantage Drophead Coupé,** 6 cylinders, double overhead camshafts, 2922cc, 140bhp at 5,000rpm, 4-speed manual gearbox, comprehensively restored, engine rebuilt, repainted, new upholstery, excellent condition.
£50,000–60,000 *C*

l. **1954 Aston Martin DB2/4,** 6 cylinders, 2922cc, body-off restoration, full documentation, stored in air-conditioned environment, regularly maintained, excellent condition.
£21,000–25,000 *COYS*
This model was produced for only five years, each car being hand-made to the client's own specification.

r. **1991 Aston Martin DB4 GT Zagato Sanction II,** 4.2 litres, 352bhp, 0–60mph in 5.5 seconds, 1,100 recorded miles, mint condition throughout.
£300,000+   *BKS*

Only 19 examples of the DB4 GT Zagato were made from 1961 to 1963 but, in 1991, the run was extended by a further four cars which were given the name Sanction II. The rationale behind these four cars was that in 1960 23 chassis numbers had been allocated to the project and only 19 were used. Furthermore, 1991 was the model's 30th anniversary.

1961 Aston Martin DB4 MkII, 3670cc, aluminium body, manual transmission, bare metal respray, engine rebuilt, 1,000 miles since restoration, 54,000 miles from new, excellent condition.
£37,000–42,000   *BKS*

1955 Austin-Healey 100, 2660cc, 4 cylinders, engine rebuilt, 3-speed gearbox with overdrive, new shock absorbers, brakes relined, radiator recored, chromework excellent, requires respray.
£11,500–15,000   *BRIT*

The debut of the new 100 sports car caused a sensation at the 1952 Earl's Court Motor Show. It remained in production until 1956, when it was superseded by a six-cylinder version with the BMC C-Series engine.

1964 Aston Martin DB5 Convertible, 6-cylinder in-line engine, double overhead camshafts, 3995cc, 282bhp at 5,500rpm, 5-speed manual gearbox, factory hardtop, left-hand drive, 32,000 miles from new, good condition.
£64,000–75,000   *C*

l. **1969 Aston Martin DB6,** 6 cylinders, 3995cc, chassis-up restoration, components refurbished or replaced where necessary, new ZF gearbox, excellent condition.
£26,000–32,000   *COYS*

Launched in October 1965 at the London Motor Show, the roof line of the DB6 was 2in (5cm) higher than the DB5. It had a more steeply raked windscreen, and split front and rear bumpers. Despite these changes, the DB6 was only 17lb heavier than the DB5.

l. **1930 Bentley 4½ Litre Supercharged Four-Seater Tourer,** coachwork by Vanden Plas, original fabric body, rebuilt gearbox, crown wheel and pinion fitted with new bearings, reground crankshaft, later single-wall ribbed-case blower, well maintained, excellent condition.
£400,000+ *BKS*

The inspiration behind the 'Blower' Bentley was the legendary Tim Birkin. However, W. O. Bentley did not support the development of the supercharged car, but with backing by Woolf Barnato production went ahead.
This car is one of the most original of the surviving 'Blowers'.

r. **1936 Bentley 4¼ Sportsman's Coupé by Barker,** sliding sunroof, excellent overall condition.
£25,000–30,000 *COYS*

This unique sporting Derby Bentley was designed by Barkers exclusively for the 1936 London Motor Show. It has numerous interesting features associated with being a show car, and is one of the most exciting Derby Bentleys in existence.

l. **1936 Bentley 4¼ Sports Tourer,** coachwork by Vanden Plas, extensively restored, full weather equipment, fold-down windscreen, 2 additional Brooklands screens, black hood, red leather interior, restoration photographs, special tools, owner's manual, excellent condition.
£32,000–37,000 *S*

Early in the car's life, the original Rippon sports saloon body was replaced with a Vanden Plas body.

1935 Bentley 3½ Litre Three-Position Drophead Coupé, coachwork by Thrupp & Maberly, 6 cylinders, 3669cc, 4-speed transmission with synchromesh, hypoid bevel rear axle, 105bhp, 90mph, well-documented early history, polished alloy wheel discs, walnut facings to interior, excellent condition.
£48,000–55,000 *COYS*

This car was once the property of the world-renowned British actor, Albert Finney.

l. **1935 Bentley 3½ Litre Drophead Coupé,** coachwork by Barker, propeller shaft serviced, clutch centre disc and linings replaced, servo and shock absorbers overhauled, stainless steel exhaust fitted, front suspension overhauled, rewired, wheel centres, radiator shell and slats, pram irons and front bumper rechromed, fully equipped custom tool compartment in drop-down boot lid, hood and full tonneau cover, excellent condition.
£55,000–65,000 *BKS*

The continuation of the Bentley name was assured following its acquisition by Rolls-Royce Ltd in 1931. Bentley's sporting tradition was maintained, and even W. O. Bentley acknowledged that the 3½ Litre model was the finest car ever to bear his name.

1972 Bentley TI, dark brown interior, 62,000 recorded miles, right-hand drive, good condition mechanically.
£6,500–8,000 *PA*

1939 Bentley 4¼ Park Ward Sports Saloon, with overdrive, original condition, stored since 1989, in running order.
£16,000–18,000 *RCC*

1988 Bentley Eight, 6750cc, tan interior, 80,000 recorded miles, alloy wheels, excellent condition.
£18,000–22,000 *VIC*

1953 Bentley R-Type Radford Countryman, 4-door with 2-piece tailgate, requires attention, in running order.
£11,500–13,500 *RCC*

r. **1949 Bentley MkVI Drophead Coupé,** coachwork by Park Ward, 4257cc, 6 cylinders, 4-speed manual gearbox, factory 4-door all-steel saloon body, centre front foglight, original and operational Radiomobile radio, dashboard tool kit, well-maintained, good condition.
£34,000–39,000 *C*

The majority of these chassis were equipped with their own factory four-door all-steel saloon bodies, producing a car with wider appeal than before. However, there was still demand for the very expensive bespoke bodywork.

1973 BMW 3.0 CSL, 3.2 litres, 200bhp, very good condition.
£20,000–25,000 *MUN*
The CSL's 3003cc capacity made it eligible for Group 2 competition use.

1986 BMW 635 CSi, 3.5 litres, very good condition.
£4,000–7,000 *MUN*

1973 BMW 2002, new brakes, track rod ends, wheel bearings, full history, restored, very good condition.
£1,500–1,800 *PA*

1972 BMW 2002 Tii, 0–60mph in 8.2 seconds, 118mph top speed, very good condition.
£4,000–5,000 *MUN*

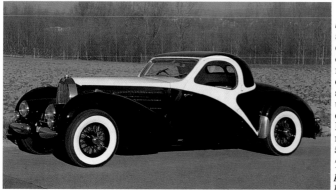

l. **1938 Bugatti Type 57 Atalante,** aluminium coachwork by Gangloff, chassis No. 57660, engine No. 459, covered 30,000km before WWII, remained unused until 1950s, engine rebuilt, 16in wheels fitted, small rear bumpers, ivory leather upholstery and black carpets, original owner's manual, tool kit, Louis Vuitton case, completely restored, excellent condition. **£270,000+** *BKS*

This was the 27th Atalante produced, and one of only four with aluminium bodies.

r. **1930 Cadillac V8 Series 353 Roadster,** V8 engine, 95bhp at 3,000rpm, 3-speed manual gearbox, replica Fleetwood style coachwork, fully restored, excellent condition. **£44,000–48,000** *C*

The Cadillac Motor Car Company was started by Henry Martin Leland. Having rescued the Detroit Motor Company in 1902, he wanted to build quality cars, and called his company Cadillac after the early French explorer of the mid-west. In 1908 the company became part of GM and soon were leaders of that group.

l. **1957 Chevrolet Corvette Fuel-Injected Roadster,** V8 engine, 250hp at 4,800rpm, 4-speed manual gearbox, restored 1988–90, bodywork rebuilt, new accessories fitted, excellent condition. **£140,000–150,000** *C*

Chevrolet introduced the Corvette at the 1953 Motorama show and started production that year. Beginning in 1955, Corvettes had a V8 engine which improved their performance. For 1957, the engine became the hottest of all – the base engine gave 220hp, and with fuel injection produced 250hp, while with dual four-barrels it generated 283hp.

1937 Delahaye 135M Open Tourer, 3557cc, 6 cylinders, chassis and engine No. 48715, stored during 1960s, restoration commenced 1981, Figoni-style coachwork, ash frame completed in 1991 and clad in aluminium, chassis and mechanical components fully restored, excellent condition. **£100,000–115,000** *COYS*

The Type 135, with its 3½ litre straight-six and Cotal gearbox, was a genuinely fast car with excellent handling, and posed stiff competition for the Bugatti Type 57 and 4½ litre Talbot Lago. Some of the most spectacular coachwork of the day is to be found on 135s.

1960 Ferrari 250 Pininfarina Convertible, 2953cc,
12 cylinders, restoration costing £20,000, new paintwork,
chrome, hide interior and hood, excellent condition.
£65,000–75,000   *COYS*

1962 Ferrari 250 GT, 3 litres, short wheelbase,
totally restored, right-hand drive, excellent condition.
£380,000+   *TALA*

1967 Ferrari 330 GT MkII, V12 engine,
4 litres, excellent condition.
£33,000–35,000   *FOS*

l. **1967 Ferrari 275GTB/4,** coachwork by Pininfarina, V12 engine, 3286cc, 300bhp at 8,000rpm, 5-speed manual gearbox, 4-wheel disc brakes, engine completely overhauled in 1990, 73,000km recorded, excellent condition.
£230,000+ *C*

The 275 GTB/4 was unveiled at the Paris Salon in October 1966. The redesigned cylinder heads featured twin overhead camshafts directly operating on the valves. A dry sump system, as previously used in competition cars, was introduced to improve lubrication at high revs.

r. **1968 Ferrari 330GTC Coupé,** coachwork by Pininfarina, 3960cc, 12 cylinders, 27,000km recorded, excellent original condition.
£47,000–57,000 *COYS*

Introduced at the Geneva Show, this model incorporated the short wheelbase chassis of the 275, but had the larger 4 litre engine from the 330. It was hailed as Ferrari's best all-round Gran Turismo to date, with its 300hp engine, all-round independent suspension and disc brakes on all four wheels. Top speed was 150mph.

l. **1973 Ferrari 365GTS/4 Daytona Spyder,** coachwork by Pininfarina, built by Scaglietti, V12 engine with 4 overhead camshafts, 4390cc, 355bhp at 7,500rpm, 5-speed manual gearbox, 4-wheel disc brakes, 3,427 recorded miles from new, completely restored, excellent condition.
£300,000+ *C*

The Daytona was announced in 1968. The new engine provided a top speed in excess of 180mph, making it the fastest production car in the world, a title it retained during the six years it was on sale. The soft-top Spyder version was unveiled in September 1969.

r. **1974 Ferrari 246GTS Dino,** V6 mid-engine, double overhead camshafts, cast iron block, light alloy heads, 2418cc, 178bhp at 7,000rpm, 5-speed manual gearbox, air conditioning, Blaupunkt radio, 24,726 miles from new, repainted, excellent condition.
£57,000–65,000 *C*

This Dino is a very late example. After two years in coupé form, the Spyder version of the 246 was unveiled at the 1972 Geneva Show and was designated as the GTS. 1,180 GTS models were built.

1971 Ferrari 365GT 2+2, 12 cylinders, 4390cc, 120,000km recorded, 5-speed manual gearbox, air conditioning, radio, excellent condition.
£15,500–20,000 *Pou*

1972 Ferrari 246GT Dino, excellent condition.
£38,000–42,000 *FOS*

l. **1974 Ferrari 308GT4,** 2926cc, 8 cylinders, 255bhp at 7,700rpm, maximum speed 155mph, 0–60mph in 6.5 seconds, steel tubular spaceframe, 5-speed transaxle gearbox, twin distributors, new wings, front valance, door skins, inner and outer sills, rear wheel arches, new Wilton carpets, engine rebuilt in 1988, used only in dry weather, comprehensive history files, excellent condition. **£16,000–20,000** *COYS*

r. **1982 Ferrari 512BBi,** Berlinetta coachwork by Pininfarina, seats reupholstered in black, 52,000km recorded, fuel injection, restored, excellent condition throughout. **£37,000–42,000** *S*

The successor to the Daytona was a radical design for the traditionally conservative Ferrari. Manufacture ceased in 1984.

l. **1984 Ferrari 288GTO,** excellent condition. **£200,000+** *FOS*
The Ferrari 288GTO, produced from 1984 to 1987, rekindled memories of the fabled 250GTO 20 years before. 200 examples of the 288GTO were built, with a four-cam 2855cc V8 engine and twin turbochargers pumping out around 400bhp, enough to enable the car to do 0–60mph in five seconds and a claimed top speed of 190mph.

r. **1989 Ferrari 328 Conciso Show Car,** 3.2 litres, V8 engine, 270bhp, 5-speed transaxle gearbox, 0–100km/h in 5 seconds, top speed 278km/h, lightweight aluminium alloy body, suede leather upholstery, excellent condition throughout. **£32,000–38,000** *BKS*

Almost a 'two-seater Grand Prix car', the lightweight, mid-engined Conciso, with its open-topped coachwork, puts function first. There is no weather or roll-over protection – the driver and passenger wear crash helmets, which are stowed in fitted bins on each side of the car.

1977 Ferrari 512BB, 16,800 recorded miles, original service book and manuals, excellent condition. **£50,000–55,000** *TALA*

1984 Ferrari 308QV, excellent condition. **£30,000–35,000** *FOS*
The 308 switched to a 32-valve version of the 2927cc V8 engine in 1982.

l. **1940 Fiat 2800 Two-Door,** Berlinetta coachwork by Touring, red leather interior, 1,000km since restoration, excellent condition throughout.
£72,000–80,000 *BKS*

In 1940, Benito Mussolini gave this car to his mistress, Claretta. When they were both killed, their car was pushed into Lake Garda. It was then retrieved, hidden under hay on a train and smuggled into Switzerland. It remained in the same family from 1950.

r. **1953/57 Fiat 8V Coupé,** coachwork by Vignale, overhead valve 1996cc engine, 4-speed gearbox, 105bhp, 110mph, tubular chassis frame, steel body, all-independent suspension by coil springs and double wishbones, restored, good condition throughout.
£53,000–60,000 *BKS*

This car was a Giovanni Michelotti design from the period when he was doing his very best work, which led to him becoming a major international influence.

1969 Fiat Dino Spyder, 6 cylinders, 1986cc, 160hp at 7,200rpm, restored, excellent condition.
£7,500–10,000 *Pou*

1969 Fiat Samantha by Vignale, very good condition throughout.
£2,300–2,500 *EPP*

r. **1971 Fiat 124 Spyder,** fully rebuilt in 1996, photographic record of restoration, engine and gearbox reconditioned, rechromed, new hood, carpets and mats, new wheels and tyres, new door panels, resprayed, very good condition throughout.
£5,250–6,000 *H&H*

The Fiat 124 Spider has always been regarded as one of the Agnelli empire's prettiest sports cars.

1927 Fiat Tipo 503 Spyder, 12hp, restored, excellent original condition.
£15,000–19,000 *FCV*

1980 Fiat 124 Spyder, 2 litres, excellent condition.
£4,250–4,750 *EPP*

1931 Ford Model A Roadster, 2-seater sports
type bodywork with separate dickey seat, 3300cc,
4-cylinder in-line engine, 40bhp at 2,300rpm,
3-speed gearbox with synchromesh, 55mph,
spare wheel side-mounted on front wing,
chromium-plated headlights, 2 sidelights
mounted on cowl, used sparingly since
restoration, excellent overall condition.
£8,750–11,000 *C*

1934 Ford Model 'Y' Saloon, good condition.
£1,650–2,000 *H&H*

*In 1935, the 933cc Ford Model Y became Britain's
first £100 saloon. From 1932 to 1937, over 150,000
were made.*

l. **1957 Ford Thunderbird
F-Series Convertible,**
supercharged V8 engine, 312cu in,
300hp at 4,800rpm, Ford-O-Matic
gearbox, frame-off restoration,
power windows, Town & Country
signal seeking radio that
automatically increases the
volume in proportion to the speed
of the engine, hard and soft tops,
excellent condition.
£90,000–105,000 *C*

r. **1967 Ford GT40 MkIII,** 4736cc,
V8 engine, 306bhp at 6,000rpm, ZF
5-speed manual gearbox, original
paintwork, engine and transmission,
tinted glass, air conditioning, 3 owners
from new, 11,410 recorded miles,
excellent condition.
£200,000+ *C*

*The MkIII is the only street GT40, and
it represents one of the most significant
road-going cars produced in the 1960s.
It is also considered to be one of the
most important Anglo/American
sports cars produced in the post-war
period. This example is one of only
four built in left-hand drive form.*

l. **1956 Ford
Thunderbird,** 4785cc,
8 cylinders, 200bhp,
chromework replated,
exhaust system replaced,
upholstery 'as-new', new
white vinyl hood, excellent
condition throughout.
£17,500–20,000 *BRIT*

*Thunderbirds produced
between 1955 and 1957
are, without doubt, the
most sought-after by
connoisseurs of the model.
The 1956 Series is
distinguishable by its
'continental' spare wheel.*

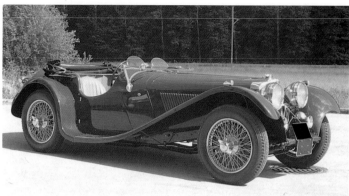

l. **1938 SS100 Jaguar 3½ Litre Two-Seater Sports,** 125bhp at 4,500rpm, totally restored, tan hide upholstery and matching carpets, black double-duck hood, side screens, twin rear-mounted spare wheels, excellent condition. **£105,000–115,000** *S*

Factory publicity described the sensational SS100 as 'primarily intended for competition work and sufficiently tractable to use as a fast tourer without modification. The Heynes-designed overhead valve engine was capable of a genuine 100mph, and the styling reflected William Lyons' influence.

r. **1952 Jaguar XK120 Roadster,** 3.4 litres, fully restored and original, excellent condition. **£26,000–30,000** *FCV*

When the XK120 was launched, it was considered so potent that one British motoring magazine wouldn't allow married men to conduct high-speed tests in it! 85 per cent of all XK120s were exported. The famed six-cylinder twin-cam XK made its debut in the XK120 and went on to power Le Mans-winning C-Type and D-Type racing Jags, the 1961 E-Type and Jaguar saloons until 1986.

l. **1955 Jaguar XK140 MC Drophead Coupé,** 6 cylinders, double overhead camshafts, 3442cc, 210bhp at 5,750rpm, 4-speed manual gearbox with synchromesh, independent front suspension, semi-elliptic rear leaf springs, 4-wheel drum brakes, left-hand drive, frame-off restoration in 1994, excellent condition. **£38,000–42,000** *C*

The XK140, introduced in October 1954, had sturdier bumpers and a tougher grille than the XK120. A chrome strip ran down the length of the bonnet and the boot. The rear bumper wrapped around the wings and sported over-riders.

r. **1954 Jaguar XK120 Drophead Coupé,** 6 cylinders, 3442cc, double overhead camshafts, 160bhp, twin SU carburettors, 126mph, 0–60mph in 10 seconds, restored, left-hand drive, excellent condition. **£34,000–37,000** *COYS*

This rare and highly desirable drophead coupé model of the XK120 offers the sportiness of the open roadster, yet has the comfort and elegance of the closed fixed head coupé.

l. **1956 Jaguar XK140 Roadster,** 3.4 litres, twin-cam 6-cylinder engine, 190bhp, gearbox with overdrive, 3,000 recorded miles since restoration, conversion to disc brakes, with original drum brakes and fittings, Mulberry interior, left-hand drive, excellent condition. **£32,500–36,000** *BKS*

The XK140 differed from the XK120 in the positioning of the engine which was 3in (7.5cm) further forward, and the adoption of rack-and-pinion steering as used on the racing C-Type.

1955 Jaguar XK140 Fixed Head Coupé,
fully restored, excellent condition.
£26,000–30,000 *BC*

1966 Jaguar MkII Four-Door Saloon,
3.8 litres, 6 cylinders, double overhead
camshafts, 125mph, new chromium-plated
brightwork, interior leather and woodwork,
wire wheels, all-synchromesh gearbox
with overdrive, totally restored, excellent
condition throughout.
£28,000–33,000 *BKS*

*Slimmer windscreen pillars and deeper side
windows greatly enlarged the MkII's glass area,
and the deletion of its predecessor's rear wheel
spats enabled the rear track to be widened –
a move which increased roll-resistance
and stability.*

1963 Jaguar E-Type 3.8 Roadster, 3800cc,
150 recorded miles since restoration, converted from
left to right-hand drive, dry-stored in heated
conditions, excellent condition throughout.
£23,000–27,000 *H&H*

1966 Jaguar E-Type 4.2 Series I 2+2 Coupé,
6-cylinder engine, double overhead camshafts,
4235cc, 265bhp at 5,400rpm, excellent condition.
£14,000–17,000 *C*

**1965 Jaguar E-Type 4.2 Litre Fixed Head
Coupé,** engine rebuilt, gearbox overhauled,
new black leather upholstery, chrome wire wheels,
Webasto sunroof, ground-up restoration to
concours standards.
£21,000–24,000 *BKS*

1974 Jaguar E-Type Series III V12 Roadster,
5343cc, 272bhp, 4 Zenith carburettors, vented front
disc brakes, 4-speed manual gearbox, new black
hood and tonneau, Mota-Lita steering wheel,
chrome wire wheels, left-hand drive, excellent
original condition.
£20,000–23,000 *S*

**1966 Jaguar E-Type Series I 4.2 Litre
Roadster with Detachable Hardtop,**
6-cylinder in-line engine, double overhead
camshafts, 4235cc, 265bhp at 5,400rpm,
4-speed manual gearbox, 16,900 recorded miles,
covered headlamps, excellent condition.
£44,000–49,000 *C*

l. **1968 Jaguar 420G Four-Door Saloon,** engine rebuilt, bodywork repainted, brightwork renewed, original beige upholstery and wood trims, 64,500 recorded miles, original tools, owner's manual, maintenance and sales books, service record, new battery, exhaust system and spare tyre, overhauled, very good condition throughout. **£4,500–7,000** *S*

r. **1973 Jaguar E-Type V12 Roadster,** 14,000 recorded miles, hard and soft tops, one owner, original and mint condition. **£45,000–50,000** *THOR*

The first E-Types had 3.8 litre units, then 4.2 from 1964. In 1971, in response to US emissions regulations, the Series 3 emerged with 5.3 litre V12 engine. The Series 3 was also based on the layout of the longer 2+2 fixed head.

l. **1977 Jaguar XJ6 Coupé,** 4.2 litres, 6 cylinders, 4235cc, 162bhp at 4,750rpm, 3-speed automatic gearbox, new Biscuit-coloured roof, fully restored, complete service record from new, bills amount to $25,000, excellent condition. **£11,000–13,000** *C*

This JCNA Concours winning Jaguar is one of only 3,899 left-hand drive versions built, which were on sale in the US between 1975 and 1977.

r. **1991 Jaguar XJ12 V12 Two-Door Convertible,** new mohair hood and headlining, recarpeting in leather-piped Wilton, Italvolanti wood-rim steering wheel, brake discs and pads replaced, new exhaust fitted, fuel injection system stripped down and repaired, Mo-Mo aluminium alloy wheels, 48,000 recorded miles, fully restored, excellent condition. **£19,000–25,000** *BKS*

BUGATTI

1925 Bugatti Type 35 Grand Prix de Lyon Racing Two-Seater, chassis No. 4449,
engine No. 27, 1991cc, 8 cylinders, restored and rebodied in 1974, original coachwork available,
correct beaded-edge Dunlop tyres, cast aluminium wheels and brake drums, full race trim.
£155,000–185,000 *BKS*

*After the poor showing of his Type 32 'Tanks' at the 1923 Tours Grand Prix, Ettore Bugatti conceived an
entirely new type of racing car. Designated Type 35, it was more elegant and compact, and had a chassis
that followed the shape of the bodywork. Although its debut at the 1924 French Grand Prix at Lyon was
marred by a batch of faulty Dunlop racing tyres, it went on to become one of the most successful racers in
history. The first ten production cars were sold to selected customers from the end of 1924 and were
designated 'Type Grand Prix de Lyon' on the factory invoices. Output of the Type 35 and its variants
steadily increased, peaking at the remarkable total for a racing car of more than 250 examples in 1926.
Production continued until 1931.*

1926 Bugatti Type 35A, chassis No. 4771, 1991cc, 8 cylinders, magneto ignition, brass oil tank beneath
passenger seat, cockpit-mounted oil pump, beaded-edge alloy wheels, finished in French Blue, beige
interior, rebuilt in 1996, little use in recent years, one of 135 built, in race trim, original.
£135,000–150,000 *COYS*

*There were several versions of the Type 35, although its basic specification remained largely unchanged
throughout its life. The first was the 1.5 litre model, initially listed as a Type 35, but later officially known
as the Type 39, its capacity achieved by reducing the stroke. With the addition of a supercharger, it became
the Type 39A. Less highly tuned than the 2 litre Type 35 was the 35T (Targa), a machine better suited to
sports car events than Grands Prix. When the capacity was increased to 2262cc in 1927, and a
supercharger fitted, the Type 35B was born. This would come to be regarded as the personification of the
Grand Prix Bugatti. Later the same year, it was joined by the similar, but 2 litre, Type 35C. The Type 35A
was basically a Type 35 fitted with the 2 litre touring engine from the Type 30 road car, Bugatti's first
eight-cylinder model.*

BUGATTI Model	ENGINE cc/cyl	DATES	CONDITION 1	2	3
13/22/23	1496/4	1919-26	£40,000	£32,000	£25,000
30	1991/8	1922-36	£45,000	£35,000	£30,000
32	1992/8	1923	£45,000	£35,000	£30,000
35A	1991/8	1924-30	£110,000+	£90,000	£80,500
38 (30 update)	1991/8	1926-28	£44,500	£34,000	£28,000
39	1493/8	1926-29	£120,000	£90,000	£80,000
39A Supercharged	1496/8	1926-29	£140,000+	-	-
35T	2262/8	1926-30	£140,000+	-	-
37 GP Car	1496/4	1926-30	£110,000+	£90,000	£75,000
40	1496/4	1926-30	£50,000	£42,000	£35,000
38A	1991/8	1927-28	£48,000	£40,000	£35,000
35B Supercharged	2262/8	1927-30	£300,000+	£170,000+	-
35C	1991/8	1927-30	£170,000+	-	-
37A	1496/4	1927-30	£125,000+	-	-
44	2991/8	1927-30	£50,000+	£40,000	£35,000
45	3801/16	1927-30	£150,000+	-	-
43/43A Tourer	2262/8	1927-31	£180,000+	-	-
35A	1991/8	1928-30	£140,000	£110,000	£90,000
46	5359/8	1929-36	£140,000	£110,000	£90,000
40A	1627/4	1930	£55,000	£45,000	£35,500
49	3257/8	1930-34	£55,000	£45,000	£35,500
57 Closed	3257/8	1934-40	£40,000+	£35,000	£30,000
57 Open	3257/8	1936-38	£80,000	£60,000	£55,000
57S	3257/8	1936-38	£250,000+	-	-
57SC Supercharged	3257/8	1936-39	£250,000+	-	-
57G	3257/8	1937-40	£250,000+	-	-
57C	3257/8	1939-40	£140,000+	-	-

Bugatti continues to be popular with not much movement in prices during 1998.
Racing history is an important factor with the GP cars.

l. **1926 Bugatti Type 40 Grand Sport,** chassis No. 40775, engine No. 656, 1496cc, 4 cylinders, Grand Sport Torpedo coachwork, Marchal lighting, starting handle, some tools, good condition, original, recently recommissioned following storage, top speed 75mph.
£38,000–43,000 *S*

A touring edition of the racing Type 37, the Type 40 utilised the 1.5 litre plain-bearing engine and typically was fitted with a scaled-down Type 43 body. When new, it sold for £365 in the UK.

1931 Bugatti Type 50 Roadster, chassis No. 50123, engine No. 18, 4972cc, 8 cylinders, double overhead camshaft, supercharged, 225bhp at 4,000rpm, 3-speed manual gearbox, hollow axle with semi-elliptic leaf-sprung front suspension, live axle with reversed quarter-elliptic leaf-sprung rear suspension, friction-type shock absorbers, 4-wheel drum brakes, right-hand drive, 2 seater with dickey coachwork designed by Jean Bugatti, replacement Type 50 engine, regularly maintained by Bugatti specialists.
£220,000–260,000 *C*

The Type 50 Bugatti, introduced in October 1930, featured the first of Ettore Bugatti's twin-camshaft engine designs. It was a luxury model based on the running gear of the previous Type 46, but initially on a shorter-wheelbase chassis. Its supercharged 4.9 litre engine was formidably powerful, so much so that the English concessionaires were reluctant to import the model, fearing that it was too fast for the great majority of their clientele. Although available until 1933, only 65 examples of the Type 50 were produced, no doubt due to its high price at a time of world recession.

BUICK

1910 Buick Model 'F' Tourer, 2600cc,
3-speed gearbox, vertical-tube radiator,
right-hand drive, excellent condition.
£8,500–9,500 *H&H*

1951 Buick Series 50 Super Four-Door Saloon,
263cu in, 8 cylinders, maroon, excellent condition.
£7,000–7,500 *CTP*

BUICK Model	ENGINE cc/cyl	DATES	CONDITION 1	2	3
Veteran	various	1903-09	£18,500	£12,000	£8,000
18/20	3881/6	1918-22	£12,000	£5,000	£2,000
Series 22	2587/4	1922-24	£9,000	£5,000	£3,000
Series 24/6	3393/6	1923-30	£9,000	£5,000	£3,000
Light 8	3616/8	1931	£18,000	£14,500	£11,000
Straight 8	4467/8	1931	£22,000	£18,000	£10,000
50 Series	3857/8	1931-39	£18,500	£15,000	£8,000
60 Series	5247/8	1936-39	£19,000	£15,000	£8,000
90 Series	5648/8	1934-35	£20,000	£15,500	£9,000
40 Series	4064/8	1936-39	£19,000	£14,000	£10,000
80/90	5247/8	1936-39	£25,000	£20,000	£15,000
McLaughlin	5247/8	1937-40	£22,000	£15,000	£10,000

Various chassis lengths and bodies will affect value. Buick chassis fitted with English bodies previous to 1916 were called Bedford-Buicks. Right hand drive can have an added premium of 25%.

1953 Buick Riviera Series 50 Super,
5250cc, 8 cylinders, 170bhp, 2-speed automatic
transmission, rebuilt engine and gearbox, new
interior, new braking system, complete respray,
chrome renewed, stainless steel trim repaired or
replaced, 10,000 miles since restoration in 1990,
very good condition.
£5,000–6,000 *H&H*

1959 Buick Le Sabre Convertible, 5965cc, V8,
red paintwork, red and white upholstery, engine
and transmission rebuilt, suspension overhauled,
good condition throughout.
£7,000–8,000 *BRIT*

BUICK Model	ENGINE cu in/cyl	DATES	CONDITION 1	2	3
Special/Super 4 Door	248/ 364/8	1950-59	£6,000	£4,000	£2,000
Special/Super Riviera	263/ 332/8	1950-56	£8,000	£6,000	£3,000
Special/Super Convertible	263/ 332/8	1950-56	£7,500	£5,500	£3,000
Roadmaster 4 door	320/ 365/8	1950-58	£11,000	£8,000	£6,000
Roadmaster Riviera	320/ 364/8	1950-58	£9,000	£7,000	£5,000
Roadmaster Convertible	320/ 364/8	1950-58	£14,500	£11,000	£7,000
Special/Super Riviera	364/8	1957-59	£10,750	£7,500	£5,000
Special/Super Convertible	364/8	1957-58	£13,500	£11,000	£6,000

CADILLAC

Quaker-born Henry Martyn Leland founded Cadillac in 1902, naming his company after le Sieur de la Mothe Cadillac, a French explorer who had discovered Detroit in the early 18th century. The Model A of 1903 showed an unusual refinement for the day, and other early models displayed an envied degree of precision engineering. By 1909, the fledgling company had been acquired by General Motors and since then has remained GM's flagship marque, notching up a creditable number of pioneering achievements, including: electric self-starting and electric lighting in 1912; one of the very first production V8 engines in 1914; and synchromesh gearboxes, chromium-plating and safety glass in 1929. In the post-war fins-and-chrome era, the Harley Earl-designed 1959 Cadillac stands out as an icon of American culture.

1904 Cadillac Model A Runabout, 6½hp, single cylinder, planetary transmission, dark blue with red wheels, brown leather upholstery, period brass sidelamps, rear lamp, detachable tonneau, modified with drum brakes and Zenith carburettor, dry stored for a number of years.
£21,000–25,000   *S*

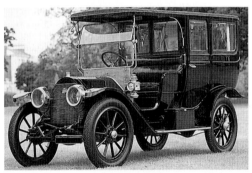

l. **1911 Cadillac Model 30 40hp Open-Drive Limousine,** 4.7 litre, electric starter, finished in black with red pinstriping, Gray & Davis acetylene and oil lamps, bevelled glass windows, black leather trimmed driver's compartment, cloth upholstered rear compartment with roller blinds, speaking tube to driver's compartment, fold-out occasional seats and companion units.
£21,000–25,000   *BKS*

1914 Cadillac Four 50hp Touring, 6 litre, 4 cylinders, original 6 volt Dynastart system, built in tyre pump, 2-speed back axle giving 6 forward speeds, 27in rims, open touring bodywork.
£23,000–27,000   *BKS*

The 1914 model was particularly significant as having the last four-cylinder engine to be produced by Cadillac for a remarkable 67 years, as 1915 saw the introduction of the Type 51 V8.

CADILLAC Model	ENGINE cc/cyl	DATES	CONDITION 1	2	3
Type 57-61	5153/8	1915-23	£20,000	£14,000	£6,000
Series 314	5153/8	1926-27	£22,000	£15,000	£6,000
Type V63	5153/8	1924-27	£20,000	£13,000	£5,000
Series 341	5578/8	1928-29	£22,000	£15,000	£6,000
Series 353-5	5289/8	1930-31	£32,500	£22,000	£12,000
V16	7406/16	1931-32	£50,000+	£32,000+	£18,000
V12	6030/12	1932-37	£42,000+	£25,000	£15,000
V8	5790/8	1935-36	£30,000+	£15,000	£6,000
V16	7034/16	1937-40	£50,000+	£30,000	£18,000

CADILLAC Model	ENGINE cu in/cyl	DATES	CONDITION 1	2	3
4 door sedan	331/8	1949	£8,000	£4,500	£3,000
2 door fastback	331/8	1949	£10,000	£8,000	£5,000
Convertible coupé	331/8	1949	£22,000	£12,000	£10,000
Series 62 4 door	331/ 365/8	1950-55	£7,000	£5,500	£3,000
Sedan de Ville	365/8	1956-58	£8,000	£6,000	£4,000
Coupé de Ville	331/ 365/8	1950-58	£12,500	£9,500	£3,500
Convertible coupé	331/ 365/8	1950-58	£25,000	£20,000	£10,000
Eldorado	331/8	1953-55	£35,000	£30,000	£18,000
Eldorado Seville	365/8	1956-58	£11,500	£9,000	£5,500
Eldorado Biarritz	365/8	1956-58	£30,000	£20,000	£15,000
Sedan de Ville	390/8	1959	£12,000	£9,500	£5,000
Coupé de Ville	390/8	1959	£15,000	£9,000	£5,500
Convertible coupé	390/8	1959	£28,000	£20,000	£10,000
Eldorado Seville	390/8	1959	£13,000	£10,000	£6,000
Eldorado Biarritz	390/8	1959	£30,000	£20,000	£14,000
Sedan de Ville	390/8	1960	£10,000	£8,000	£4,500
Convertible coupé	390/8	1960	£27,000	£14,000	£7,500
Eldorado Biarritz	390/8	1960	£25,000	£17,000	£10,000
Sedan de Ville	390/ 429/8	1961-64	£7,000	£5,000	£3,000
Coupé de Ville	390/ 429/8	1961-64	£8,000	£6,000	£4,000
Convertible coupé	390/ 429/8	1961-64	£15,000	£9,000	£7,000
Eldorado Biarritz	390/ 429/8	1961-64	£19,500	£14,000	£9,000

1918 Cadillac Type 57 Tourer, 5153cc, V8, maroon and black coachwork. **£13,500–15,000** *DB*

1941 Cadillac Series 62 Deluxe Convertible, 346cu in, V8, 150bhp at 3,400rpm, 3-speed manual gearbox, V-windscreen, restored. **£35,000–38,000** *C*

1961 Cadillac Series 62 Fleetwood Saloon, 390cu in, V8, 6 seater, finished in white with Canberra cloth/Florentine vinyl interior, original sales literature, owner's manual, 83,000km from new, excellent original condition. **£4,800–5,800** *BKS*

Restyled and re-engineered, the 1961 Cadillac range continued the previous year's trend towards slightly less outrageous tailfins. The striking pillarless coachwork, which had debuted in 1959, was also continued, and all models were powered by the 390cu in V8 introduced that same year. Automatic transmission, power-assisted steering and power brakes were standard features, while the list of options included cruise control, power-operated windows and seats, central locking, air conditioning and tinted glass.

1967 Cadillac Limousine,
leather upholstered interior.
£7,000–7,750 *CTP*

1969 Cadillac De Ville Two-Door Convertible,
472cu in, V8, excellent condition throughout.
£5,500–6,500 *BKS*

CHALMERS-DETROIT

Backed by Hugh Chalmers of the National Cash Register Company, Chalmers-Detroit was the chosen make of millionaires like the Vanderbilts and Rockefellers. The company began life as the Detroit branch of the E. R. Thomas Company of Buffalo, New York, builders of the immortal Thomas-Flyer, but in 1907 Howard Coffin and Roy Chapin – who had persuaded Thomas to endorse the idea in the first place – decided to strike out on their own. In 1908, they renamed the company Chalmers-Detroit and brought out a fine new 30hp model, which remained in production until 1913. The company fell victim to the post-WWI recession, and in 1922 merged with Maxwell. Two years later, Maxwell-Chalmers gave way to a new marque – Chrysler.

1912 Chalmers-Detroit Model 11 30hp Fore-Door Pony Tonneau, 3.7 litre, 4 cylinder monobloc engine, 3-speed gearbox, multi-disc clutch, Gray & Davis acetylene headlamps, running board-mounted Klaxon.
£20,000–25,000 *BKS*

CHENARD-WALCKER

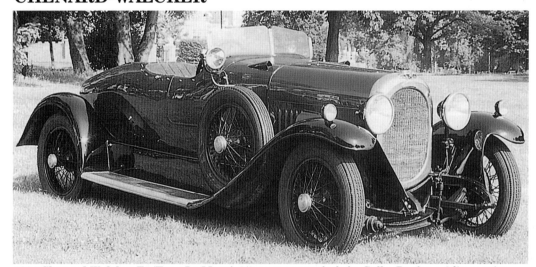

1924 Chenard-Walcker T5 'Type Le Mans', 2/3 seater sports body by Coffey Brothers, 2 litre engine and servo braking system fully restored.
£32,000–38,000 *BKS*

After their outright victory with a 3 litre car in the first Le Mans 24-hour race in 1923, Chenard-Walcker returned to the fray in 1924 with a racing version of their overhead-camshaft 2 litre model. While that year saw the first Bentley victory at Le Mans, two 2 litre Chenard-Walckers tied for fourth place and took the 2 litre class. To celebrate the achievement, Chenard-Walcker produced a limited-edition 2 litre model, the T5 'Type Le Mans'. Its novel braking system combined front drums and a servo-assisted transmission brake – there were no brakes on the rear wheels. In all, 16 T5 models were built.

CHEVROLET

l. **1954 Chevrolet Corvette Roadster,** 235cu in, 6 cylinders, 150bhp at 4,200rpm, automatic transmission, chassis restored, excellent condition.
£22,000–25,000 *C*

At the first Motorama, in 1953 at New York's Waldorf-Astoria Hotel, Chevrolet unveiled the new Corvette. It was sleek and sporty with a rounded body, mesh stone guards over inset headlamps, a wrapped windscreen and thrusting 'jet-pod' tail lamps. Its soft top folded out of sight beneath a lift-up panel, while side curtains replaced roll-up windows. Power was provided by the Chevrolet 'Blue Flame' six. The Corvette was the most exciting car GM had ever offered and was America's first true post-war sports car.

CHEVROLET Model	ENGINE cc/cyl	DATES	CONDITION 1	2	3
H4/H490 K Series	2801/4	1914-29	£9,000	£5,000	£2,000
FA5	2699/4	1918	£8,000	£5,000	£2,000
D5	5792/8	1918-19	£10,000	£6,000	£3,000
FB50	3660/4	1919-21	£7,000	£4,000	£2,000
AA	2801/4	1928-32	£5,000	£3,000	£1,000
AB/C	3180/6	1929-36	£6,000	£4,000	£2,000
Master	3358/6	1934-37	£9,000	£5,000	£2,000
Master De Luxe	3548/6	1938-41	£9,000	£6,000	£4,000

l. **1960 Chevrolet Impala Convertible,** 62,000 miles.
£11,000–12,000 *PALM*

1960 Chevrolet Corvette, 283cu in, 4-speed manual gearbox, Horizon Blue.
£27,000–30,000 *COR*

1961 Chevrolet Corvette, 4.7 litre, 245bhp, 4-speed manual gearbox, Honduras Maroon, Fawn interior, power top, original, excellent condition.
£23,000–25,000 *COR*

CHEVROLET Model	ENGINE cu in/cyl	DATES	CONDITION 1	2	3
Stylemaster	216/6	1942-48	£8,000	£4,000	£1,000
Fleetmaster	216/6	1942-48	£8,000	£4,000	£1,000
Fleetline	216/6	1942-51	£8,000	£5,000	£2,000
Styleline	216/6	1949-52	£8,000	£6,000	£2,000
Bel Air 4 door	235/6	1953-54	£6,000	£4,000	£3,000
Bel Air sports coupé	235/6	1953-54	£7,000	£4,500	£3,500
Bel Air convertible	235/6	1953-54	£12,500	£9,500	£6,000
Bel Air 4 door	283/8	1955-57	£8,000	£4,000	£3,000
Bel Air sports coupé	283/8	1955-56	£11,000	£7,000	£4,000
Bel Air convertible	283/8	1955-56	£16,000	£11,000	£7,000
Bel Air sports coupé	283/8	1957	£11,000	£7,500	£4,500
Bel Air convertible	283/8	1957	£14,500+	£10,500+	£8,000
Impala sports sedan	235/6, 348/8	1958	£12,500	£9,000	£5,500
Impala convertible	235/6, 348/8	1958	£14,500	£11,000	£7,500
Impala sports sedan	235/6, 348/8	1959	£8,000	£5,000	£4,000
Impala convertible	235/6, 348/8	1959	£14,000	£10,000	£5,000
Corvette roadster	235/6	1953	£18,000	£14,000	£10,000
Corvette roadster	235/6, 283/8	1954-57	£16,500	£13,000	£9,000
Corvette roadster	283, 327/8	1958-62	£16,000	£12,000	£9,000
Corvette Stingray	327, 427/8	1963-67	£15,500	£12,000	£10,000
Corvette Stingray DHC	327, 427/8	1963-66	£22,000	£15,000	£8,000
Corvette Stingray DHC	427/8	1967	£16,000	£13,000	£10,000

Value will also be regulated by build options, rare coachbuilding options, and de luxe engine specifications etc.

1966 Chevrolet Corvette Sting Ray Convertible, 5.4 litre, 4-speed manual gearbox, new interior and paintwork.
£17,000–20,000   *COR*

1966 Chevrolet Corvette Sting Ray Convertible, 7 litre, manual gearbox, Rally Red, red leather interior, hard and soft tops, knock-off hubs, side pipes.
£24,000–27,000   *COR*

l. **1972 Chevrolet Corvette Stingray T-Roof,** 5.7 litre, high-performance engine, manual gearbox, Mille Miglia Red, new red interior, excellent condition.
£11,000–12,500   *COR*

r. **1973 Chevrolet Corvette Stingray Convertible,** 7.4 litre, manual gearbox.
£13,500–15,500   *COR*

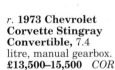

l. **1977 Chevrolet Corvette,** 5.7 litre, manual gearbox, low mileage, stainless steel exhaust.
£8,000–10,000   *COR*

1978 Chevrolet Corvette Indianapolis Pace Car Replica, 5.7 litre, automatic transmission, black and silver paintwork, leather interior, excellent original condition, 41,000 miles.
£13,000–15,000   *COR*

1980 Chevrolet Corvette, 5.7 litre, automatic transmission.
£10,000–12,000   *COR*

1989 Chevrolet Corvette 5.7 litre, automatic transmission, air conditioning, low mileage.
£13,000–15,000   *COR*

l. **1980 Chevrolet Corvette,** 5.7 litre, body and paintwork in very good condition.
£8,500–10,000   *H&H*

1991 Corvette ZR1, 5.7 litre, 375bhp, 6-speed manual gearbox.
£20,000–23,000   *COR*

CHRYSLER

1938 Chrysler Imperial C-19 Rumble Seat Convertible, 298.7cu in, 8 cylinders, 3-speed synchromesh gearbox, repainted Riviera Blue, original dark blue moleskin upholstery, windscreen spotlight, whitewall tyres, fender skirts, exhaust fishtail, rear leaf springs protected by gaiters, only 15,000km since new.
£16,500–18,500   *BKS*

The Rumble Seat Convertible represents the final availability of a rumble seat (dickey) on the prestigeous Imperial series. It was only in production for the start of the 1938 model year and was withdrawn after only 80 examples had been built.

CITROEN

1925 Citroën C3 5CV 'Cloverleaf' Tourer,
856cc, 4 cylinders, sidevalve engine, former
museum exhibit, restored in 1984, good
condition throughout, some movement in body
panel joints apparent.
£4,000–5,000 *BKS*

*Citroën's first truly outstanding design – the
Type C – was introduced in 1922. Also known as
the Cloverleaf because of its 2+1 seating and 5CV
for its tax rating, the Type C brought 'real' car
ownership within reach of the man in the street.
Its small sidevalve engine ensured that it was
more renowned for longevity than speed. An
example was driven all around Australia in 1925.*

1951 Citroën 11BL/Light 15 Saloon,
original condition.
£2,750–3,250 *PA*

Make the most of Miller's

*Condition is absolutely vital when
assessing the value of a vehicle. Top class
vehicles on the whole appreciate much
more than less perfect examples. Rare,
desirable cars may command higher
prices even when in need of restoration.*

1950 Citroën 15/6 Cabriolet, coachwork by
Carrosserie CTA, 2.9 litre, 6 cylinders, high-
compression pistons, clutch and transmission rebuilt,
steel body, all mechanical components renovated,
rack-and-pinion steering overhauled, wiring run in
stainless steel conduits, battery isolator switch.
£14,000–16,000 *BKS*

*Built on the floorpan of a 15/6 saloon, this car
is a recreation of a 'lost' Citroën model. While the
convertible version of the original 11CV four-cylinder
Traction Avant is well-known, the six-cylinder
variant was only available to the public with saloon
coachwork. However, Citroën built five 15/6
cabriolets, two of them for the controlling Michelin
family. The model never went into production, and
only one example is known to have survived.*

1951 Citroën 11BL/Light 15, 1911cc, 4 cylinders,
56bhp, French built, restored, concours condition.
£4,750–5,250 *COYS*

*The revolutionary Traction Avant was introduced
in March 1934. It not only featured front-wheel
drive, but also a low-slung body of unitary
construction. The front suspension was independent
with wishbones and torsion bars, while the brakes
were hydraulically operated. Known as the 7A in
Europe (later evolving into the 7B and 7C), or
Super Modern 12 if built in Citroën's Slough
factory, it was praised for its excellent roadholding,
ride and performance. Its new overhead-valve, four-
cylinder engine, initially of 1303cc, was mated to a
three-speed gearbox with dashboard change. In
October 1934, the Onze range was announced, all
models having a 1.9 litre engine in one of two states
of tune. Slough-built versions of the 11A were called
Super Modern 15 and Sports 12, and when the 11B
and 11L arrived in 1937, the British models became
the Light 15 and Big 15 respectively.*

CITROËN Model	ENGINE cc/cyl	DATES	CONDITION 1	2	3
A	1300/4	1919	£4,000	£2,000	£1,000
5CV	856/4	1922-26	£7,000	£4,000	£2,000
11	1453/4	1922-28	£4,000	£2,000	£1,000
12/24	1538/4	1927-29	£5,000	£3,000	£1,000
2½litre	2442/6	1929-31	£5,000	£3,000	£1,500
13/30	1628/4	1929-31	£5,000	£3,000	£1,000
Big 12	1767/4	1932-35	£7,000	£5,000	£2,000
Twenty	2650/6	1932-35	£10,000	£5,000	£3,000
Ten CV	1452/4	1933-34	£5,000	£3,000	£1,000
Ten CV	1495/4	1935-36	£6,000	£3,000	£1,000
11B/Light 15/Big 15/7CV	1911/4	1934-57	£9,000	£5,000	£2,000
Twelve	1628/4	1936-39	£5,000	£3,000	£1,000
F	1766/4	1937-38	£4,000	£2,000	£1,000
15/6 and Big Six	2866/6	1938-56	£7,000	£4,000	£2,000

CITROEN Model	ENGINE cc/cyl	DATES	CONDITION 1	2	3
2CV	375/2	1948-54	£1,000	£500	£250
2CV/Dyane/Bijou	425/2	1954-82	£1,000	£800	£500
DS19/ID19	1911/4	1955-69	£5,000	£3,000	£800
Sahara	900/4	1958-67	£5,000	£4,000	£3,000
2CV6	602/2	1963 on	£750	£500	£250
DS Safari	1985/4	1968-75	£6,000	£3,000	£1,000
DS21	1985/4	1969-75	£6,000	£3,000	£1,000
DS23	2347/4	1972-75	£6,000	£4,000	£1,500
SM	2670/ 2974/6	1970-75	£9,000	£6,000	£4,500

Imported (USA) SM models will be 15% less.

1953 Citroën 11BL/Light 15 Saloon, Paris-built, left-hand drive, dry stored for a number of years, repainted in black, original interior trim.
£2,900–3,400 *S*

This car was imported to the UK from France at the beginning of the 1980s by a motion picture company. Later, it appeared in the television series Till We Meet Again *and the film* The Contract.

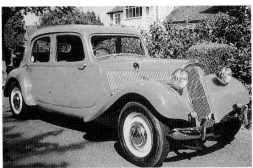

1955 Citroën Light 15 Saloon, Slough-built, new pistons, liners, valves and loom, VW tail lights, original semaphores, stainless steel exhaust, sunroof in working order, interior retrimmed in maroon leather, very good condition.
£6,000–6,500 *S*

l. **1963 Citroën 2CV Sahara,** twin 425cc 2 cylinder engine, body stripped and restored, excellent condition.
£13,000–15,000 *Pou*

1975 Citroën DS23 EFI Pallas Four-Door Saloon, 2347cc, 4 cylinders, right-hand drive, manual gearbox, fuel injection, luxury equipment package, restored.
£8,250–9,000 *BKS*

As they had done 21 years before, with the revolutionary Traction Avant, Citroën stunned the world in 1955 with the strikingly-styled DS. Beneath its aerodynamic, low-drag bodyshell was all-independent, self-levelling, hydro-pneumatic suspension, together with power-operated brakes, clutch and steering. No European car would match the ride quality of the DS for several years, the fundamental soundness of the suspension design being demonstrated by its survival in the present-day XM and Xantia models.

CLEMENT-BAYARD

The industrial and personal activities of Adolphe Clément are complex. With a background in the bicycle industry and having made a fortune from acquiring the French rights to Dunlop tyres, he became involved with many makes of car, and manufactured aero engines, dirigibles and aeroplanes. He added the name of a medieval knight to that of his own to become Monsieur Clément-Bayard, and ran his companies as private enterprises so that their details were not in the public domain. A bewildering range of models bore his name.

1913 Clément-Bayard Type CB1 12hp Tourer, 4 seater, finished in blue with black wings, brass fittings throughout, Ducellier acetylene headlamps with running board-mounted generator, Securit oil sidelamps, double-twist bulb horn, retains much original black upholstery, original condition. **£10,500–12,000** *S*

CROSSLEY

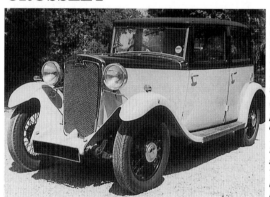

l. **1934 Crossley Torquay 10hp,** 1122cc, 4 cylinders, aluminium-panelled body, fabric roof, good condition mechanically, coachwork and structure in excellent condition, original brown leather upholstery in excellent condition, well maintained, 26,000 warranted miles. **£6,250–7,000** *BRIT*

Crossley began building cars in 1904 and, following a line of high-quality, powerful motor cars, entered the small car market in 1923 with the 12/14 model. This gained considerable success and remained in production until the late 1920s. The small car theme was continued with the 10hp Torquay, offered for the 1933/34 seasons. Crossley's last cars were made in 1937, but the company built bus bodies until 1958.

DAIMLER

The British Daimler company's name and origins go back to 1891, when inventor and businessman Frederick Simms acquired British rights to Gottleib Daimler's engines. The Daimler Motor Company Ltd was formed in 1896, and the first car – which required 60 workers to produce – emerged in March 1897. The 4hp machine had tiller steering and solid tyres, yet was capable of twice the new 12mph speed limit. By 1900, Daimler had attracted royal patronage, which was to continue for more than 50 years. In 1910, the company received welcome stability and capital with its acquisition by Birmingham Small Arms (BSA). In the 1920s, Daimler's engines matched Rolls-Royce's for smoothness and silent running, and in 1926 Daimler produced Britain's first series-production V12.

After WWII, Daimler struggled to retain its pre-war eminence and produced some curious models, none more so than the fibreglass-bodied Dart SP250 sports car. Intended as a dollar winner, the ungainly, but appealing, machine propelled the company into Jaguar's hands in 1960. The last true Daimler model was the DS420 limousine (1968–92), but Daimler's fluted radiator surround remains a badge of distinction, worn by the luxury flagship of the Jaguar marque.

In the 1960s Daimler and Jaguar products converged, and today Daimler variants can be more affordable than their Jaguar counterparts. Instead of a MkII Jaguar you might consider a Daimler 250 V8 saloon or a Daimler Sovereign as an alternative to a Jaguar 420.

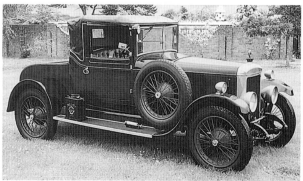

l. **1927 Daimler 16/55hp Type L Doctor's Coupé with Dickey,** 1872cc, 6 cylinders, nickel electric lighting, windscreen-mounted spotlamp, side-mounted spare, calorimeter, wooden lathed petrol tank, opening windscreen, carriage-style door handles, in good running order. **£9,500–11,500** *BKS*

For the 1927 season, Daimler listed five different chassis, ranging from the 12-cylinder, 7136cc Types P, O and W to the smallest of the range, the compact 1872cc six-cylinder Type L with a maker's rating of 16/55hp.

DAIMLER	ENGINE Model	DATES cc/cyl	CONDITION		
			1	2	3
Veteran (Coventry built)	var/4	1897-1904	£75,000	£60,000	£30,000
Veteran	var/4	1905-19	£35,000	£25,000	£15,000
30hp	4962/6	1919-25	£40,000	£25,000	£18,000
45hp	7413/6	1919-25	£45,000	£30,000	£20,000
Double Six 50	7136/12	1927-34	£40,000	£30,000	£20,000
20	2687/6	1934-35	£18,000	£14,000	£12,000
Straight 8	3421/8	1936-38	£20,000	£15,000	£12,000

Value is dependent on body style, coachbuilder and condition of the sleeve valve engine.

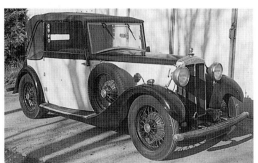

1933 Daimler 15 Drophead, coachwork by Tickford, 1805cc, 6 cylinders, fluid-flywheel gearbox, cream over black livery, original dark brown leather upholstery, luggage trunk, hood in good condition.
£5,250–6,000 *S*

The body of this particular Daimler 15 was designed to allow its first owner to wear his hat inside the car.

1939 Daimler DB18 Drophead Coupé, 2552cc, straight 6, finished in black, original green leather interior, opening windscreen, some original tools, good overall condition.
£14,500–16,000 *S*

In March 1939, Stratstone delivered this DB18 Drophead to King George VI for his own personal use. Ownership passed to Mary Beatrice, Lord Bath's sister. The Sixth Marquess later acquired the car and commissioned its restoration in 1980, since when it has been displayed at Longleat.

1936 Daimler 4½ Litre Six-Light Limousine, coachwork by Mann Egerton, 4624cc, overhead-valve straight 8, finished in black with matching leather front seats, beige upholstery to rear, comprehensive tool kit, restored.
£13,500–15,000 *BKS*

1949 Daimler 15 2.5 Litre Saloon, coachwork by Hooper, 2522cc, 6 cylinders, black paintwork, 3 piece alloy bonnet, electric driver's window, refurbished trim, wooden flooring, seats, ash frame and body panels, carefully maintained, dry-stored for the past 5 years, only 200 miles covered since engine rebuilt.
£3,000–4,500 *COYS*

This car is most unusual in being effectively a DB18 built on a 1939 15 chassis, one of a handful laid down prior to WWII. During the war, it was stored at the Daimler factory in Coventry, where it was damaged during the Blitz. After the war, it was sold to royal coachbuilder Hooper who rebuilt it to a high standard.

l. **1956 Daimler Conquest Drophead Coupé,** 2433cc, 6 cylinders, 100bhp, twin carburettors, fluid-flywheel transmission, aluminium-panelled body, finished in yellow, natural leather trim, 3-abreast seating, wind-up windows, good condition.
£9,500–11,000 *BKS*

Only 54 examples of the Drophead Coupé were built before production ended in 1957.

Daimler Dart SP250, 1959–64

This Daimler is like no other, a drastic plastic cocktail of a sports car with a menacing grouper-like mouth, fanciful fins and a beautiful turbine-smooth 2.5 litre V8. After Daimler fell into the clutches of Jaguar, it was overshadowed by the E-Type. Today, the Dart is quaint and distinctive, and that gorgeous V8 engine really redeems this rather eccentric device.
Engine: 2548cc, iron-block V8.
Power output: 140bhp at 5,800rpm.
Brakes: Discs all-round.
Transmission: Four-speed manual or three-speed automatic.
Top speed: 125mph.

0–60mph: 8.5 seconds.
Production: 2,644.
Price in 1959: £1,395.
Price today: £5,000–17,000.
Pick of the bunch: So-called 'B-specification' cars from 1961 had a more robust chassis and a few more creature comforts. The last 'C-spec' cars from 1963 were marginally more refined.
Dart facts: The Dart was a flop in the US where it was primarily aimed. It's a measure of the hasty development that even the name had to be changed because Dodge had legal rights to 'Dart' and threatened to sue. The Metropolitan Police ran a fleet of 30 black Dart automatics.

1957 Daimler One-O-Four, 3468cc, 6 cylinders, pre-selector gearbox, new starter motor, black coachwork in good order, original tan leather trim, stored 1976–90, fewer than 1,000 miles covered during the last 6 years, runs well.
£1,100–1,600 *BRIT*

The One-O-Four, produced between 1955 and 1959, continued the theme of the earlier Regency. Its 3½ litre engine developed 137bhp, while servo-assisted braking was standard. From late 1956, automatic transmission became available. Only 569 were built.

1965 Daimler 250 V8 Saloon, 2548cc, V8, automatic transmission, optional wire wheels, fair general condition.
£4,600–5,200 *S*

The V8 250 Daimler, the luxury alternative to the Jaguar MkII, was launched at the 1962 London Motor Show. It used the Jaguar MkII body, but was powered by Daimler's 2.5 litre V8 engine, which was far lighter than its Jaguar counterpart. Dunlop disc brakes were fitted all-round. The familiar fluted design on the grille and boot plinth, and the 'D' emblem on the hub caps, distinguished the new saloon as a Daimler. Road tested by The Autocar, *it achieved a maximum speed of 113mph and overall fuel consumption of 19.3mpg.*

    r. **1968 Daimler 250 V8 Saloon,** 2548cc, automatic transmission, power steering, original sunroof, service books, receipts and bills, £2,000 recently spent on mechanical work, 62,000 guaranteed miles, original, unrestored.
£6,000–7,000 *H&H*

1962 Daimler Dart SP250, 2548cc, V8, rebuilt and race modified.
£10,500–12,000 *WILM*

1964 Daimler Majestic Major, 4561cc, V8, silver and black paintwork, largely original interior in very good condition, front passenger seat retrimmed, original rugs and carpets, new stainless steel exhaust 68,500 guaranteed miles.
£3,750–4,250 *H&H*

1965 Daimler 250 V8, 42,000 miles, unrestored, excellent condition.
£10,000–13,000 *THOR*

1968 Daimler 250 V8, 2548cc, V8, manual/overdrive transmission, new rear spats and jacking points, bumpers replated, refurbished interior, new head lining and carpets, woodwork relacquered, service book, well maintained, excellent mechanical condition.
£6,000–7,000 *BRIT*

1969 Daimler 420 Sovereign, 4235cc, 6 cylinders, automatic transmission, good condition throughout.
£2,000–2,500 *H&H*

1973 Daimler Double Six Vanden Plas, 5343cc, V12, 3-speed automatic transmission, 42,620 miles.
£2,750–3,250 *H&H*

Only 342 Vanden Plas Double Six Series 1 cars were built.

1971 Daimler DS240 Limousine, 4235cc, 6 cylinders, finished in silver and maroon, maroon interior, some refurbishment.
£1,750–2,250 *BRIT*

These large motor cars were produced between 1968 and 1992.

l. **1973 Daimler 4.2 Series 1,** 4235cc, 6 cylinders, genuine 43,000 miles, very good condition throughout.
£3,000–3,500 *PA*

| DAIMLER | ENGINE | DATES | CONDITION | | |
Model	cc/cyl		1	2	3
DB18	2522/6	1946-49	£7,500	£4,000	£1,000
DB18 Conv S/S	2522/6	1948-53	£14,000	£7,000	£2,000
Consort	2522/6	1949-53	£5,000	£3,000	£1,000
Conquest/Con.Century	2433/6	1953-58	£4,000	£2,000	£1,000
Conquest Roadster	2433/6	1953-56	£12,000	£7,000	£4,000
Majestic 3.8	3794/6	1958-62	£5,000	£2,000	£1,000
SP250	2547/8	1959-64	£12,000	£10,000	£4,500
Majestic Major	4561/8	1961-64	£6,000	£4,000	£1,000
2.5 V8	2547/8	1962-67	£8,000	£5,250	£2,500
V8 250	2547/8	1968-69	£8,000	£4,000	£2,000
Sovereign 420	4235/6	1966-69	£5,000	£3,500	£1,500

DATSUN

1973 Datsun 240Z, 5735cc, Chevrolet V8, £6,000 engine rebuild, bright red paintwork, good mechanical condition, bodywork and underside in good condition.
£4,000–5,000 *BRIT*

1902 De Dion Bouton Model K2 8hp Rear Entrance Tonneau, single cylinder, self starter, 4 seater, dark blue livery, varnished wooden wheels, 'King of the Road' oil front lamps, double-twist bulb horn, Smith's 0–50mph speedometer, red leather upholstery.
£29,000–33,000 *BKS*

This car was supplied new to the Duke of Bedford's Woburn Estate. It comes with a photographic and history file covering the period from 1902 to date.

r. **1903 De Dion Bouton 8hp Type R Rear Entrance Tonneau,** single cylinder, 4 seater, red livery, Lucas oil lamps, Sparton hand klaxon, Stewart speedometer, wicker umbrella holder, grey upholstery, all major components including engine and gearbox rebuilt, new exhaust.
£19,500–23,500 *BKS*

DE DION BOUTON

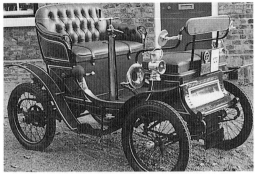

1902 De Dion Bouton Type G 4½hp Vis-à-Vis, finished in crimson livery with gold leaf lining, brass oil lights, rear-view mirrors, horn and warning bell, full engine rebuild, reupholstered in deep buttoned leather, new tyres, history file.
£26,500–29,000 *BKS*

De Dion Bouton's 3½hp Voiturette of 1899 was a new generation of motor car. Its rear-mounted, smooth and fast-revving, single-cylinder engine drove through a system of gears to the rear wheels, unlike the slow-running Benz engine with its drive chains and belts that was typical of the period. A 4½hp engine was offered in the Vis-à-vis models from 1900, giving the car a comfortable speed of 25mph, and still more achievable where brakes were unlikely to be needed. This particular car is one of the most original survivors and was one of the last of this model to be produced. It has completed The New London to New Brighton Run in Minnesota as well as the British run, has been a consistent concours winner and has been maintained regardless of cost.

l. **1913 De Dion Bouton Model EK Two-Seater,** 4 cylinders, magneto ignition, steel channel frame, honeycomb radiator, wooden steering wheel.
£13,500–17,000 *S*

This car was originally registered in April 1924 to the well-known motoring pioneer Sir David Salomons, whose advice to fellow motorists is revealing: 'The first thing to be done by the purchaser of a mechanical carriage is to have it completely dismantled under his eyes, and to thoroughly comprehend the whole mechanism.' Salomons built the first properly equipped 'motor house' in England and held the first British motor show in Tunbridge Wells, where he was Mayor, in 1895.

DELAGE

Louis Delage set up his own components business in 1905 before turning to the manufacture of motor cars for those who preferred individuality to mass production. A successful, if costly, racing programme was pursued in the 1920s and a line of excellent fast tourers was produced. The Courbevoie-sur-Seine firm disappeared in the Hotchkiss takeover of 1953.

1928 Delage DM, fabric bodied by C. T. Weymann, 3.2 litre, 6 cylinders, right-hand drive, stored between 1956 and 1978, then fully restored, concours standard.
£22,000–25,000 *S*

1937 Delage D670 Sports Saloon, coachwork by University Motors, later D670 straight 6 engine, 3418cc, Cotal 4-speed electric-change gearbox, right-hand drive, completely restored during 1979/80, good overall condition.
£12,750–14,250 *S*

Louis Delage's withdrawal from the Courbevoie firm in 1935 was followed by the merger of his former company with Delahaye. Thereafter, the Delage was built alongside the products of its new owner in a Paris factory.

DELAHAYE

1951 Delahaye 135M 'Competition' Two-Door Coupé, coachwork by Chapron of Paris, 3557cc, 6 cylinders, Cotal electric-change gearbox, complete with all original features, aluminium bodywork in good condition, original leather interior trim.
£8,500–10,000 *BKS*

DELOREAN

The DeLorean Motor Company was founded in 1975 by John Z. DeLorean, the former Vice President of General Motors. The technical specification of the DMC-12 made interesting reading, the box section steel chassis was double epoxy-coated and of Lotus design, whilst the body was of GRP clad with a brushed stainless steel outer skin. The Renault V6 engine was fitted with Bosch K-Jetronic fuel injection and Girling dual circuit power brakes were specified. The striking body was designed by Giugiaro of Ital Design in Turin and the first prototype was completed late in 1977. Following further development the first production car was completed in January 1981 and by the Summer production was in full swing. By the end of that year some 6,539 vehicles had been built. By 1983 production had ceased and the company was liquidated during October that year, after a total of 8,583 cars had been built, most of which were exported to the USA.

l. **1981 DeLorean DMC-12,** 2849cc, 6 cylinders, turbocharger, converted to right-hand drive, original unpainted stainless steel finish in very good condition, new clutch and tyres, original grey leather interior trim, all equipment functional except air conditioning.
£8,500–10,000 *BRIT*

DE TOMASO

r. **1978 De Tomaso Longchamp,** 5.7 litre, automatic transmission, mechanically good, interior trim and bodywork in excellent condition.
£6,000–6,500 *LF*

This car is a short-chassis example, of which 395 were built between 1973 and 1985. It is one of only five provided with right-hand drive.

DODGE

l. **1936 Dodge Senior 6 De Luxe Saloon,** overdrive, side-mounted spare, original dark brown leather interior, generally sound condition, 31,974 miles.
£3,500–4,500 *S*

John and Horace Dodge produced their first car in Detroit in 1914, and by 1920 the brothers were placed second overall in US sales. Walter P. Chrysler acquired the company in 1928, changing the name from Dodge Brothers to simply Dodge during the following decade, which also saw the introduction of overdrive, synchromesh and independent front suspension. Only Sixes were produced from 1934 to the outbreak of war and, for the UK market, cars were built in right-hand drive form near Kew Gardens, Surrey.

DUESENBERG

By 1913 the Duesenberg brothers, Fred and August, had set up their own small factory where they built four-cylinder 'walking beam' engines mainly for the motor racing community. In 1920 a Duesenberg-powered record car topped 156mph at Daytona. A Duesenberg won the 1921 French Grand Prix and the marque won the Indianapolis 500 four times in the 1920s. The first Duesenberg road car had a 100bhp straight-eight engine with a single overhead camshaft and hydraulic front brakes. Both these innovations derived from competition practice and Duesenberg was the first to actually go into production with them. Production did not begin until late 1921, but for all their engineering brilliance the brothers were poor business managers, and the company went into receivership in 1924. It was revived with fresh capital, floundered again and was taken over by E.L. Cord in 1926 to add to his growing empire. By then a total of about 500 Model A's had been delivered. Ironically this period coincided with Duesenberg's greatest success on the race track.

l. **1922 Duesenberg Model A Doctor's Coupé,** coachwork by Fleetwood, 4260cc, 8 cylinders, 2 seater with dickey seat, good all-round condition.
£23,000–26,000 *COYS*

FACEL VEGA

Forges et Ateliers de Construction d'Eure et Loire, or Facel, founded by Jean Daninos in 1938, produced *inter alia,* machine tools for the aircraft industry and was best known for supplying specialist bodies to Panhard, Simca, Bentley and Ford France. Daninos exhibited his first car, the Vega, at the Paris Salon in 1954, fulfilling his dream of building true *Grandes Routiéres.* Following the practice of using American V8 engines allied to Continental styling and chassis behaviour, the Pont-à-Mousson concern employed 4.5 litre, 5.8 litre and latterly 6.3 litre units of Chrysler origin for their stylish motor cars. A total of 46 of these very expensive cars were sold during 1954 and 1955. By 1956 the models were designated Facel Vega. The ultimate Franco-American creation by Daninos was the supremely elegant Facel HK2 series, powered by the 6286cc V8 overhead camshaft Chrysler engine, developing over 380bhp. Support from Mobil, Pont-à-Mousson and Hispano-Suiza notwithstanding, a receiver was appointed in 1962 and the original company wound up in 1964.

1961 Facel Vega HK2 Cabriolet, 6.3 litre, manual gearbox, restored.
£44,000–48,000 *S*

This example was the second production car made and was exhibited at the 1961 London and Paris motor shows. About 10 years ago, it was converted into a cabriolet.

1959 Facel Vega HK500, 6.3 litre, left-hand drive, disc brakes, power-assisted steering, cylinder heads and carburettor missing, no gearbox, original, unrestored.
£11,000–13,000 *S*

FERRARI

Enzo Ferrari, ex-racing driver and team manager for Alfa Romeo through the 1930s, began the legend of the Prancing Horse when he went his own way and produced his first 1.5 litre racing car in 1940. The first true production Ferrari, the 166 of 1948, employed a V12 engine that was to become a hallmark of the Maranello make. It is often said that, in the early days, Ferrari built road cars to finance his true passion for racing, and the long line of classic stunning-looking sports cars have benefited their few lucky owners with impeccable race-car breeding and, often, staggering performance.

1949 Ferrari Tipo 166 Stabilimenti Berlinetta chassis No. 021S, 2 litre, black paintwork, tan hide interior.
£120,000–125,000   *TALA*

This is probably the best known of the four Stabilimenti Farina-bodied cars.

1951 Ferrari 195 Ghia Coupé, chassis No. 0129S, 2.3 litre, cream paintwork, tan hide interior, restored during the late 1980s.
£120,000–125,000   *TALA*

This triple-carburettor example is one of only 10 Ghia-bodied cars.

1953 Ferrari 250 Europa Two-Door Coupé, chassis No. 0323EU, engine No. 0323EU, coachwork by Pinin Farina, 2963cc, original V12, triple Weber carburettors, 200–220bhp, restored during the late 1980s.
£90,000–100,000   *BKS*

Introduced alongside the larger-engined 375GT America, the 250 Europa shared the former's long-wheelbase chassis and Lampredi-designed 60° V12. There was no 'standard' bodywork, coachbuilding being shared by Pinin Farina and Vignale. Production was short-lived, however, with only about 18 examples being produced before being superseded by the outwardly-similar 250GT Europa in late 1954.

1957 Ferrari 250 GT 'Low Roof' Boano Coupé, chassis No. 0547, engine No. 0547, 3 litre, V12, restored 5–6 years ago, silver over dark red, tan hide upholstery, matching carpets, cream head lining, Borrani wheels, Marchal driving lights.
£45,000–49,000   *S*

Fewer than 80 Boano Coupés were made between 1956 and 1957.

l. **1958 Ferrari 250 GT Two-Door Coupé,** chassis No. 1157GT, engine No. 1157GT, coachwork by Pininfarina, 2953cc, V12, 220–240bhp, dark blue paintwork, tan interior, mechanics overhauled in 1990, only 155 miles since engine rebuilt, period modification to front disc brakes.
£31,000–35,000   *BKS*

This is one of the few Ferraris of the period not to have undergone cosmetic restoration.

FERRARI Model	ENGINE cc/cyl	DATES	CONDITION 1	2	3
250 GTE	2953/12	1959-63	£32,000	£22,000	£20,000
250 GT SWB (steel)	2953/12	1959-62	£235,000+	£185,000	-
250 GT Lusso	2953/12	1962-64	£85,000	£65,000	£50,000
250 GT 2+2	2953/12	1961-64	£30,000	£21,000	£18,000
275 GTB	3286/12	1964-66	£120,000	£80,000	£70,000
275 GTS	3286/12	1965-67	£90,000	£70,000	£50,000
275 GTB 4-cam	3286/12	1966-68	£170,000+	£150,000	£100,000
330 GT 2+2	3967/12	1964-67	£27,000	£18,000	£15,000
330 GTC	3967/12	1966-68	£55,000	£40,000	£25,000
330 GTS	3967/12	1966-68	£80,000	£70,000	£60,000
365 GT 2+2	4390/12	1967-71	£30,000	£20,000	£15,000
365 GTC	4390/12	1967-70	£40,000	£35,000	£30,000
365 GTS	4390/12	1968-69	£150,000+	£100,000	£80,000
365 GTB (Daytona)	4390/12	1968-74	£90,000	£70,000	£50,000
365 GTC4	4390/12	1971-74	£45,000	£38,000	£30,000
365 GT4 2+2/400GT	4390/ 4823/12	1972-79	£25,000	£20,000	£10,000
365 BB	4390/12	1974-76	£55,000	£38,000	£30,000
512 BB/BBi	4942/12	1976-81	£50,000	£40,000	£30,000
246 GT Dino	2418/6	1969-74	£35,000	£30,000	£15,000
246 GTS Dino	2418/6	1972-74	£45,000	£32,000	£20,000
308 GT4 2+2	2926/8	1973-80	£15,000	£10,000	£8,000
308 GTB (fibreglass)	2926/8	1975-76	£25,000	£18,000	£15,000
308 GTB	2926/8	1977-81	£22,000	£16,000	£10,000
308 GTS	2926/8	1978-81	£26,000	£18,000	£11,000
308 GTBi/GTSi	2926/8	1981-82	£24,000	£17,000	£10,000
308 GTB/GTS QV	2926/6	1983-85	£21,500	£16,500	£9,500
400i manual	4823/12	1981-85	£12,000	£11,000	£10,000
400i auto	4823/12	1981-85	£12,000	£11,000	£8,000

1960 Ferrari 250 GT Series II Two-Door Cabriolet, chassis No. 1761GT, engine No. 1761GT, coachwork by Pininfarina, V12, 240bhp, left-hand drive, overdrive transmission, red with beige leather interior, restored. **£90,000–100,000** *BKS*

The 250GT was the most successful Ferrari of its time, over 900 being built, of which 200 were Series II Cabriolets.

l. **1962 Ferrari 400 Superamerica Aerodinamica Coupé,** chassis No. 3621SA, 3967cc, V12, pale silver green, blue hide interior. **£120,000–125,000** *TALA*

This car is the 11th of 12 Aerodinamica Coupés, from a total production of 33 cars.

l. **1964 Ferrari 250 GT Lusso,** chassis No. 5449, 3 litre, recently repainted in silver, original black hide interior, Borrani wire wheels, 50,800km recorded, one of 350 cars built, excellent condition. **£90,000–100,000** *TALA*

1964 Ferrari 330 GT 2+2 Coupé, chassis No. 6879, engine No. 209, coachwork by Pininfarina, 4 litre, V12, 3 twin-choke Weber carburettors, 300bhp at 7,000rpm, Borrani knock-on wire wheels, Koni shock absorbers, Dunlop disc brakes, restored in 1989/90 at a cost of over £70,000, engine retuned by Mototechnic in 1992. **£25,000–30,000** *S*

This car was originally owned by Jimmy Stewart, ex-racing driver and brother of Jackie. He held the Ferrari franchise for Scotland, and modified and tuned the engine to produce one of the fastest four-seater GT cars of its time.

1965 Ferrari 275 GTB/2 Berlinetta, chassis No. 6639 GT, engine No. 6639, coachwork by Scaglietti, 3.3 litre, V12, fitted with optional 6 twin-choke Weber carburettors, original condition, 68,000km. **£98,000–112,000** *S*

The 275GTB, successor to the 250GT Lusso, was Ferrari's first all-independently-sprung production car and was intended for the Gran Turismo *competition market. The race-bred V12 engine, fitted as standard with three Weber twin-choke carburettors, was said to produce 280bhp at 7,650rpm, or almost 300bhp with the optional six twin-choke Weber set-up. Approximately 250 examples of the 'short nose' 275GTB were completed in its year of production.*

1965 Ferrari 500 Superfast Coupé, chassis No. 5983, engine No. 208 5983, coachwork by Pininfarina, 4962cc, V12, 400bhp at 6,500rpm, top speed 175mph, cream hide interior, 24,000km, original, excellent condition. **£105,000–120,000** *COYS*

The 500 Superfast was an evolution of the 410 and 400 Superamerica, which made its debut at the 1964 Geneva Show. It was considered the ultimate grand tourer of its day, a production run of only 36 cars and a price tag of almost £12,000 (making it the most expensive car in the world) guaranteeing its exclusivity. With unequal length wishbones and coil springs at the front, and a semi-elliptically sprung live axle with parallel trailing arms at the rear, the elegantly styled 500 Superfast had roadholding to match the performance of its Colombo-designed 5 litre engine. Wide Borrani wire wheels and four-wheel disc brakes complemented the package.

Did You Know?
British comic actor Peter Sellers, star of the *Pink Panther* films, was also a keen motoring enthusiast. His passions ranged from Minis to Rolls-Royces, and in 1965 he bought a very rare right-hand drive Ferrari 500 Superfast.

1968 Ferrari 275 GTB/4, chassis No. 226/10243, engine No. 10243, 3286cc, V12, six twin-choke Weber carburettors, dry sump lubrication, 300bhp at 8,000rpm, Rosso Corsa paintwork, retrimmed in tan hide, Borrani wire wheels, 18,000 miles, concours condition.
£190,000–230,000 *COYS*

In 1966, a long-nosed version of the 275GTB was introduced, offering better aerodynamics and improved appearance. More importantly, the slender shaft that transmitted power from the engine to the rear-mounted transaxle, which was prone to severe flexing and vibration, was enclosed in a rigid torque tube. Further improvements came later the same year when the '4 cam' was introduced. This car is one of approximately 280 built.

Market Comment

In the late 1980s, Ferrari prices sky-rocketed. Back then, speculators had serious fun with Ferraris. One Japanese collector paid £10 million for a fabled Ferrari 250 GTO, another paid £5 million for a 250 LM. The fabled blood-and-thunder 365 GTB/4 Daytona was once bankable at £250,000. Look at our price table for today's values. If not accessible to all, there is a large stable of classic Ferraris that are once more in reach of the enthusiast, particularly the 2+2 and four-seater models, such as the 308 GT4, the 330 GT 2+2 (1964–67), 365 GT 2+2 (1967–71), 365 GT4 2+2 (1972–76), and the follow-on 400 and 412 models. However, although many Ferraris are now far more attainable, it's worth remembering that ownership costs remain as high as ever.

1969 Ferrari 330 GTC, chassis No. 11313, engine No. 11313, coachwork by Pininfarina, left-hand drive, silver paintwork, black hide upholstery, cream head lining, bodywork, trim and interior in excellent condition, new exhaust and tyres, 2 complete tool rolls, spare Borrani wheel, handbooks, 15,600km.
£38,500–43,500 *S*

The 330 GTC was announced at Geneva in March 1966, being based on the short-wheelbase chassis of the 275GTB/GTS range. It was fitted with a single overhead camshaft V12 of 3967cc, rated at 300bhp at 7,000rpm. Three twin-choke Weber carburettors were used, and a five-speed all-synchromesh gearbox was mounted to the rear. Borrani knock-off wire wheels and disc brakes were fitted all-round.

1971 Ferrari 365 GT 2+2 Coupé, chassis No. 13571, engine No. 13571, coachwork by Pininfarina, 4390cc, V12, right-hand drive, restored in 1988 at a cost of £45,000, Rosso Corsa paintwork, light tan leather upholstery, excellent condition.
£24,000–28,000 *COYS*

Ferrari introduced the 365GT 2+2 at the 1967 Paris Salon. It was the first 2+2 Ferrari to have four-wheel independent suspension, which also featured a hydro-pneumatic self-levelling system. Power steering and air conditioning were standard. The engine was the new 4.4 litre Type 245, with single overhead camshafts and three Weber carburettors, producing 320bhp at 6,600rpm. With a top speed of 152mph, the car could achieve 0–60mph and 0–120mph times of 7.2 seconds and 26.2 seconds respectively. Only 800 examples of the 365GT 2+2 were produced.

1972 Ferrari 365 GTB/4 Daytona Berlinetta, chassis No. 15915, engine No. 15915, 4390cc, V12, 4 overhead camshafts, aluminium doors, bonnet and boot lid, optional wider wheel arches, finished in black, interior retrimmed in Connolly hide, new exhaust, 68,101km, excellent condition.
£65,000–70,000 *S*

1972 Ferrari 365 GTS/4 Daytona Spyder, chassis No. 14829, coachwork by Pininfarina, built by Scaglietti, 4390cc, V12, 4 overhead camshafts, 6 Weber 40DCN twin-choke carburettors, 355bhp at 7,500rpm, 5-speed integral manual gearbox with final drive, all-independent suspension, 4-wheel disc brakes, left-hand drive, 14,700 miles. **£260,000+** *C*

What would become the 365GTB/4 Daytona made its debut at the Paris Salon in 1968. It was an immediate success, and the press gave it the nickname 'Daytona' in honour of its victory in the American 24-hour race. Production ended in 1974, after approximately 1,400 Daytonas had been made. Only about 120 Spyders were built, this being one of 96 US models.

1972 Ferrari 365 GTS/4 Daytona Spyder, chassis No. 16465, 4.4 litre, pale yellow with black hide and carpets, black hood, air conditioning, original US specification, original books and tools, 16,800 miles. **£220,000+** *TALA*

1973 Ferrari 246 GTS, chassis No. 05856, 2.4 litre, yellow with black leathercloth interior, black carpets, headlamp covers, one of 235 UK cars, 55,000 miles. **£55,000–60,000** *TALA*

1971 Ferrari Dino 246 GT Two-Door Berlinetta, coachwork by Pininfarina, restored between 1988 and 1990, only 2,000km covered since, excellent condition. **£40,000–45,000** *BKS*

Ferrari Dino 246GT (1969–1974)

In its day, the pretty little Dino was the cheapest Ferrari ever marketed, a budget super-car that was pitched directly at the Porsche 911. It rang changes in other ways, too, for in place of Ferrari's traditional V12 up front, the Dino had a V6 mounted transversely amidships. In fact, it seems that the Dino was intended as a cheaper 'companion' marque in its own right, as the 246 Dino was initially completely bare of Ferrari script and prancing horse insignia. Even so, despite a mere 2.4 litres, its near-150mph performance was very Ferrari-like, with brilliant handling to match. As for the Pininfarina shape, many rate it as one of the prettiest and purest of all Ferraris: lithe, lean and free of the steroid strakes and brutal 'Rambo' garnishes that infected Ferraris in the 1980s and beyond.

Engine: Four-cam, 2418cc V6.
Power output: 195bhp at 7,600rpm.
Transmission: Five-speed manual.
Brakes: Discs all-round.
Top speed: 142–148mph.
0–60mph: 7.1 seconds.
Production: Dino 246 GT, 2,732; Dino 246 GTS (Spyder), 1,180.
Ferrari facts: The Dino was named in tribute to Enzo Ferrari's son, Alfredino, who died of a kidney disease at the age of 24 in 1956. Dino had been closely involved with V6-engined sports-racing cars in the early 1950s. In the 1970s television series, *The Persuaders*, Tony Curtis drove a Dino.

1972 Ferrari 365 GTC/4, chassis No. 15803, 4390cc, V12, 4 overhead camshafts, 320bhp at 6,200rpm, 5-speed manual gearbox, all-independent suspension, 4-wheel disc brakes, left-hand drive, 35,074 miles, excellent condition.
£50,000–55,000 C

Introduced at Geneva in 1971, the 365 GTC/4 featured 2+2 seating. Its V12 engine produced 330–340bhp at 6,800rpm, leading to a top speed of 152mph and a 0–60mph time of 7.3 seconds. In all, 500 365 GTC/4s were built.

l. **1972 Ferrari 246 GTS,** chassis No. 04206, engine No. 1410, 2418cc, 6 cylinders, restored at a cost of almost £50,000, well maintained, excellent condition.
£52,000–57,000 COYS

1979 Ferrari 308 GT4 Two-Door Coupé, 5-speed manual gearbox, resprayed, original leather interior, air conditioning, 56,700 miles, good condition.
£11,500–14,000 BKS

1974 Ferrari 365 GT4 2+2, coachwork by Pininfarina, 4390cc, V12, 6 sidedraught Weber carburettors, 340bhp at 7,000rpm, 5-speed automatic transmission, all-independent suspension, power steering, right-hand drive, Chromodora alloy wheels, air conditioning, 31,000 miles.
£13,000–16,000 S

Ferrari's family of successful V8-engined road cars began with the 308 GT4 of 1973, which was intended as a replacement for the previous Dino and was badged as such until 1977. Its wedge-shaped styling was by Bertone, while power came from a mid-mounted, double overhead camshaft 3 litre V8 that produced 236bhp. With a top speed of 150mph and a 0–60mph time of a little under seven seconds, the 308 GT4 had stunning handling.

1979 Ferrari 400 Convertible, coachbuilt conversion.
£22,000–25,000 EPP

1975 Ferrari 365 GT4/BB, 4390cc, 12 cylinders, excellent condition.
£60,000–70,000 *COYS*

The 365 GT4/Berlinetta Boxer was shown at the Turin Salon in 1971, but did not enter production until 1973. Styled by Pininfarina, it was powered by a 4.4 litre light alloy engine that produced 380bhp at 7,700rpm. The horizontal cylinder layout kept the engine's weight low in the chassis to aid handling. A larger-engined 512 version was introduced in 1976, after fewer than 400 of the 365 had been built. Despite its larger engine, the 512 was less powerful than the earlier car, and it was heavier with softer suspension to cater for the American market. This particular 365 holds the world record for the top price paid for this type, having previously changed hands for more than £200,000.

l. **1979 Ferrari 308 GTS,** 3 litre, V8, sports exhaust, Rosso red paintwork, deep front spoiler, air conditioning, 40,000 miles, excellent condition.
£30,000–35,000 *VIC*

1978 Ferrari 512 Berlinetta Boxer Two-Door Coupé, coachwork by Pininfarina, 4942cc, 12 cylinders, right-hand drive, genuine 11,000 miles, very good condition.
£42,000–48,000 *BKS*

The 512BB appeared in 1976 with a new larger engine than the 365 it replaced. However, emissions restrictions meant that, at 340bhp, maximum power was slightly down, although the larger engine did provide a useful increase in torque. In addition, improvements were made to the 512BB's aerodynamics, suspension and tyres. US emissions legislation forced the adoption of Bosch electronic fuel injection in 1981.

1979 Ferrari 308 GTB, 2962cc, V8, 255bhp at 7,600rpm, Koenig body kit, Compomotive split-rim wheels, 9,000 miles covered since engine rebuilt at a cost of over £11,000, excellent condition.
£22,500–27,500 *BRIT*

> **Miller's is a price GUIDE not a price LIST**

l. **1986 Ferrari 328 GTB,** 3.2 litre, red paintwork, colour-coded rear aerofoil, tan hide interior, red carpets, air conditioning, one of only 130 UK cars, 21,800 miles.
£38,000–42,000 *TALA*

1985 Ferrari 288 GTO, 2.8 litre, red paintwork, black hide interior and carpets, air conditioning, electric windows, one of only 273 cars built, 14,000 miles.
£200,000+ *TALA*

r. **1983 Ferrari Mondial QV Coupé,** coachwork by Pininfarina, electric windows, air conditioning, 27,000km.
£13,500–17,000 *BKS*

1987 Ferrari 412 Two-Door Coupé, coachwork by Pininfarina, 5-speed manual gearbox, finished in Rosso Corsa, unmarked cream leather interior, red carpets, restored in 1994/95.
£15,000–18,000 *BKS*

Directly descended from the 365 GT4 2+2, which it closely resembled, and launched at the 1976 Paris Salon, the 400 featured self-levelling rear suspension, power-assisted steering, electric windows, and optional air conditioning. Its arrival reaffirmed Ferrari's determination to compete with the world's finest luxury saloons. The series culminated in the 412, which appeared in 1985. The first Ferrari Gran Turismo with anti-lock brakes, the 412 boasted a 5 litre engine that developed 340bhp. Production of the 400 series ceased in 1989 after 2,386 cars had been built, 576 of them being 412s.

1990 Ferrari 348 TS, 3405cc, V8, service history, very low mileage.
£30,000–35,000 *COYS*

The 348 was introduced in 1990 to replace the popular 328, its quad-cam V8 engine being claimed to produce 320bhp at 7,200rpm. This was achieved through four-valve-per-cylinder heads and Bosch motronics. A 0–60mph time of 5.3 seconds was quoted, while the claimed top speed was 169mph. The two-seat 348 was originally offered in two versions: a closed berlinetta and a targa-roofed variant, known as the TS. When the 348 TS ceased production, it retailed for over £80,000.

1990 Ferrari Testarossa, silver paintwork, navy blue hide interior and carpets, 16,800 miles.
£55,000–60,000 *TALA*

FIAT

Founded in 1899 by Giovanni Agnelli, whose family still controls the company, Fiat has grown into an Italian industrial colossus. The company's initials originally stood for Societa Anonimo Fabbrica Italiana di Automili Torini. Cars are only one area of Fiat's wide-ranging interests, and in the motoring field alone the company controls Ferrari, Lancia, Abarth and Alfa Romeo. In the early days, Fiat devoted considerable effort to racing and won the Targa Florio and French Grand Prix in 1907. Some of the early cars had monstrous engines, up to 11 litres. The first model built in quantity was the 1912 Tipo Zero, of which about 200 were made. In 1919, with the 1.5 litre 501, the company became mass producers, and in 1936 the little 500 Topolino revolutionised personal transport, a feat repeated in 1957 with the 500 Nuova. From the 1960s, Fiat's model range broadened considerably. Two models that stand out and have a strong following today are the long-running 124 Spyder, which makes an interesting alternative to an MGB roadster, and the very pretty and slightly exotic Dino Spyder.

A double-sided pressed tin Fiat advertising sign, some edge damage, otherwise good condition, 37in (94cm) diam.
£425-475 *BKS*

c1933 Fiat 508 Balilla Saloon, 995cc, 4 cylinders, restored, retrimmed maroon cloth interior, good condition, stored for a number of years, requires recommissioning and cosmetic attention.
£2,000–2,500 *BRIT*

Introduced in 1932, the Balilla was available as a four-door pillarless saloon, a two-seater tourer and a two-door saloon. Powered by a sidevalve engine, it bore a strong family resemblance to the larger 522. To reduce the cost, its specification was both conventional and simple, and included a gravity-feed fuel tank and a three-speed crash gearbox.

1936 Fiat 500 'Topolino' Two-Door Coupé, 570cc, 4 cylinders, sidevalve, 13bhp, right-hand drive, restored in 1995.
£4,000–4,500 *BKS*

Better equipped than many cars twice its size, the Fiat 500 – nicknamed Topolino *(mouse) – brought a degree of refinement hitherto unknown to small cars when launched in 1936. Lockheed hydraulic brakes, independent front suspension and 12 volt electrics were all part of the package, while an engine mounted ahead of the front axle line helped maximise cabin space. The Topolino could manage 50+mph under favourable conditions.*

1965 Fiat Gamine, limited edition, 500cc, restored.
£3,750–4,000 *EPP*

FIAT Model	ENGINE cc/cyl	DATES	CONDITION 1	2	3
501	1460/4	1920-26	£6,000	£3,500	£1,500
519	4767/6	1923-29	£9,000	£7,000	£3,000
503	1473/4	1927-29	£8,000	£4,000	£2,000
507	2297/4	1927-28	£9,000	£5,500	£3,500
522/4	2516/6	1932-34	£10,000	£8,000	£3,500
508	994/4	1934-37	£5,000	£2,500	£1,500
527 Sports	2516/6	1935-36	£14,000	£8,000	£3,500
1.5 litre Balilla	1498/6	1936-39	£10,000	£7,000	£3,000
500	570/4	1937-55	£6,000	£2,500	£1,000
1100 Balilla	1089/4	1938-40	£4,500	£2,000	£1,000

1967 Fiat Dino Two-Door Spyder, coachwork
by Pininfarina, restored in the early 1980s, major
refurbishment in 1996.
£6,750–7,500 *BKS*

*An agreement to build the four-cam V6 for the mid-
engined Ferrari Dino led to a spin-off model for Fiat.
Launched in Spyder form at the 1966 Turin Show,
the Fiat Dino had its 2 litre 160bhp engine ahead of
the driver in conventional manner. Steel-bodied, it
employed a Fiat five-speed gearbox and featured
independent front suspension, a live rear axle and
four-wheel disc brakes. The Dino offered a top speed
in excess of 125mph and a 0–60mph time of around
eight seconds. A coupé model with Bertone coachwork
appeared in 1967 and, in 1969, the V6's capacity was
increased to 2418cc, while a ZF gearbox and
independent rear suspension were adopted.*

1970 Fiat 850 Spyder, needs restoration.
£500–750 *S*

*Fiat launched the new 850 model at the Geneva
Show in 1965, initially as a sports coupé with a
rear-mounted four-cylinder in-line engine. It was
followed by a two-seat Spyder version, on a 79.8in
wheelbase, with styling by Bertone.*

1976 Fiat 124 Two-Door Coupé, 1.8 litre, stainless
steel exhaust, sunroof, electric windows, central
locking, alloy wheels, alarm, original condition.
£4,200–4,600 *BKS*

*Introduced in 1969 and based on the 124 saloon's
floorpan and running gear, the attractive four-
seater Coupé proved an outstanding success for
Fiat, over 270,000 being sold before production
ended in 1975. Initially available in two-headlamp
form with a 1.4 litre twin-cam engine, the Coupé
was given a 1.6 litre engine in 1969, gaining a four-
lamp front end at the same time. New 1.6 and 1.8
litre power units were introduced in 1972, examples
equipped with the latter being capable of nudging
110mph. Four-wheel disc brakes were part of the
package from the outset, and all but a few home-
market cars came with five-speed gearboxes.*

Miller's
Starter Marque

Starter Fiats: *Fiat 500 – 1957 onwards; Fiat
600; Fiat 850 Coupé, Fiat X1/9; Fiat 124
Coupé and Spyder.*

- Fiat 500: When the Fiat 500 Nuova appeared
  in 1957, long-time Fiat designer Dante
  Giacosa defended his frugal flyweight by
  saying, 'However small it might be, an
  automobile will always be more comfortable
  than a motor scooter.' Today, though, the
  diminutive scoot-about needs no defence, for
  time has justified his faith, with production of
  more than 4 million 500s and derivatives up
  to the demise of the Giardiniera estate in
  1977. The original 500 Nuova was rather
  frantic with its 479cc tiddler of a two-pot
  motor. But in 1960, it grew to maturity with
  the launch of the 500D, which was pushed
  along by an enlarged 499.5cc engine. Now at
  last the baby Fiat could almost touch 60mph
  without being pushed over the edge of a cliff.
  Many Fiat 500 proponents commend the car
  as a usable every-day commuter classic, and
  fitting larger Fiat engines up to 650cc is a
  common practice. The engines are generally
  robust and long-lasting, but the monocoque
  chassis and body are fairly prone to rusting.

- Fiat 850 Coupé: The Fiat 850 Coupé is a
  delectable little package combining up to
  45mpg economy, peppy performance (90+mph
  for the 903cc versions), front disc brakes,
  super handling and delightfully neat styling.
  Again, rust is the main enemy. Even though
  around 380,000 were built between 1965 and
  1973, they have never been common in the
  UK. If you take your time to find a good one
  you'll discover a rewarding little car.

- Fiat X1/9: The merits of the sharp-edged
  Bertone design are a matter of divided
  opinion, but the X1/9 is just about the only
  truly affordable and practical, volume-
  produced, mid-engined sports car, and it also
  has exceptional handling. The engine is a
  little jewel, reliable and generally long-
  lasting, too. Unfortunately, the same can't be
  said of the body, so the best buy will usually
  be a later model that's had less time to rust.

- Fiat 124 Spyder: Elegant Pininfarina styling,
  all-round disc brakes, twin-cam power and
  excellent five-speed gearbox add up to a very
  appealing and fine-handling fresh-air sporting
  package. The model was produced from 1966
  to 1982 by Fiat. From then until 1985
  Pininfarina took over production and built it
  as the Spyder Europe. Once again, rust can
  strike hard, the front suspension struts, inner
  sills, and the front and rear edges of
  the floorplan being particularly susceptible.
  Right-hand drive versions are rare, but left-
  right conversion is viable. Of the 200,000
  built, a large number went to the USA, so
  there's every chance of picking up a car that's
  spent most of its life in a rust-free climate.
  The best all-round model is the 2 litre
  carburettor version.

Prices

***The price ranges given reflect the average
price a purchaser should pay for a similar
vehicle. Condition, rarity of model, pedigree,
restoration and many other factors must be
taken into account when assessing values.***

FIAT Model	ENGINE cc/cyl	DATES	CONDITION 1	2	3
500B Topolino	569/4	1945-55	£5,000	£2,000	£750
500C	569/4	1948-54	£4,000	£1,700	£1,000
500 Nuova	479,499/2	1957-75	£3,000	£1,500	£750
600/600D	633, 767/4	1955-70	£3,000	£2,000	£1,000
500F Giardiniera	479, 499/2	1957-75	£3,000	£1,500	£1,000
2300S	2280/6	1961-68	£3,000	£1,700	£1,000
850	843/4	1964-71	£1,000	£750	-
850 Coupé	843, 903/4	1965-73	£1,500	£1,000	-
850 Spyder	843, 903/4	1965-73	£3,000	£2,000	£1,000
128 Sport Coupé 3P	1116/1290/4	1971-78	£2,500	£1,800	£1,000
130 Coupé	3235/6	1971-77	£5,500	£4,000	£2,000
131 Mirafiori Sport	1995/4	1974-84	£1,500	£1,000	£500
124 Sport Coupé	1438/1608/4	1966-72	£3,000	£2,000	£1,000
124 Sport Spyder	1438/1608/4	1966-72	£4,000	£2,500	£1,500
Dino Coupé	1987/2418/6	1967-73	£8,000	£5,500	£2,500
Dino Spyder	1987/2418/6	1967-73	£12,000	£7,000	£5,000
X1/9	1290/1498/4	1972-89	£4,000	£2,000	£1,500

l. **1984 Fiat X1/9 V5 Targa,** 1500cc, rustproofed from new, 44,000 miles, excellent condition. **£2,100–2,600** *H&H*

The 1.5 litre five-speed Fiat X1/9 was introduced in 1978 to replace the original 1300cc model, Bertone having taken over the assembly and marketing of the car.

1984 Fiat X1/9, 1.5 litre, 5-speed gearbox, targa top, 78,000 miles. **£2,500–3,000** *WILM*

FLETCHER

l. **1970 Fletcher Ogle SX1000,** 1275cc Cooper S engine on standard block, Fletcher front end, original Ogle rear end, may have been built for racing, complete and running. **£3,900–4,400** *BKS*

Norman Fletcher, a boat builder, took over the moulds of the Ogle SX1000 and modified the original design by adding a sharper tail and recessed front headlights behind Perspex covers. Initially, this version was produced for competition. Fletcher received an order for 30 cars from Switzerland, but BMC could not, or would not, supply the components, and the deal fell through. Thus, the project was abandoned after only four had been made.

FORD

Born in Michigan in 1863, the son of an Irish immigrant farmer, Henry Ford's incredible automotive career got under way in 1893 when he built an internal-combustion engine on the kitchen table of his Detroit home. In 1896, his first motorised vehicle took to the streets, and in 1903 the Ford Motor Company was established and started producing the Model A runabout. It was the launch of its replacement, the Model T, in 1908 that really brought the company to prominence.

The story of Ford in England also began with the Model T when Henry Ford set up his first overseas assembly plant at Trafford Park, Manchester, in 1911. From the 1930s, Fords became as much a part of Britain's motoring landscape as our own domestic makes, like Austin and Morris, once were. From the enthusiast's point of view, British-built Fords offer a wide variety of affordable classics, both from before and after the war. American Fords from the 1950s onwards offer a touch of transatlantic glamour, and the later Mustang is firmly established as a motoring icon, coveted the world over.

1910 Ford Model T Speedster, 2900cc.
£6,600–7,200 *LF*

1924 Ford Model T Runabout, black wheels, black leathercloth upholstery, restored c1990.
£8,500–11,500 *BKS*

Model T production peaked at 2,055,309 units in 1923, and approximately half the cars in the world were 'Tin Lizzies'. This was hardly surprising, for the price of a new two-seater Runabout was only $265 (about £53). The low price was achieved by Henry Ford's pioneering mass-production methods. From the time that iron ore (from Ford mines) was unloaded at the company's River Rouge plant to the arrival of the finished car in the dealership took between 18 and 33 hours. About 100,000 Model Ts survive worldwide.

l. **1926 Ford Model T Tourer,** left-hand drive, finished in Old English white, new black hood, trim and sidescreens, original wooden wheels, new tyres, good condition.
£6,000–7,000 *H&H*

Ford Milestones

1863:	Henry Ford born on July 30 in Wayne County, Michigan.	1961:	Parent company bought outstanding British Ford shares at a price of £119,595,645.12s.
1903:	Ford incorporated in the USA; first two Ford cars in Britain were Model As imported from the USA.	1962:	Ford Cortina introduced.
1911:	Ford Motor Company (England) Limited incorporated. Assembly plant set up at Trafford Park, Manchester.	1963:	New assembly plant opened at Halewood, Merseyside.
		1966:	Ford GT40 won Le Mans; victory repeated for next three years.
1918:	Ford produced its first British truck, a one-ton vehicle.	1968:	New Escort launched.
		1969:	Capri introduced.
1925:	The 250,000th British Ford, a Model T, produced.	1971:	Millionth Escort built less than four years after launch.
1929:	Henry's son, Edsel, cut the first sod on marshy Dagenham site.	1976:	Millionth Transit built.
		1981:	Escort voted Car of The Year.
1931:	First vehicle produced at the Dagenham plant was a 30cwt Model A truck.	1982:	Sierra replaces Cortina.
		1987:	Ford buys Aston Martin Lagonda.
1947:	Henry Ford died on April 7 after a brain haemorrhage.	1989:	Ford acquired majority shareholding in Jaguar Cars.
1950:	Transatlantic styling of the new MkI Consul, Zephyr and Zodiac were a highlight of the 1950 London Motor Show.	1992:	Ford regained position of UK bestseller with 121,140 Escort registrations.
		1993:	Mondeo launched as world car.

1937 Ford Model Y Tudor Popular,
8hp, good condition.
£2,500–3,000 *FYC*

1928 Ford Model A Two-Door Coupé, 2 seater
with dickey seat, left-hand drive, restored, good
running order, concours winner in USA.
£8,000–9,000 *BKS*

1929 Ford Model A Tudor Two-Door Saloon,
3280cc, 4 cylinders, 40bhp, left-hand drive, chassis in
good condition, all other parts in excellent condition.
£4,750–5,250 *BKS*

*In 1929, Ford used the Model A to beat Chevrolet to
the title of world's number one car manufacturer.
A year later, the Model A hit production levels that
would not be surpassed throughout the 1930s. The
Model A was Ford's only product in the late 1920s,
but no fewer than 18 body styles were offered.
Although not the cheapest model, the Tudor saloon
was the most popular and accounted for around
40 per cent of Model A production.*

Miller's Starter Marque

Starter Fords: *Anglia, Prefect, Popular
models from 1948 onwards; MkI, II, III
Consul, Zephyr and Zodiac, MkIV
Zephyr/Zodiac; Consul Classic 315/
Consul Capri.*

- Whatever your taste, there's a Ford you can
afford – in fact more than we have space to
mention. Their list of virtues as starter
classics is almost as long as the list of
models there are to choose from. Importantly,
many were made in their millions, and
generally there's a ready stock of cars and
spares, backed by a healthy network of clubs
and specialists.

- Consul, Zephyr, Zodiac – MkI, II and III:
These are what you might term lifestyle
Fords – there's one to match your taste in
clothes and music. The MkI and II models are
favoured as Brit-sized chunks of Americana
for the retro crowd. For MkI models read
early Elvis, rockabilly rather than rock 'n'
roll. The MkII is mainstream Elvis,
structurally reinforced quiffs, pedal pushers,
bowling shirts and Levi 501s. As for the
MkIII that's Elvis at Vegas, teddy boy drape-
coats, long sideboards and a tub of Swarfega
in the hair. All models are eminently viable
for the DIY enthusiast. While performance is
hardly shattering by today's standards, they
are fast enough to go with the flow of modern
traffic without causing a tail-back.

- Anglia: In 1959, Ford's new Anglia
represented the shape of fins to come, a
pretty, compact little saloon that was an
instant hit with buyers who might otherwise
have opted for something drearily and
domestically familiar, like an Austin A40,
Morris Minor or Triumph Herald. The Anglia
105E was a stylish device with a miniature
full-width version of the 'dollar-grin' grille up
front and voguish US-hand-me-down rear
fins. Under the skin there was a little
innovation, too, with the first overhead valve
engine for a small Ford and – wonder of
wonder – four gears. The Anglia was a worthy
and peppy workhorse that went on to sell
more than a million before making way for
the Escort.

- **Pick of the bunch:** The Anglia Super 123E;
this has an 1198cc engine compared with the
997cc of the 105E, so you'll get to 60mph in
22 seconds rather than 29, and eventually
you'll nudge 85mph instead of running out
of puff at 75mph.

FORD Model	ENGINE cc/cyl	DATES	CONDITION 1	2	3
Model T	2892/4	1908-27	£12,000	£7,000	£4,000
Model A	3285/4	1928-32	£8,500	£6,000	£3,500
Models Y and 8	933/4	1933-40	£5,000	£3,000	£1,500
Model C	1172/4	1933-40	£4,000	£2,000	£1,000
Model AB	3285/4	1933-34	£10,000	£8,000	£4,500
Model ABF	2043/4	1933-34	£9,000	£6,000	£4,000
Model V8	3622/8	1932-40	£8,500	£6,000	£4,500
Model V8-60	2227/8	1936-40	£7,000	£5,000	£2,000
Model AF (UK only)	2033/4	1928-32	£9,000	£6,000	£3,500

A right-hand drive vehicle will always command more interest than a left-hand drive. Coachbuilt
vehicles, and in particular tourers, achieve a premium at auction. Veteran cars
(ie manufactured before 1919) will often achieve a 20 per cent premium.

1952 Ford Prefect Four-Door Saloon, restored, paintwork tired, sound in most other respects, original interior, heater.
£1,550–1,800 *BKS*

Introduced in 1939 in a variety of body styles, the Prefect continued post-war as a four-door saloon only. Powered by an 1172cc sidevalve engine with a three-speed gearbox, the Anglia's big brother was roomier and better suited to family motoring. It offered a top speed of over 60mph and fuel consumption of around 35mpg on runs. Restyled for 1949 with integral headlamps, revised bonnet and radiator grille, it continued in production until 1953, over 350,000 being built.

r. **1958 Ford Prefect,** 1172cc, 3-speed gearbox, reconditioned engine, Raydot signpost lamp, sunvisor, wind-up clock, original interior, new carpets, 73,000 miles, excellent condition.
£1,250–1,650 *H&H*

1955 Ford Zodiac MkI Saloon, 2262cc, 6 cylinders, 3-speed gearbox with column change, good condition.
£3,700–4,000 *S*

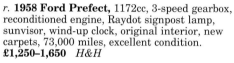

FORD (British built) Model	ENGINE cc/cyl	DATES	CONDITION 1	2	3
Cortina Mk I	1198/4	1963-66	£1,550	£600	£150
Cortina Crayford Mk I	1198/4	1963-66	£3,500	£1,800	£950
Cortina GT	1498/4	1963-66	£1,800	£1,000	£650
Lotus Cortina Mk I	1558/4	1963-66	£10,000	£7,500	£4,500
Cortina Mk II	1599/4	1966-70	£1,000	£500	£100
Cortina GT Mk II	1599/4	1966-70	£1,200	£650	£150
Cortina Crayford Mk II DHC	1599/4	1966-70	£4,000	£2,000	£1,500
Lotus Cortina Mk II	1558/4	1966-70	£6,000	£3,500	£1,800
Cortina 1600E	1599/4	1967-70	£2,800	£1,400	£450
Consul Corsair	1500/4	1963-65	£1,100	£500	£250
Consul Corsair GT	1500/4	1963-65	£1,200	£600	£250
Corsair V4	1664/4	1965-70	£1,150	£600	£250
Corsair V4 Est.	1664/4	1965-70	£1,400	£600	£250
Corsair V4GT	1994/4	1965-67	£1,300	£700	£250
CorsairV4GT Est.	1994/4	1965-67	£1,400	£700	£350
Corsair Convertible	1664/1994/4	1965-70	£4,300	£2,500	£1,000
Corsair 2000	1994/4	1967-70	£1,350	£500	£250
Corsair 2000E	1994/4	1967-70	£1,500	£800	£350
Escort 1300E	1298/4	1973-74	£1,900	£1,000	£250
Escort Twin Cam	1558/4	1968-71	£8,000	£5,000	£2,000
Escort GT	1298/4	1968-73	£3,000	£1,500	£350
Escort Sport	1298/4	1971-75	£1,750	£925	£250
Escort Mexico	1601/4	1970-74	£4,000	£2,000	£750
RS1600	1601/4	1970-74	£5,000	£2,500	£1,500
RS2000	1998/4	1973-74	£4,500	£2,200	£1,000
Escort RS Mexico	1593/4	1976-78	£3,500	£2,000	£850
Escort RS2000 Mk II	1993/4	1976-80	£6,000	£3,500	£2,000
Capri Mk I 1300/1600	1298/1599/4	1969-72	£1,500	£1,000	£550
Capri 2000/3000GT	1996/4 2994/6	1969-72	£2,000	£1,000	£500
Capri 3000E	2994/6	1970-72	£4,000	£2,000	£1,000
Capri RS3100	3093/6	1973-74	£6,500	£3,500	£2,000
Cortina 2000E	1993/4	1973-76	£2,500	£550	£225
Granada Ghia	1993/4 2994/6	1974-77	£4,000	£900	£350

l. **1962 Ford Consul MkII,** 1703cc, 4 cylinders, 3-speed gearbox. **£3,250–3,750** *WILM*

1964 Ford Lotus Cortina MkI, 1588cc, 4 cylinders, restored, bare metal respray, new aluminium doors, bonnet and boot lid, new front and rear suspension, rebuilt engine, gearbox, rear axle, brakes, and instruments, little use since, standard specification, never raced or rallied. **£8,250–9,000** *COYS*

In the early 1960s, Ford asked Lotus's Colin Chapman to produce a sports/racing version of the new Cortina. The resulting Lotus Cortina sported white paintwork, green side flashes, front quarter bumpers and discreet Lotus badging. Inside, there were bucket seats, a wood-rim wheel and a special fascia. The bonnet, boot lid and doors were alloy, as were the clutch and diff housings, and the gearbox tailshaft. The MacPherson strut front suspension was lowered and stiffened, while the rear leaf springs were replaced by an A-bracket, coil springs and trailing arms. Wide wheels and servo-assisted disc front/drum rear brakes, along with 105bhp from the new 1588cc twin-cam engine and a close-ratio gearbox, completed the package.

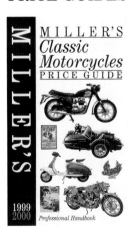

1962 Ford Anglia Saloon, 997cc, 4 cylinders. **£850–1,100** *H&H*

l. **1968 Ford Cortina Savage,** 3000cc, V6, 4-speed manual gearbox, restored at a cost of over £8,000, all body panels with the exception of the floorpan replaced, engine rebuilt and tuned, interior renewed, concours winner. **£5,250–5,750**   *H&H*

1970 Ford Cortina 1600E, finished in champagne, black interior, completely restored, excellent condition. **£4,000–4,500**   *BC*

1968 Ford Cortina 1600E Four-Door Saloon, 48,250 miles, good condition. **£2,800–3,400**   *BKS*

Ford added a new dimension to family motoring in 1967 with the launch of the Cortina 1600E at the Paris Salon. It was an astute combination of components from some of the most desirable Cortina models, including the high-compression 1.6 litre engine from the GT and the suspension from the Lotus Cortina. It also featured wide-rimmed Rostyle sports wheels, a painted coachstripe and a well-appointed interior with a polished wooden dashboard and comprehensive instrumentation.

Did You Know?

The breeze-block MkIV Zephyrs and Zodiacs of 1966 were the last all-British Fords. Since then, each subsequent new model has been increasingly European in design and production, and lately even global with the Mondeo.

FORD (British built) Model	ENGINE cc/cyl	DATES	CONDITION 1	2	3
Anglia E494A	993/4	1948-53	£2,000	£850	£250
Prefect E93A	1172/4	1940-49	£3,500	£1,250	£900
Prefect E493A	1172/4	1948-53	£2,500	£1,000	£300
Popular 103E	1172/4	1953-59	£1,875	£825	£300
Anglia/Prefect 100E	1172/4	1953-59	£1,350	£625	£250
Prefect 107E	997/4	1959-62	£1,150	£600	£200
Escort/Squire 100E	1172/4	1955-61	£1,000	£850	£275
Popular 100E	1172/4	1959-62	£1,250	£600	£180
Anglia 105E	997/4	1959-67	£1,400	£500	£75
Anglia 123E	1198/4	1962-67	£1,550	£575	£150
V8 Pilot	3622/8	1947-51	£7,500	£5,000	£1,500
Consul Mk I	1508/4	1951-56	£2,250	£950	£400
Consul Mk I DHC	1508/4	1953-56	£6,000	£3,500	£1,250
Zephyr Mk I	2262/6	1951-56	£3,000	£1,250	£600
Zephyr Mk I DHC	2262/6	1953-56	£7,000	£4,000	£1,300
Zodiac Mk I	2262/6	1953-56	£3,300	£1,500	£700
Consul Mk II/Deluxe	1703/4	1956-62	£2,900	£1,500	£650
Consul Mk II DHC	1703/4	1956-62	£5,000	£3,300	£1,250
Zephyr Mk II	2553/6	1956-62	£3,800	£1,800	£750
Zephyr Mk II DHC	2553/6	1956-62	£8,000	£4,000	£1,500
Zodiac Mk II	2553/6	1956-62	£4,000	£2,250	£750
Zodiac Mk II DHC	2553/6	1956-62	£8,500	£4,250	£1,800
Zephyr 4 Mk III	1703/4	1962-66	£2,100	£1,200	£400
Zephyr 6 Mk III	2552/6	1962-66	£2,300	£1,300	£450
Zodiac Mk II	2553/6	1962-66	£2,500	£1,500	£500
Zephyr 4 Mk IV	1994/4	1966-72	£1,750	£600	£300
Zephyr 6 Mk IV	2553/6	1966-72	£1,800	£700	£300
Zodiac Mk IV	2994/6	1966-72	£2,000	£800	£300
Zodiac Mk IV Est.	2994/6	1966-72	£2,800	£1,200	£300
Zodiac Mk IV Exec.	2994/6	1966-72	£2,300	£950	£300
Classic 315	1340/ 1498/4	1961-63	£1,400	£800	£500
Consul Capri	1340/ 1498/4	1961-64	£2,100	£1,350	£400
Consul Capri GT	1498/4	1961-64	£2,600	£1,600	£800

Miller's Starter Marque

Starter Fords: *Cortina MkI, II, III; Corsair, Capri, Escort.*

- **Cortina MkI:** The Cortina appeared late in 1962 and soon you couldn't miss it on Britain's roads as sales soared. With a mean price-tag of £639 it undercut rivals and, in many cases, offered a lot more. Overall, it added up to the anatomy of a best seller, in fact the best-selling British car of its time.

- **Pick of the bunch:** 1500GT and Lotus Cortina MkI; the 1500GT gave a creditable 13-second 0–60mph and 95mph top speed; the Lotus Cortina, with 1558cc, 105bhp Lotus twin-cam and uprated suspension scorched its way to 108mph. There were only 4,012 genuine MkI Lotus Cortinas. They're highly prized, so watch out for fakes – there are plenty.

  Capri: In the transatlantic crossing from Detroit to Dagenham, and with a Mediterranean name thrown in, the theme of Ford America's hot-selling Mustang fastback resurfaced in Europe in 1969 as the Capri. The Mustang, with an options list longer than the Golden Gate bridge, was promoted as Ford's 'personal car', while on this side of the pond, the advertising scribes reckoned the Capri was 'the car you always promised yourself.' Like its American cousin, the Capri offered kaleidoscopic customer choice, from the sheep-in-wolf's clothing 89mph 1300 to rorty V6-engined RS, GT and injected models, some with 130+mph performance. Over the years, there were an astonishing 900 variants on the Capri theme.

- **Pick of the bunch:** V6-engined models, including RS, GT and E designations; troublesome V4 engines best avoided; ordinary 1300 and 1600 models are pretty lame; 1600GT an option in the go-less-slowly stakes.

Did You Know?

It's difficult to think of a Ford failure, but if you count failure as selling less than a million vehicles, there are a few contenders. The ungainly Consul Classic of 1961–63 struggled to pass 100,000. Its sporting sister, the two-door Consul Capri, was a pretty thing with its pillarless tear-drop window. However, except for the rare GT version, of which only 2,002 were built, it was gutless and production tailed off at 20,000. Another contender is the square-cut MkIV Zephyr/Zodiac of 1966–72, with a bonnet you could land a Harrier jump-jet on. Production totalled under 200,000.

1968 Ford Cortina MkII Estate De Luxe, 1300cc, 4 cylinders, 20,750 miles, original condition.
£2,300–2,800 *BKS*

1968 Ford Lotus Cortina Two-Door Saloon, 1558cc.
£4,600–5,200 *BKS*

The MkII Lotus Cortina was launched early in 1967, but unlike the MkI, which had been assembled by Lotus, it was a product of Ford's factory at Dagenham. It still incorporated many of the features that had made the original Lotus Cortina such a successful competition car, but the valve timing had been improved by Ford engineers, and the special-equipment version of the Lotus-built engine (previously a costly extra) was adopted as standard. Only 4,320 MkII Lotus Cortinas were built.

1980 Ford Escort 1300 Saloon, 1298cc, 4 cylinders, 4-speed manual gearbox, 68,000 miles, very good condition.
£600–1,000 *H&H*

l. **1984 Ford Capri 1.6 Laser,** new tyres and exhaust, good condition.
£400–700 *PA*

FORD – USA

1956 Ford Thunderbird, 5113cc, V8, 225bhp at 4,600rpm.
£14,000–17,000 *Pou*

In 1954, Ford countered Chevrolet's Corvette by announcing the Thunderbird. However, while the Corvette remained true to its sporting origins, the Thunderbird became softer. Today, the most prized models are the 1955–57 cars, with a slight preference for the 1956 Thunderbirds offered with the porthole-windowed, hardtop and Continental spare wheel kit. From 1957, the Thunderbird mutated into a larger four-seater.

1957 Ford Thunderbird 'E' Model, 312cu in, V8, 2 4-choke carburettors, 255bhp at 4,600rpm, Ford-O-Matic 3-speed transmission, removable hardtop, power windows, four-way seat, Town and Country radio and heater, fully restored in 1989, limited use since.
£24,000–27,000 *C*

The universal appeal of the Thunderbird's styling made it an instant success, the 1955 model outselling the more expensive Corvette by 24 to one.

l. **1958 Ford Edsel,** blue with white roof.
£7,000–7,500 *CTP*

FORD (American built) Model	ENGINE cu in/cyl	DATES	CONDITION 1	2	3
Thunderbird	292/ 312/8	1955-57	£18,500	£13,500	£9,000
Edsel Citation	410/8	1958	£9,000	£4,500	£2,500
Edsel Ranger	223/6- 361/8	1959	£6,000	£3,500	£2,000
Edsel Citation convertible	410/8	1958	£12,000	£6,000	£4,000
Edsel Corsair convertible	332/ 361/8	1959	£10,500	£7,000	£4,500
Fairlane 2 door	223/6- 352/8	1957-59	£8,000	£4,500	£3,000
Fairlane 500 Sunliner	223/6- 352/8	1957-59	£12,000	£8,000	£6,500
Fairlane 500 Skyliner	223/6- 352/8	1957-59	£14,000	£10,000	£8,000
Mustang 4.7 V8		1964-66	£9,000	£4,000	£2,000
Mustang GT 350		1966-67	£15,000	£10,000	£6,000
Mustang hardtop	260/6- 428/8	1967-68	£6,000	£4,000	£3,000
Mustang GT 500			£20,000	£14,000	£6,000

l. **1967 Ford Mustang Coupé,** 289cu in, V8, automatic transmission, rust free, original metallic green paintwork in need of attention, black interior, 74,000 miles. **£7,000–7,500** *RCC*

r. **1965 Ford Thunderbird Special Landau,** 390cu in, rustproofed from new, some minor renovations to paintwork, no rust or filler, original. **£5,000–6,000** *H&H*

1966 Ford Mustang Shelby GT 350, 289cu in, V8, 306bhp at 6,000rpm. **£17,000–20,000** *Pou*

1969 Ford Mustang Convertible, 302cu in, V8, 220bhp, finished in metallic blue, white hood and upholstery, chrome wire wheels, good condition. **£7,500–9,000** *BRIT*

l. **1972 Ford Mustang Mach 1,** 351cu in, V8, FMX automatic transmission, Traction Lok rear axle, restored to show standard, finished in red with correct side decals, black vinyl interior, 8-track stereo, mechanically in very good condition. **£8,000–9,000** *BRIT*

One of the most loved of American muscle cars, the Mach 1 version of the Mustang was powered by the formidable 351cu in Cleveland engine, equipped with the Ram Air induction system.

GEORGES RICHARD

l. **1900 Georges Richard Model 5 10hp Rear Entrance Tonneau,** 2.9 litres, 2 cylinders.
£46,000–50,000 *BKS*

In 1897, Georges Richard began production of a fragile four-wheeler at Ivry-Port. By 1899, the quest for speed and the need for a more robust motor car saw Richard building a superior machine. This had a substantial timber chassis with a horizontal, forward-mounted twin-cylinder engine and could carry six passengers. This particular car is believed unique, and for 40 years it was exhibited at the Pichon Museum in Northern France. It was recommissioned in time to take part in the Victorian Extravaganza for pre-1900 cars at Beaulieu in 1996, and participated in the Centenary London to Brighton run.

GORDON-KEEBLE

Introduced in 1964, the Gordon-Keeble was one of a select band of 1960s GTs that combined British chassis engineering with American horsepower and Italian style. The car featured a space-frame chassis with independent front suspension, De Dion rear axle and four-wheel disc brakes. Styled by Giugiaro at Bertone, its elegant fibreglass bodywork was manufactured in Britain by Williams & Pritchard. A 5.3 litre Chevrolet V8 provided effortless cruising and a top speed in the region of 140mph.

1965 Gordon-Keeble Two-Door Coupé, reconditioned engine fitted 1995, manual gearbox, new brakes, reconditioned alternator and starter motor, interior refurbished, very good condition.
£12,000–14,000 *BKS*

This car is number 68 of the 99 cars built.

GROUT

1904 Grout Steam Runabout Light Touring Car, 2 cylinder steam engine, 7–10hp, original paint, leather interior and floor mats, mechanics restored.
£26,000–30,000 *C*

The Grout Brothers began building steam cars in Orange, Massachusetts, in about 1900. By 1903, the Grout Steam Carriage had developed in many respects with the addition of headlamps and mudguards. Grout steamers were always recognised for their quality, receiving many accolades.

HEALEY

Donald Mitchell Healey's name is normally associated with Austin-Healey sports cars, but the Cornishman's career weaved a meandering path through the British motor industry. As a driver, he had considerable talent and, in 1931, drove an Invicta to outright victory in the Monte Carlo Rally. In 1933, he joined the Riley experimental team, and in 1935 moved across Coventry to become experimental manager and technical director at Triumph until the company collapsed in 1939. From 1946 until 1954, he produced his own Healeys at Warwick, using proprietary engines from Riley and, later, Nash and Alvis.

All Healeys were sporting in character, particularly the early Riley-powered examples, which were among the first post-war British high-performance cars. In fact, in 1948, a 2.4 litre Riley-engined Healey Elliot recorded 110mph on the Jabbeke autoroute in Belgium, setting a benchmark for saloons. The cars' styling was always individual and not universally admired. However, with total Healey production at under 1,200, these fine sporting machines remain very collectable.

1947 Healey Duncan Saloon, 2.4 litres, restored in the 1980s, original bill of sale, instruction book, many invoices.
£12,500–14,000 *CGC*

The Healey Duncan originally cost £2,987 10s 8d, an expensive car in 1947.

1949 Healey Westland, 2.5 litre, 4 cylinder, twin-cam Riley engine, aluminium bodywork, mechanics and interior restored, original paintwork in fair condition.
£9,000–10,000 *Mot*

1951 Healey Silverstone Special, 2443cc, 4 cylinders, converted from a Tickford in 1992, chassis and engine rebuilt at a cost of over £30,000, professionally made body, gas-flowed exhaust, otherwise unmodified.
£16,500–19,000 *H&H*

HILLMAN

Hillman was founded in 1907 and taken over by Humber in 1928, then coming under control of the Rootes Group. Most models were pretty conventional but are often quite stylish. In the post-war era through to the mid-1960s the company persisted with a comprehensive range of convertible saloons. The name disappeared in 1976.

r. **1935 Hillman Minx 10hp Saloon,** 1056cc, 4 cylinders, 4-speed manual gearbox, new head lining, leather seats renovated, interior wood refurbished, bodywork in need of attention.
£1,300–1,500 *H&H*

HILLMAN Model	ENGINE cc/cyl	DATES	CONDITION 1	2	3
Minx Mk I-II	1184/4	1946-48	£1,750	£800	£250
Minx Mk I-II DHC	1184/4	1946-48	£3,500	£1,500	£250
Minx Mk III-VIIIA	1184/4	1948-56	£1,750	£700	£350
Minx Mk III-VIIIA DHC	1184/4	1948-56	£3,750	£1,500	£350
Californian	1390/4	1953-56	£2,000	£750	£200
Minx SI/II	1390/4	1956-58	£1,250	£450	£200
Minx SI/II DHC	1390/4	1956-58	£3,500	£1,500	£500
Minx Ser III	1494/4	1958-59	£1,000	£500	£200
Minx Ser III DHC	1494/4	1958-59	£3,750	£1,500	£400
Minx Ser IIIA/B	1494/4	1959-61	£1,250	£500	£200
Minx Ser IIIA/B DHC	1494/4	1959-61	£3,750	£1,250	£500
Minx Ser IIIC	1592/4	1961-62	£900	£500	£200
Minx Ser IIIC DHC	1592/4	1961-62	£3,000	£1,500	£500
Minx Ser V	1592/4	1962-63	£1,250	£350	£150
Minx Ser VI	1725/4	1964-67	£1,500	£375	£100
Husky Mk I	1265/4	1954-57	£1,000	£600	£200
Husky SI/II/III	1390/4	1958-65	£1,000	£550	£150
Super Minx	1592/4	1961-66	£1,500	£500	£100
Super Minx DHC	1592/4	1962-64	£3,500	£1,250	£450
Imp	875/4	1963-73	£800	£300	£70
Husky	875/4	1966-71	£800	£450	£100
Avenger	var/4	1970-76	£550	£250	£60
Avenger GT	1500/4	1971-76	£950	£500	£100
Avenger Tiger	1600/4	1972-73	£2,000	£1,000	£500

l. **1948 Hillman Minx Three-Position Drophead Coupé,** 1185cc, body and interior in fair condition, some corrosion around the wheel arches, hood requires repairing, unused for 5 years.
£2,100–2,400 *LF*

The Phase III Minx was built between 1948 and 1953. Of unitary construction, it was propelled by a sturdy sidevalve engine that became the mainstay of Rootes Group products for some years. Some sources suggest that only 80 Drophead Coupés were built.

HORCH

1935 Horch 750B Six-Seater Tourer, 4486cc, 8 cylinder, overhead-valve engine, 4-speed gearbox.
£42,000–46,000 *S*

August Horch's early cars were built to the highest standards, the first to bear the Horch name leaving the Cologne factory in 1900. The marque enjoyed pre-WWI success in the Herkomer and Prince Henry Trials. Post-war production concentrated initially on four- and six-cylinder cars, the first straight-eight, the 300, appearing in 1927. The 750B was only produced between 1934 and 1935. This particular example was restored by Le Coq in Paris in the early 1980s, and since then has remained on display in the International Musée de l'Automobile, Geneva.

1938 Horch Roadster, 8 cylinders.
£125,000–135,000 *FHF*

HOTCHKISS

Benjamin B. Hotchkiss, an American, was the founder of the famous French armaments concern, which sought a new line of manufacturing when the ordnance business slowed. The first car emanated from Saint Denis for the Automobile Show in 1903 and attracted much interest. The Edwardian Hotchkiss was preferred by wealthy automobilists who might retain a chauffeur. Hotchkiss made its last car in 1954.

1910 Hotchkiss Sedanca de Ville.
£25,000–35,000 *FHF*

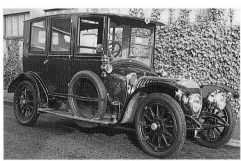

l. **1912 Hotchkiss Saloon,** 'Top-Hat' saloon coachwork with drop-down partition window by Hamshaw's, 4 cylinder engine, black livery including some original paintwork, good original condition.
£24,750–28,750 *S*

In no year before WWI did Hotchkiss make more than 200 of its high-priced cars.

l. **1951 Hotchkiss Anjou 13.50,** 2.3 litres, 72bhp, 4-speed synchromesh gearbox, 5 seater, top speed of just over 80mph, partially restored in 1997, good condition.
£4,000–5,000 *BKS*

For 50 years, Hotchkiss was one of France's most distinguished car makers, and was the winner of the Monte-Carlo Rally six times on the 10 occasions the event was run between 1932 and 1950.

HRG

1946 HRG 1100, restored in 1987, non-original front wings, good history.
£16,000–18,500 *Mot*

HUDSON

1935 Hudson Straight-Eight Saloon, 3000cc, 6 cylinders, 3-speed manual gearbox, original right-hand drive, restored, very good condition.
£8,500–10,000 *H&H*

This car has a host of special features and is believed to have been imported to the UK for the Earl's Court Motor Show.

1946 Hudson Super Six, 3475cc, 6 cylinders, right-hand drive, interior in excellent condition, mechanically sound and in running order, stored for a number of years, needs recommissioning.
£4,500–5,500 *BRIT*

The Hudson Motor Company of Detroit, founded in 1908, became renowned for producing well engineered, distinctively styled and competitively priced motor cars. After building aircraft and engines during WWII, the company recommenced car production for 1946 with essentially face-lifted pre-war models.

HUMBER

A once distinguished British make, Humber was brought low in its later days by an epidemic of badge-engineering when the Humber name became little more than a dubious emblem of suburban rank on upmarket Hillmans and Singers. Humber, like so many early British makes, had graduated to cars from bicycles in the early years of the century. In 1928, the company took over Hillman, and both were absorbed into the growing Rootes empire in 1931. Humber's role during this period was to furnish cars for the sober upper-middle-class market. In the 1930s, the majestic six-cylinder Humber Pullmans and Super Snipes received official patronage and went on to do sterling duty as staff cars during WWII. The Super Snipe of the late 1940s continued the tradition as a superior bank manager's carriage. Increasingly, in the 1960s, the Humber marque lost its individual identity. Chrysler absorbed the Rootes Group in 1964, and 12 years later the Humber name disappeared for ever.

1913 Humberette 8hp Two-Seater, air-cooled V-twin engine, maroon livery, beige hood, H & B acetylene lighting, bulb horn, folding windscreen.
£5,750–6,500 *BKS*

Initially a bicycle maker, Humber began serious car production with 5 and 6½hp models in 1903–4. In many ways, these successful little cars were the forerunners of the V-twin Humberette cyclecar, introduced in 1913 and possibly the sturdiest of the many cyclecars of the era.

HUMBER	ENGINE	DATES	CONDITION		
Model	cc/cyl		1	2	3
Veteran	var	1898			
		1918	£25,000	£20,000	£14,000
10	1592/4	1919	£7,000	£5,000	£3,000
14	2474/4	1919	£8,000	£6,000	£4,000
15.9-5/40	2815/4	1920-27	£9,500	£7,000	£4,000
8	985/4	1923-25	£7,000	£5,000	£2,500
9/20-9/28	1057/4	1926	£7,000	£5,000	£4,000
14/40	2050/4	1927-28	£10,000	£8,000	£5,000
Snipe	3498/6	1930-35	£8,000	£6,000	£4,000
Pullman	3498/6	1930-35	£8,000	£6,000	£4,000
16/50	2110/6	1930-32	£9,000	£7,000	£5,000
12	1669/4	1933-37	£7,000	£5,000	£3,000
Snipe/Pullman	4086/6	1936-40	£7,000	£5,000	£3,000
16	2576/6	1938-40	£7,000	£5,000	£3,000

Pre-1905 or Brighton Run cars are very popular.

r. **1963 Humber Super Snipe,** 2965cc, straight 6, overhead-valve engine, automatic transmission, interior and mechanics in good condition, paintwork requires attention, 12,000 miles in last 10 years, fewer than 75,000 recorded miles.
£1,100–1,500 *LF*

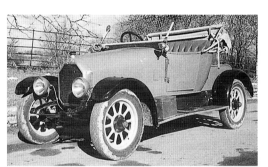

1919 Humber 10hp Open Tourer, beige paintwork, red trim, electrical equipment in working order, good tyres, converted to well-base wheels, original beaded-edge wheels included, good overall condition.
£10,500–13,000 *S*

The 10hp Humber, a newcomer for 1914, featured a four-cylinder monobloc sidevalve engine with a detachable head and unit construction of the engine and gearbox. Available in open two- and four-seater form, the 'Ten' represented the very best touring practice of the period. During WWI, Humber built aeroplanes and motor cycles. When hostilities ceased, the main pre-war models – the 'Ten' and 'Fourteen' – were revived and formed the basis of a range that continued until 1927. This particular car was one of three assembled in 1919 from 1915 parts, and is thought to be the first car to leave the works following the Armistice.

1964 Humber Super Snipe, 2965cc, 6 cylinders, bare metal respray in 1995, structure and mechanics in good condition, interior wood trim repolished, original red leather upholstery needs refurbishing, very good condition.
£1,700–2,000 *BRIT*

Miller's Starter Marque

Starter Humbers: *Hawk and Super Snipe from 1957 onwards; 1965–67 Imperial; Sceptre, 1963–76.*

- The 1959 Super Snipe and later Imperial were the last of the true Humbers. The former was a bigger, six-cylinder, more luxurious version of the 1957 four-cylinder Hawk, with the short-lived Imperial topping the range with even more luxury trimmings. The interiors were the usual British drawing-room mix of leather, wood and quietly ticking clock, and by all accounts these last big Humbers handled pretty much like a drawing-room, too. Then again, Humber owners weren't really inclined to hustle a car along like those flashy types in tyre-squealing MkII Jags. And that's why, if you're lucky, you might just be able to find one that hasn't been caned into the ground by a succession of lead-footed owners.
- Snipe I models had a 2655cc overhead-valve straight-six, but Snipe II onwards, and associated Imperials, offer better 3 litre performance (90–100+mph) and front disc brakes. Transmission could be a three-speed manual with optional overdrive, a Borg Warner automatic, or an optional four-speed manual on the Imperial.
- Look for structural rot in the unitary shell; prices are low, but all the leather, wood and other luxury fittings are as expensive to restore as in a more valuable car. Many body panels and trim items are unavailable, so you want a car that's complete.
- In 1960, the revised Super Snipe became the first British car to be equipped with twin headlamps.

HUMBER Model	ENGINE cc/cyl	DATES	CONDITION 1	2	3
Hawk Mk I-IV	1944/4	1945-52	£2,750	£1,500	£600
Hawk Mk V-VII	2267/4	1952-57	£2,500	£1,500	£400
Hawk Ser I-IVA	2267/4	1957-67	£2,500	£850	£325
Snipe	2731/6	1945-48	£5,000	£2,600	£850
Super Snipe Mk I-III	4086/6	1948-52	£4,700	£2,400	£600
Super Snipe Mk IV-IVA	4138/6	1952-56	£5,500	£2,300	£550
Super Snipe Ser I-II	2651/6	1958-60	£3,800	£1,800	£475
Super Snipe SIII VA	2965/6	1961-67	£3,500	£1,800	£400
Super Snipe S.III-VA Est.	2965/6	1961-67	£3,950	£1,850	£525
Pullman	4086/6	1946-51	£4,500	£2,350	£800
Pullman Mk IV	4086/6	1952-54	£6,000	£2,850	£1,200
Imperial	2965/6	1965-67	£3,900	£1,600	£450
Sceptre Mk I-II	1592/4	1963-67	£2,200	£1,000	£300
Sceptre Mk III	1725/4	1967-76	£1,600	£600	£200

l. **1974 Humber Sceptre,** 1725cc, 4 cylinders, manual/overdrive gearbox, 16,000 miles recorded, very good condition.
£1,300–1,500 *BRIT*

The late-series Humber Sceptre was effectively a luxury version of the contemporary Hillman Minx, powered by the robust 1725cc, aluminium-head Rootes engine. It offered good value and a high level of finish and equipment.

INVICTA

Invicta's life was short, turbulent, but sometimes glorious. The cars were all 'assembled' models based on Meadows 2.5 and 4.5 litre engines and the 1.5 litre Blackburne unit. The company enjoyed brief renown in the early 1930s with the lovely and potent 4½ litre low-chassis S-Type, a purposeful 115bhp, 95+mph sports car that achieved considerable competition success. Very few were made, possibly only 50, but they are keenly sought after and highly valued, both for their imposing but stark styling and their Bentley-baiting performance. The company finally succumbed for good in 1950.

1933 Invicta 4½ Litre Low Chassis Tourer, coachwork by Carbodies, 4467cc, straight 6, 4-speed gearbox, dark blue livery, matching hood, red upholstery and interior trim, fold-flat windscreen, side-mounted spare, restored.
£165,000–185,000 *S*

The origins of Captain (later Sir) Noel Macklin's Invicta Company date from 1924, when early models using Coventry Climax engines were produced. The first Henry Meadows-engined 4½ litre version appeared in 1928. In the following year, Macklin announced the entirely new sports chassis – the type 'S' – which became known as the '100mph Invicta'. Although the makers never endorsed this name, in tuned form, the car could easily attain the 'magic century'. Very few models were made before production ceased in 1934. This car was originally supplied to 'B. Bira' (Prince Birabongse Bhanuban of Siam), a very successful racing driver of the inter-war period.

ISO

Like Ferruccio Lamborghini, Renzo Rivolta was a wealthy industrialist who entered motor manufacturing with an eye for high-performance sports and GT cars. Chief designer Giotto Bizzarrini's brief was to design a car that would provide the power and performance of a Ferrari or Maserati, with the ease of use and maintenance of a mass-produced vehicle. The solution was to design a chassis along the lines of the best European sports cars, but powered by a large capacity American V8 engine. Bizzarrini, designer of Ferrari's 250 GTO and Lamborghini's V12 engine, rose to the challenge with aplomb, the first car being the Rivolta. This was followed by an out-and-out two-seater sports car, the fabulous Grifo, which in Italian means Griffin. This, of course, is the legendary bird that preys on horses, an allusion to Iso's desire to conquer Ferrari in the sports car stakes.

1969 Iso Grifo, coachwork by Bertone, 5359cc Chevrolet V8, 365bhp, manual gearbox, right-hand drive, top speed 160mph, fully restored, bare metal respray, history file.
£18,500–22,500   COYS

1974 Iso Rivolta Lele, 5762cc, Ford V8.
£3,100–3,600   H&H

ISO Model	ENGINE cc/cyl	DATES	CONDITION		
			1	2	3
Rivolta V8	5359cc/8	1962-70	£15,000	£10,000	£3,500
Grifo V8	5359/6899/8	1965-74	£28,000	£16,000	£12,000
Lele 2 door fastback coupé	5359/8	1967-74	£12,000	£8,000	£5,000
Fidia V8 4 door exec. saloon	5359/8	1967-74	£10,000	£7,000	£5,000

ISOTTA FRASCHINI

r. 1925 Isotta Fraschini Type 8A, 7 seater tourer coachwork by Cowley Coach & Motor Co, 7.4 litre, overhead-valve straight 8, 4-wheel servo brakes, restored mechanically, new upholstery, 79,000 miles, full service history, excellent original condition.
£65,000–70,000   Mot

ITALA

c1907 Itala 35/40hp Raceabout, 5.7 litre T-head engine, 4-speed gearbox, correct torque-tube drive, staggered 2 seater coachwork based on Targa Florio cars, brass Rushmore acetylene lighting, generator, petrol pressure pump and Boa Constrictor horn, drip-feed oiler system, petrol pressure gauge, Bosch coil, Edwardian speedometer, meticulous restoration, excellent condition.
£35,000–40,000   S

Fabrica Automobili Itala, of Turin, entered motor car production with a 3½hp De Dion-engined voiturette. The company's most famous achievement was gaining victory in the 1907 Peking to Paris Trial, and the marque was also active in Grand Prix racing.

JAGUAR

William Lyons was born in Blackpool in 1901. Before he dabbled with cars, he was an enthusiastic motorcyclist who, on his 21st birthday, formed the Swallow Sidecar Company with partner William Walmsley. In 1927, the company made the transition to four wheels, clothing a strengthened Austin 7 chassis with a stylish two-toned sports body. In 1931, the rakish SS1 appeared, and in 1935, with Lyons now sole proprietor of the company, the Jaguar name was used for the first time. Most prized among the pre-war models is the beautifully rakish and fast SS100. In 1948, at the first post-war Motor Show at Earl's Court, William Lyons stole the show with perhaps the most cat-like of all Jaguars, the XK120. Since then, virtually all Jaguars, whether sports cars or sporting saloons, have become objects of desire, perhaps none more so than the 1961 E-Type. Even so, several models remain a little overlooked and are worth considering by the Jaguar enthusiast on a budget. The S-Type saloon is, in effect, a MkII with a stretched boot and better-handling independent rear suspension that made it a gangland favourite as a get-away car. Another option is the 420, an S-type with MkX-style frontal treament and 4.2 litre engine. Other models to consider are the 'thrift' late-model Jaguar MkII variants, namely the 240 and 340, and Daimler 250 V8 saloon, a MkII with Daimler grille and a lovely compact V8 engine.

1936 SS Jaguar 100 Two-Seater Sports Roadster, chassis No. 18031, 2663cc, 6 cylinder in-line overhead-valve engine, twin SU carburettors, 101bhp at 4,600rpm, 4-speed synchromesh gearbox, completely restored, concours winner.
£100,000–110,000 *C*

When the young William Lyons introduced his handsome SS Jaguar 100 Sports two-seater in 1935, it was viewed with some scepticism by the rather conservative sporting motorists of the day. Rakishly low, with 90+mph readily available and acceleration to match, it was well equipped and finished, yet cost a mere £398. In the few seasons before WWII, only 198 were sold, plus 116 of the 3.5 litre version introduced in 1937. This particular car was the last to be built in 1936, and the 31st produced.

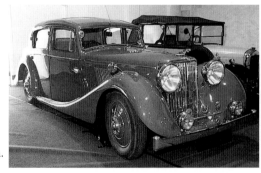

r. **1948 Jaguar 3½ Litre Saloon,** excellent condition.
£16,500–18,000 *CGC*

JAGUAR Model	ENGINE cc/cyl	DATES	CONDITION 1	2	3
SSI	2054/6	1932-33	£25,000	£18,000	£12,000
SSI	2252/6	1932-33	£22,000	£17,000	£13,500
SSII	1052/4	1932-33	£18,000	£15,000	£11,000
SSI	2663/6	1934	£26,000	£22,000	£15,000
SSII	1608/4	1934	£18,000	£15,000	£12,000
SS90	2663/6	1935	£60,000+		
SS100 (3.4)	3485/6	1938-39	£80,000+		
SS100 (2.6)	2663/6	1936-39	£70,000+		

Very dependent on body styles, completeness and originality, particularly original chassis to body.

1950 Jaguar XK120 Roadster, 3442cc, 6 cylinder, in-line engine, 160bhp at 5,250rpm, 4-speed manual gearbox, 4-wheel drum brakes, left-hand drive, completely restored.
£37,500–42,500   *C*

It was at the 1948 London Motor Show that Jaguar launched its stunning XK120, a car offering incredible style and performance at a remarkably low price – a quarter of that for a comparable V12 Ferrari. At the heart of the William Lyons-styled roadster was a new 3442cc, double-overhead-camshaft XK engine that gave 160bhp via twin SU carburettors – enough for 126mph and 0–60mph in 10 seconds.

1954 Jaguar XK120SE Sports Roadster, 3442cc, 6 cylinder in-line engine, 160bhp at 5,200rpm, 4-speed manual gearbox, complete frame-off restoration, engine updated with 1⅝in diam exhaust valves and enlarged valve throats, stelite valve seats to permit use of unleaded fuel, complete street and racing trim, supplied with full windshield, convertible top and side curtains, metal racing tonneau.
£43,000–47,000   *C*

1950 Jaguar XK120 Roadster, 3442cc, 160bhp, right-hand drive, restored, still requires some work.
£19,500–22,500   *P(E)*

XK120

- The 120 in the name really did stand for 120mph, thanks to the fabulous double overhead cam engine that went on to power six-cylinder E-types and Jaguar saloons until 1986. At the time cynical motoring scribes were sceptical and in 1949 William Lyons, by now an accomplished publicist, hired a Dakota aircraft and flew a band of hacks to Belgium to witness the XK120 perform a 132mph run on the unrestricted Jabbeke autoroute. That Jag did have a little aerodynamic tweaking but he'd proved his point, the XK120 was the fastest series production car in the world. In fact the 3.4 litre XK engine pumped out as much power as the 5.4 litre Cadillac engine of the same period.
- One of the earliest XK120 customers was car connoisseur and actor Clark Gable and he reckoned the XK120 was 'a masterpiece of design and construction'.

1952 Jaguar XK120 Fixed-Head Coupé, 3.8 litre, 6 cylinder XK engine and 4-wheel disc brakes, left-hand drive, restored.
£15,500–17,000   *COYS*

The appearance of the XK120 in 1948 generated such a clamour from potential buyers that instead of producing the few hand-built cars originally intended, Jaguar had to tool up for serious production. Competition success and the 126.45mph (133.5mph without windscreen) achieved by 'Soapy' Sutton on a Belgian autoroute further increased demand for the car, which did not become widely available until the 1950s. Even then, export orders were so great that significant home-market sales did not materialise until 1951.

1954 Jaguar XK120SE Roadster, 3.4 litres, 6 cylinders, C-Type cylinder head, 210bhp, restored, newly rebuilt engine.
£23,000–27,000   *BKS*

l. **1954 Jaguar XK120SE Roadster,** fitted optional 190bhp engine with high-lift camshafts, lightened flywheel and competition crankshaft damper, 4-speed manual gearbox, dual exhaust system, uprated suspension, wire wheels, left-hand drive, restored, interior reupholstered in red leather, brightwork rechromed, excellent condition.
£42,000–48,000 *BKS*

JAGUAR Model	ENGINE cc/cyl	DATES	CONDITION 1	2	3
XK120 roadster aluminum	3442/6	1948-49	£50,000+	£28,000	£15,000
XK120 roadster	3442/6	1949-54	£26,000	£20,000	£15,000
XK120 DHC	3442/6	1953-54	£22,000	£17,000	£12,000
XK120 Coupé	3442/6	1951-55	£16,000	£12,000	£10,000
C-type	3442/6	1951	£150,000+		
D-type	3442/6	1955-56	£500,000+		
XKSS (original)	3442/6	1955-57	£400,000+		
XK140 roadster	3442/6	1955-58	£30,000+	£23,000	£16,000
XK140 DHC	3442/6	1955-58	£25,000+	£20,500	£15,000
XK140 Coupé	3442/6	1955-58	£15,000+	£10,000	£7,500
XK150 roadster	3442/6	1958-60	£28,000	£22,000	£15,000
XK150 DHC	3442/6	1957-61	£25,000	£18,000	£10,000
XK150 Coupé	3442/6	1957-60	£15,000	£10,000	£6,000
XK150S roadster	3442/ 3781/6	1958-60	£40,000	£26,000	£20,000
XK150S DHC	3442/ 3781/6	1958-60	£34,000	£22,000	£18,000
XK150S Coupé	3442/ 3781/6	1958-61	£22,000	£18,000	£14,000

D-Type with competition history considerably more.
Watch out for left-hand to right-hand drive conversions in the XK series of cars.

1955 Jaguar XK140 Drophead Coupé,
3.4 litre, 6 cylinder twin-cam engine, 190bhp, standard trim, restored, converted from left-to right-hand drive in 1994/95.
£35,000–38,000 *BKS*

1955 Jaguar XK140 Roadster, 3.4 litre, 6 cylinder twin-cam engine, 190bhp, disc brakes, standard trim, left-hand drive, completely restored in 1991, only 10,000 miles covered since.
£32,000–36,000 *BKS*

1955 Jaguar XK140 Fixed-Head Coupé,
finished in British Racing Green, green leather upholstery, right-hand drive, automatic transmission, stainless steel exhaust, rally equipment, paintwork needs attention, otherwise excellent condition.
£18,500–20,000 *BKS*

1956 Jaguar XK140 Fixed-Head Coupé, 3442cc, 6 cylinders, 190bhp, bare metal respray and engine rebuilt in 1995.
£16,000–19,000 *Pou*

1957 Jaguar XK140 Drophead Coupé, C-Type head, twin stainless steel exhausts, close-ratio overdrive gearbox, front disc brakes, Koni shock absorbers, original Lucas spot and fog lamps, completely rebuilt, 5,800 miles since, award winner.
£46,500–52,000 *COYS*

This XK140 was originally owned by racing driver Mike Hawthorn.

r. **1958 Jaguar XK150 Drophead Coupé.**
£27,000–30,000 *BLE*

l. **1958 Jaguar XK150S Roadster,** 3.4 litres, manual overdrive gearbox, left-hand drive, finished in British Racing Green, tan leather interior, beige mohair hood, chrome wire wheels.
£40,000–44,500 *BC*

1960 Jaguar XK150 Fixed-Head Coupé, 3781cc, 3-speed automatic transmission, original trim and brightwork, chassis, battery boxes, suspension and back axle stripped and repainted, new propshaft bearings, brake pipes, servo, engine hoses, and ignition components, wire wheels, Webasto sunroof, 69,816 miles recorded.
£15,000–18,000 *H&H*

1953 Jaguar MkVII, original carpets and head lining, 70,000 miles, excellent original unrestored condition.
£15,000–18,000 *THOR*

Roy Nockolds, Monte Carlo Rally 1956, depicting the winning Jaguar MkVII of Adams at speed in the mountains above Monaco, handpainted silkscreen print with inscribed title, unframed, 24 x 33in (61 x 84cm).
£115–130 *S*

1957 Jaguar MkI 3.4 Saloon, 4-wheel disc brakes, finished in Warwick Grey, red leather interior, 34,000 miles, unrestored.
£12,000–15,000 *VIC*

Jaguar's range of compact sports saloons first rolled off the production line at Brown's Lane in 1955, heralding a new chapter in Jaguar history. Initially offered in 2.4 litre form, the range was developed to include 3.4 and 3.8 litre models.

1958 Jaguar MkI 2.4 Saloon, 2483cc, manual overdrive gearbox, 4-wheel disc brakes, restored, only 10,000 miles covered in last 20 years.
£3,500–4,000 *H&H*

1960 Jaguar MkII 2.4 Saloon, 2483cc, 6 cylinders, manual overdrive gearbox, wire wheels, largely original, mechanics, body and underside in good condition.
£3,600–4,000 *BRIT*

The 2.4 litre Jaguar MkII was introduced in 1959 along with its 3.4 and 3.8 litre stable-mates. Compared to the MkI, they featured slimmer windscreen pillars and deeper side windows, while the rear track was widened to improve stability. Otherwise, the running gear remained much as before, with independent front suspension by wishbones and coil springs, a leaf-sprung live rear axle and Dunlop four-wheel disc brakes. The interior was furnished in leather with a polished walnut instrument panel and deep pile carpets. The XK engine of the 2.4 litre car developed 120bhp at 5,750rpm.

1960 Jaguar MkII 3.8 Vicarage, 5-speed Getrag gearbox, 4-wheel servo-assisted disc brakes, gas-filled adjustable dampers, limited-slip differential, air conditioning, electric sunroof, locking and windows, 4-door courtesy lights, fully restored.
£27,500–32,000 *BKS*

Ten years ago, a base-specification Vicarage Jaguar MkII cost £62,500 exclusive of VAT. For that, the customer received a fully restored car with improved steering and suspension, and a superior finish to the original Jaguar paintwork.

1961 Jaguar MkII 3.8 Saloon, 3781cc, 6 cylinders, automatic transmission, chrome wire wheels, brightwork replated, original red leather interior and carpets in good condition, bills for engine rebuild.
£8,750–10,000 *BRIT*

l. **1962 Jaguar MkII 3.4 Saloon,** bare metal respray, all mechanical components replaced or rebuilt.
£17,500–20,000 *BKS*

The MkII's 3.4 litre engine developed 210bhp, giving a top speed of 120mph and effortless cruising at 100mph using the Laycock de Normanville overdrive.

JAGUAR Model	ENGINE cc/cyl	DATES	CONDITION 1	2	3
1½ Litre	1775/4	1945-49	£8,500	£5,500	£2,000
2½ Litre	2663/6	1946-49	£10,000	£7,500	£2,000
2½ Litre DHC	2663/6	1947-48	£17,000	£11,000	£8,000
3½ Litre	3485/6	1947-49	£12,000	£6,000	£4,000
3½ Litre DHC	3485/6	1947-49	£19,000	£13,500	£5,500
Mk V 2½ Litre	2663/6	1949-51	£8,000	£5,000	£1,500
Mk V 3½ Litre	3485/6	1949-51	£11,000	£7,000	£1,800
Mk V 3½ Litre DHC	3485/6	1949-51	£20,000	£17,000	£8,500
Mk VII	3442/6	1951-57	£10,000	£7,500	£2,500
Mk VIIM	3442/6	1951-57	£12,000	£8,500	£2,500
Mk VIII	3442/6	1956-59	£8,500	£5,500	£2,000
Mk IX	3781/6	1958-61	£9,000	£7,000	£2,500
Mk X 3.8/4.2	3781/6	1961-64	£7,500	£3,500	£1,500
Mk X 420G	4235/6	1964-70	£6,000	£3,000	£1,200
Mk I 2.4	2438/6	1955-59	£7,000	£5,500	£2,000
Mk I 3.4	3442/6	1957-59	£9,000	£6,000	£2,500
Mk II 2.4	2483/6	1959-67	£7,000	£5,000	£2,000
Mk II 3.4	3442/6	1959-67	£9,000	£6,500	£3,000
Mk II 3.8	3781/6	1959-67	£10,000+	£6,000	£4,000
S-Type 3.4	3442/6	1963-68	£9,000	£6,500	£2,000
S-Type 3.8	3781/6	1963-68	£10,000	£6,500	£2,000
240	2438/6	1967-68	£9,000	£6,000	£2,500
340	3442/6	1967-68	£8,000	£7,000	£3,000
420	4235/6	1966-68	£6,000	£3,000	£2,000

Manual gearboxes with overdrive are at a premium.
Some concours examples making as much as 50% over Condition 1.

l. **1965 Jaguar MkII 3.4 Saloon,** automatic transmission, restored in 1990, bare metal respray, engine rebuilt, all brightwork and badges renewed or replated, rewired where necessary, new carpet, head lining, and door trims, seats and centre console reupholstered in pale grey leather, interior wood trim reveneered, 80,181 miles.
£12,500–14,000 *BKS*

1963 Jaguar MkII 3.4 Saloon, 3442cc, 6 cylinders, manual overdrive gearbox, finished in metallic grey, burgundy leather interior, 54,000 miles, good condition.
£12,750–14,500 *BRIT*

1966 Jaguar MkII 3.8 Saloon, restored.
£13,000–14,000 *WILM*

Jaguar MkII (1960–68)

In one respect at least, 1960s cops owe a debt of gratitude to the villains. If the Krays and kindred crooks hadn't cottoned on to the get-away capabilities of the MkII and MkII-based S-Type, the police probably wouldn't have been given the MkII as the tool to catch them. This Jag is a true sports saloon – especially in larger-engined form – a rare blend of grace, pace and plenty of space in the boot for loot.

Original 1960 prices: 2.4 litre, £1,534; 3.4, £1,669; 3.8, £1,779.

Pick of the bunch: Post-1965 cars with much smoother all-synchromesh box. Most-prized is the 3.8-litre, but the extra 400cc costs an awful lot more than the 3.4, which runs it close in performance terms.

What to watch: Beware 'yuppie blow-overs'. Late-1980s price-hikes encouraged cosmetic bodges that are now losing their sheen.

MkII fact: Guildford dealer and saloon car racer John Coombs created his own highly tuned Coombs MkII that could match an E-Type on the 0–60mph sprint. Coombs Jags are identifiable by louvred vents in the bonnet, which were taken from changing-room locker doors. Cynics say that of the 28 or so Coombs MkIIs built, there are only 40 or 50 survivors!

1968 Jaguar 240 Saloon, 2438cc, manual overdrive gearbox, 67,000 miles, lightly restored, original condition.
£5,750–6,500 *H&H*

1968 Jaguar 340 Saloon, 3442cc, 4-speed manual overdrive gearbox, completely restored in 1994, only 624 miles covered since, engine rebuilt, rewired, rechromed, new stainless steel exhaust, reclining front seats, new carpets.
£13,000–15,000 *H&H*

1968 Jaguar 340 Saloon, 3442cc, 6 cylinders, overdrive, sunroof, restored in 1989, brakes overhauled, new wire wheels, brown leather interior, good condition.
£8,250–9,250 *BRIT*

1967 Jaguar S-Type, 3.8 litres, good condition.
£4,500–5,000 *PALM*

1967 Jaguar S-Type 3.4 Saloon, 3442cc, 6 cylinders, suspension overhauled, underside in excellent condition, resprayed 5 years ago, original grey/blue leather trimmed interior.
£3,500–4,000 *BRIT*

1970 Jaguar Type 420G, 4235cc, 6 cylinders, 245bhp at 5,500rpm, engine rebuilt, partially resprayed, original interior wood trim.
£5,000–6,000 *Pou*

1963 Jaguar MkX Saloon, 3781cc, 6 cylinders, 4-speed manual overdrive gearbox, stainless steel exhaust, new tyres, finished in Golden Sand, original tan leather interior, electric windows, heated rear window, Webasto sunroof.
£8,000–9,000 *H&H*

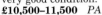

1963 Jaguar E-Type 3.8 Fixed-Head Coupé,
synchromesh gearbox, right-hand drive, restored,
very good condition.
£10,500–11,500 *PA*

**1963 Jaguar E-Type 3.8 Fixed-Head
Coupé,** 3781cc, completely restored at
a cost of over £30,000, new engine and
electrics, reconditioned gearbox,
resprayed, new interior.
£18,500–20,000 *H&H*

1964 Jaguar E-Type Roadster, 3.8 litres, several
'Eagle' upgrades, fully restored, excellent condition.
£42,000–45,000 *EAE*

1964 Jaguar E-Type Series I Roadster,
3.8 litres, 4-speed manual gearbox, good
overall condition.
£28,000–30,000 *THOR*

1965 Jaguar E-Type Fixed-Head Coupé, 4.2 litres, red paintwork, black interior, restored.
£11,000–13,000 *P(E)*

Jaguar E-Type (1961–74)

Engine: 3781cc and 4235cc straight-six;
5343cc V12.
Power output: 265–272bhp.
Top speed: 143–150mph.
0–60mph: 7–7.2 seconds.
Price when new: £2,097 19s 2d (roadster).
Production: 72,520.
The E-Type was a sensational show-stopper at
the 1961 Geneva Motor Show. British motoring
magazines had produced road tests of pre-
production models to coincide with the launch –
and yes, the fixed-head coupé really could do
150.4mph (149.1mph for the roadster), but most
owners found 145mph more realistic. What's
more, its shattering performance came relatively

cheaply. In fact, to match it, you would have had
to pay at least £1,000 more, and Aston Martins
and Ferraris were more than double the money.
E-Types took off again in the late 1980s as
speculators drove prices into orbit, nudging a
stratospheric £100,000 before the gravitational
pull of the market brought them back down to
earth in a big way. That's good news for today's
buyers, who stand a chance of owning an
E-Type for less than will have been spent on
its restoration.

E-Type facts: Of every three E-Types built, two
were exported. Originally fixed-head coupés cost
£100 more than the open roadster; today,
roadsters are far more highly prized.

1966 Jaguar E-Type Series I 2+2 Coupé, 4235cc, 6 cylinders, double overhead camshafts, twin SU carburettors, 265bhp at 5,400rpm, leather-trimmed interior, engine overhauled, good mechanical condition, body in need of minor attention.
£11,500–13,000 *C*

When the E-Type appeared in 1961, it was offered as a two-seater roadster and a Gran Turismo coupé, accommodating two in considerable comfort with space for luggage. With the introduction of the 4.2 litre engine, Jaguar took the opportunity to add a roomier third model to the range, which appeared in 1966. To produce the new 2+2 coupé, the E-Type's wheelbase was extended by 9in, and its roofline raised and lengthened. Although not really practical for adults, the rear seating arrangement provided space for two children, at some cost to the luggage capacity. Other improvements were also implemented in 1966. The 4.2 litre engine's cylinder bores were respaced, and there was a much stronger crankshaft with an improved torsional damper. A welcome feature was a new all-synchromesh gearbox with its own oil pump, supplemented by a stronger clutch.

1966 Jaguar E-Type Series I 2+2 Coupé, 4.2 litres, mechanically original and in good condition, bodywork in sound condition, restored front seats, tool kit.
£12,750–14,500 *C*

1967 Jaguar E-Type Coupé, 4.2 litres, engine rebuilt, resprayed.
£7,000–8,000 *H&H*

1968 Jaguar E-Type Roadster, 4.2 litres, converted to right-hand drive, completely restored, excellent condition.
£21,000–22,500 *Mot*

1968 Jaguar E-Type 2+2 Fixed-Head Coupé, manual gearbox, left-hand drive, bare metal respray, restored.
£10,000–11,000 *Mot*

1973 Jaguar E-Type Series III Roadster, V12, automatic transmission, power steering, completely original, excellent condition.
£32,000–34,000 *THOR*

1969 Jaguar E-Type Coupé, 4.2 litres, 4-speed manual gearbox, original.
£12,000–13,000 *WILM*

1973 Jaguar E-Type Series III Roadster, V12, 4-speed manual gearbox, resprayed, original.
£30,000–32,000 *THOR*

l. **1973 Jaguar E-Type Series III,** 5343cc, V12, restored in 1991, little use since, bare metal respray, replacement XJS engine, 5-speed manual gearbox, air conditioning, tinted glass, 8in wheel rims.
£16,000–18,000 *COYS*

1975 Jaguar E-Type Series III Roadster Commemorative Model, manual gearbox, 650 miles from new, carefully stored, coachwork in excellent condition, original black vinyl roof in good order, good mechanical condition.
£74,000–80,000 *BRIT*

Although essentially the same in appearance as its predecessors, the Series III E-Type differed in a number of ways: the wheelbase was longer, the bonnet air-intake was considerably larger, and the wheel arches were flared to clear wider wheels. When production of the legendary E-Type ceased in 1975, 50 cars were prepared as Commemorative Edition models, all having a black finish.

JAGUAR Model	ENGINE cc/cyl	DATES	CONDITION 1	2	3
E-type 3.8 flat floor roadster (RHD)		1961	£40,000	£30,000	£22,000
E-type SI 3.8 roadster	3781/6	1961-64	£30,000	£19,000	£15,000
E-type 3.8 FHC	3781/6	1961-64	£20,000	£13,000	£10,000
E-type SI 4.2 roadster	4235/6	1964-67	£28,000	£18,000	£14,000
E-type 2+2 manual FHC	4235/6	1966-67	£16,000	£11,000	£9,000
E-type SI 2+2 auto FHC	4235/6	1966-68	£14,000	£10,000	£9,000
E-type SII roadster	4235/6	1968-70	£30,000	£21,000	£14,000
E-type SII FHC	4235/6	1968-70	£18,000	£12,000	£10,000
E-type SII 2+2 manual FHC	4235/6	1968-70	£15,000	£10,000	£8,000
E-type SIII roadster	5343/12	1971-75	£40,000	£26,000	£17,000
E-type SIII 2+2 manual FHC	5343/12	1971-75	£19,000	£14,000	£10,000
E-type SIII 2+2 auto FHC	5343/12	1971-75	£17,000	£12,000	£9,000
XJ6 2.8 Ser I	2793/6	1968-73	£3,000	£1,500	£1,000
XJ6 4.2 Ser I	4235/6	1968-73	£3,500	£2,000	£1,000
XJ6 Coupé	4235/6	1974-78	£7,000	£4,000	£2,500
XJ6 Ser II	4235/6	1973-79	£3,500	£2,000	£750
XJ12 Ser I	5343/12	1972-73	£3,500	£2,250	£1,500
XJ12 Coupé	5343/12	1973-77	£9,000	£5,000	£3,000
XJ12 Ser II	5343/12	1973-79	£3,000	£2,000	£1,000
XJS manual	5343/12	1975-78	£6,000	£4,500	£2,500
XJS auto	5343/12	1975-81	£4,500	£3,000	£2,000

Jaguar E-Type Series III Commemorative Roadsters fetch more than SIII Roadsters – 50 limited editions only.

1971 Jaguar XJ6, 4235cc, 6 cylinders, finished in grey, red leather-trimmed interior, well maintained. **£1,800–2,200** *BRIT*

1974 Jaguar XJ6L, 4.2 litres, automatic transmission, long-wheelbase, finished in dark blue, beige leather interior, very good condition throughout. **£2,500–3,000** *BKS*

1973 Jaguar XJ6, 2792cc, 6 cylinders, brightwork in good condition, 71,000 miles, good original condition. **£2,750–3,250** *BRIT*

Launched to much acclaim in 1968, the XJ6's refined concepts embodied by previous Jaguar saloons created a car that rivalled the best from Mercedes-Benz. Lower, longer and wider than the preceding 420, the XJ6 was also more rigid and utilised 'crumple zone' technology for increased safety. The all-independent suspension followed 420 lines, but with anti-dive geometry up front, while rack-and-pinion steering made its first appearance on a Jaguar saloon. The six-cylinder XK engine was available in either 2.8 or 4.2 litre forms initially, the latter capable of propelling the luxuriously appointed XJ6 to a top speed of 120+mph. There was choice of four-speed manual (usually with overdrive), or three-speed automatic transmissions.

l. **1977 Jaguar XJ6C Coupé,** 4.2 litres, manual gearbox, retrimmed Biscuit leather interior, recently overhauled carburettors and air conditioning, very good condition. **£3,900–4,400** *BKS*

Only 6,505 4.2 litre Coupés were built.

1985 Jaguar XJ6 Sovereign, 4.2 litres, metallic grey with grey leather interior.
£1,900–2,400 *PA*

1975 Jaguar XJ12C, 5343cc, V12, 4 Zenith carburettors, left-hand drive, 76,000km since new.
£5,500–6,000 *Pou*

Only 1,800 XJ12 Coupés were built, 1,200 of them being in left-hand drive.

l. **1987 Jaguar Sovereign,** V12, electric sunroof, full service history.
£2,750–3,250 *PA*

r. **1978 Jaguar XJS Convertible,** 5343cc, converted from a standard fixed-head to a convertible by Lynx Engineering in 1983, electric hood, bare metal respray in black, 65,000 miles.
£4,400–5,200 *H&H*

1987 Jaguar XJS Cabriolet, left-hand drive, excellent condition.
£5,250–6,000 *PA*

1997 Jaguar XJ220 Coupé, 3.5 litre, race-derived, all-alloy, 4 cam V6 engine, 4 valves per cylinder, separate turbocharger for each cylinder bank, 5-speed and reverse transaxle with spiral-bevel final drive and VC limited-slip differential, finished in Spa Silver, Smoke Grey leather interior, left-hand drive, fewer than 1,800km recorded.
£120,000–140,000 *BKS*

This car is a late number from the limited production run, so it benefits from having larger brakes than earlier examples. It is capable of the shattering 0–60mph time of 4.0 seconds, while 0–100mph is said to take only 9 seconds. Top speed is in the order of 220mph.

JENSEN

It was the last-of-the-line Interceptor that really made Jensen a household name in the late 1960s and 1970s. With its blend of lantern-jawed Italian good looks, tyre-smoking V8 engine and genteel British craftsmanship, it was produced in far greater numbers than any previous car from the small West Bromwich company. Brothers Richard and Allen Jensen had dabbled with motor cars since the 1920s, and in 1936 began producing their own cars, always in limited numbers. The Interceptor name was first used in 1950 on an attractive two-door saloon and tourer powered by Austin's 4 litre six-cylinder engine. That engine also went on to power the fibreglass-bodied 541 of 1954 which, in 1957, became one of the first production saloons to adopt disc brakes. Next, in 1962, came the dramatic fibreglass CV8, powered by a mighty Chrysler V8, which was also used to provide motive power for the 1967 Interceptor. Although the 541 and CV8 were only produced in limited numbers, they are blessed with a high survival rate, thanks to their tough chassis and non-rusting fibreglass bodies.

c1964 Jensen CV8, 5916cc, Chrysler overhead-valve V8, 305bhp, 3-speed automatic transmission, grey leather interior in very good condition, stored for 10 years, 65,000 miles, generally sound condition, requires recommissioning.
£6,500–7,500 *C*

The CV8 was introduced at the 1962 London Motor Show, and with it the company moved confidently into the very high-performance, luxury market. It was a comfortable four-seater, very well equipped and finished. Its body, with striking four-headlamp front-end styling, was clearly descended from the 541, but underneath there was a new chassis to accommodate the powerful 6 litre Chrysler V8 engine. This drove through a Chrysler Torqueflite automatic transmission to a limited-slip differential, which helped put the powerplant's 300bhp (330bhp in later versions) down on to the road. Earlier cars were tested at 132mph top speed, but later examples were good for 140mph.

1968 Jensen Interceptor FF,
6276cc, V8, 4-wheel drive.
£15,000–16,500 *DHAM*

1971 Jensen Interceptor II, restored at a cost of over £4,000, many new body panels, bare metal respray, reconditioned alloy road wheels, overhauled air conditioning, tailored footwell carpets.
£9,500–11,000 *PA*

JENSEN Model	ENGINE cc/cyl	DATES	CONDITION 1	2	3
541/541R/541S	3993/6	1954-63	£13,000	£7,000	£4,500
CV8 Mk I-III	5916/				
	6276/8	1962-66	£14,000	£7,000	£6,000
Interceptor SI-SIII	6276/8	1967-76	£11,000	£8,000	£6,000
Interceptor DHC	6276/8	1973-76	£25,000	£16,000	£10,000
Interceptor SP	7212/8	1971-76	£13,000	£9,000	£7,000
FF	6766/8	1967-71	£17,000	£11,000	£9,000
Healey	1973/4	1972-76	£5,000	£3,000	£1,500
Healey GT	1973/4	1975-76	£6,000	£3,000	£2,000

The Jensen CV8 and 541 are particularly sought after.

1971 Jensen Interceptor FF II, rebuilt engine, automatic transmission, 4-wheel drive, differentials and axles rebuilt, new brakes, springs, shock absorbers, stainless steel exhaust, wheel bearings, relays, carburettor, distributor, fuel tank, and water, oil and petrol pumps, lights and instruments restored, steering, radiator, air conditioning and fans overhauled, bare metal respray, concours winner.
£15,000–17,000 *S*

1975 Jensen Interceptor III Convertible, 54,000 miles.
£26,000–28,000 *EPP*

JOWETT

The Bradford company founded by Benjamin and William Jowett began series car production shortly after 1910, offering a string of commendable small cars powered first by flat-twin engines, and in 1936 by flat-four engines. The company's most exciting period occurred after 1945 with the introduction of the advanced Javelin saloon and Jupiter sports model, but Jowett ceased car manufacture in 1954, shortly after announcing the fibreglass-bodied R4 sports model, of which only three are thought to have been produced.

1972 Jensen Interceptor III, 7212cc, V8, engine in good condition, suspension overhauled, new sills, resprayed.
£5,000–6,000 *H&H*

With the Interceptor's introduction in 1967, Jensen switched from fibreglass to steel for its car bodies. Underneath, however, the preceding CV8's chassis, running gear and 6276cc Chrysler engine remained substantially unchanged. Chrysler's excellent Torqueflite automatic transmission was standard equipment, a manual box being an option. With around 280bhp on tap, performance was more than adequate, The Motor recording a top speed of 140mph and 0–100mph in 19 seconds. The Series II incorporated revised front suspension, Girling brakes and a redesigned interior, while the Series III, introduced in 1971, came with a 7.2 litre (330bhp) engine, improved seats, central locking, and alloy wheels.

1952 Jowett Jupiter, 1486cc, 3 seater convertible, completely restored 1991–94, receipts and bills totalling over £23,000.
£16,000–18,000 *H&H*

l. **1949 Jowett Javelin Saloon,** 1486cc, horizontally opposed flat four, overhead valves, 52.5bhp at 4,500rpm, column change 4-speed manual gearbox, original hydraulic-tappet engine, finished in turquoise blue, beige interior, radiator rebuilt, good original condition.
£2,750–3,500 *H&H*

LAGONDA

Although quintessentially a British sporting marque, Lagonda was actually founded by an American, Wilbur Gunn. The first cars sold in the UK market appeared in 1912, although the Staines workshops had been exporting vehicles for a while. In the mid-1920s, the company moved away from light cars to concentrate on the fast sporting cars and tourers that have come to characterise the marque. A Le Mans victory came in 1935 and, with W. O. Bentley as technical director, the company produced the magnificent V12. David Brown, owner of Aston Martin, acquired Lagonda in 1947, gaining access to W. O. Bentley's last engine design, the 2580cc twin-cam six, employed in the Aston Martin DB2. Since then, the Lagonda name has been used intermittently on larger luxury versions of Astons.

1933 Lagonda 3 Litre Tourer, 3013cc, converted from saloon, fully restored with new body and replacement engine, low mileage since.
£26,000–30,000 *H&H*

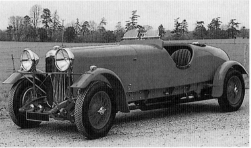

1936 Lagonda LG 45 Two-Seater Le Mans Replica, coachwork by Rod Jolley, restored 1986–91, extensive history and restoration files, finished in red with black upholstery, hydraulic brakes.
£38,000–43,000 *BKS*

l. **1939 Lagonda V12 De Ville Saloon,** 4479cc, restored in 1970s, paintwork and interior leather trim in excellent condition.
£24,000–27,000 *BKS*

Within 18 months of W. O. Bentley joining Lagonda as technical director in 1935, a V12 model was developed in time for the Motor Show of 1937. The engine, of 4479cc, had a very short stroke and gave 100mph performance. Soon after the new car went into production, Lagonda achieved great publicity and much prestige at Brooklands, where the V12 managed an average 101.5mph, with a best lap at 108mph.

1955 Lagonda 3 Litre Drophead Coupé, coachwork by Tickford, 6 cylinders, 2922cc, double overhead camshafts, restored, finished in bronze with beige hood and interior, offered with an assortment of spares.
£14,500–16,000 *P(E)*

1962 Lagonda Rapide Four-Door Saloon, restored 1990–92, underbody, sills, chassis, suspension and brakes overhauled, engine rebuilt, bare metal respray, interior refurbished, invoices for about £25,000, optional wire wheels, 6,000 miles covered since restoration.
£23,000–26,000 *BKS*

LAGONDA Model	ENGINE cc/cyl	DATES	CONDITION		
			1	2	3
12/24	1421/4	1923-26	£14,000	£10,000	£8,000
2 litre	1954/4	1928-32	£28,000	£25,000	£19,000
3 litre	2931/6	1928-34	£35,000	£30,000	£22,000
Rapier	1104/4	1934-35	£15,000	£9,000	£5,000
M45	4429/6	1934-36	£40,000	£30,000	£20,000
LG45	4429/6	1936-37	£45,000	£32,000	£22,000
LG6	4453/6	1937-39	£40,000	£28,000	£20,000
V12	4480/V12	1937-39	£75,000+	£50,000	£40,000

Prices are very dependent upon body type, dhc or saloon, originality and competition history.

LAMBORGHINI

Having owned a number of Ferraris, wealthy industrialist Ferruccio Lamborghini was convinced that he could build a better super-car. He pursued his goal by recruiting some of the best design and engineering talent for his fledgling concern, names such as Giotto Bizzarrini, Giampaolo Dallara, Franco Scaglione, Touring of Milan and Bertone. His first car, the 350 GT of 1964, certainly looked the part and was powered by a magnificent V12, but it was the launch of the staggering Miura at the 1966 Geneva Motor Show that many commentators count as the motoring sensation of the decade. When the Miura's lease of life came to an end, the brutal-looking Countach debuted in 1974 and carried the company's standard as the flagship model to the end of the 1980s. By then, Ferruccio Lamborghini had long since lost interest and the company had passed through several changes of ownership.

1965 Lamborghini 350 GT, 3464cc, V12, very good mechanical condition, original headlamps replaced by 400 GT units.
£26,000–30,000   *COYS*

The V12 engine of the first Lamborghini was the work of Bizzarrini, designer of the legendary Ferrari 250 GTO. Essentially, he reworked his design for a Ferrari F1 engine, enlarging it to 3500cc. The first dyno run released 370bhp at 9,000rpm, and the fledgling company was under way. A body was designed by Franco Scaglione, famous for the BAT designs on Alfa Romeo 1900 chassis in the 1950s, and the new car was displayed at the 1963 Turin Salon. However, it met with a lukewarm reception, for the styling was too controversial, so Carrozzeria Touring was called in to clean it up. The resultant car went into production as the 350 GT. In the interests of usability and longevity, the engine was detuned to give 280bhp at 7,000rpm, sufficient to provide a claimed top speed of 165mph. It was a triumph of design, with only 131 examples built.

1971 Lamborghini Espada Series II Coupé, coachwork by Bertone, finished in Champagne with black leather upholstery, well maintained from new, engine overhauled, resprayed, partially reupholstered, new windscreen, light lenses, seat belts and clutch.
£10,500–13,000   *BKS*

Five years after introducing its first car, Lamborghini upstaged Ferrari again by announcing a full four-seater, the Espada. With similar styling to the Marzal show car, the four-cam, V12-powered Espada boasted 325bhp, sufficient for 150+mph. Introduced in January 1970, the Series II came with an extra 25bhp and an improved dashboard.

l. **1971 Lamborghini Jarama,** 3929cc, V12, 350bhp at 7,500rpm, completely restored, 2,240km covered since.
£11,000–13,000   *Pou*

Only 177 examples of this car were built between 1970 and 1972.

LAMBORGHINI Model	ENGINE cc/cyl	DATES	CONDITION 1	2	3
350 GT fhc	3500/12	1964-67	£70,000	£45,000	£25,000
400 GT	4000/12	1966-68	£55,000	£40,000	£28,000
Miura LP400	4000/12	1966-69	£60,000	£50,000	£30,000
Miura S	4000/12	1969-71	£75,000	£60,000+	£40,000
Miura SV	4000/12	1971-72	£90,000+	£75,000	£60,000
Espada	4000/12	1969-78	£18,000	£14,000	£10,000
Jarama	4000/12	1970-78	£22,000	£15,000	£13,000
Urraco	2500/8	1972-76	£18,000	£11,000	£8,000
Countach	4000/12	1974-82	£60,000+	£40,000	£30,000

Countach limited editions are sought after as well as Miura SV.

1968 Lamborghini P400 Miura GT Berlinetta, 3929cc, V12, 4 valves per cylinder, 6 twin-choke Weber carburettors, 350/400bhp at 7,000rpm, left-hand drive, red with black leather and cloth interior, £11,397 spent in 1994 on engine top-end overhaul and other mechanical work, good oil pressure, good brakes, body showing slight signs of age.
£59,000–66,000 *C*

When it appeared as a prototype late in 1965, Lamborghini's P400 Miura coupé – named after a famous strain of fighting bulls – was the first production sports car with a mid-mounted 12 cylinder engine. It was a major sensation at that year's Turin show. The fabulous 350bhp, four-camshaft V12 was installed transversely behind the two occupants in a rigid sheet-steel chassis equipped with racing-style suspension. Clad by one of the most elegantly aggressive Berlinetta bodies ever to emerge from the workshops of the brilliant Nuccio Bertone, the Miura brought contemporary F1 design to the autostrada, a top speed of 180mph being suggested.

1972 Lamborghini Miura SV, 3929cc, V12, excellent original condition, 25,000km recorded.
£82,000–90,000 *COYS*

A natural process of evolution and improvement was maintained throughout the life of the Miura, the ultimate model, the SV, appearing at the 1971 Geneva Motor Show. Among its improvements were a stiffer chassis, redesigned rear suspension with a wider track, and wider tyres, all of which considerably improved roadholding and handling. Furthermore, the engine was uprated to produce an impressive 385bhp at 7,850rpm.

Lamborghini Miura (1966–72)

Engine: 3929cc, transverse-mounted V12, four overhead camshafts, 24 valves, four triple-choke Weber carburettors.
Power output: 350–385bhp.
Transmission: Five-speed manual.
Brakes: Four-wheel ventilated discs.
Top speed: 165–175+mph.
0–60mph: 6–6.7 seconds.
Production: 763 (some say 764).

1982 Lamborghini Countach 5000S Berlinetta, museum stored until 1991, 6,000km recorded, as new condition.
£38,000–43,000 *BKS*

The Countach was styled by Bertone's Marcello Gandini and retained Lamborghini's well-tried four-cam V12, this time installed longitudinally. To achieve the optimum weight distribution, the car's designer, Paulo Stanzani, placed the five-speed gearbox ahead of the engine, between the seats. The 375bhp aerodynamically efficient Countach could attain 170mph, but its failure to meet US emissions standards denied it the biggest potential market until the arrival of the LP500 in 1982.

LANCHESTER

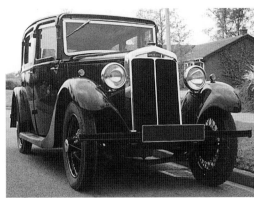

1933 Lanchester LA10 Tickford Drophead Coupé, coachwork by Salmons & Sons, finished in Fiord Blue with black wings, grey leather and Rexine upholstery, radiator and springs rebuilt, wiring in need of work, requires cosmetic attention, 6,000 miles covered in past 24 years, generally sound.
£2,900–3,400 *BKS*

1933 Lanchester LA10 Six Light Saloon, 1150cc, 4 cylinders, 4-speed pre-selector gearbox, reconditioned engine, black paint, green upholstery, wood cappings to doors, restored.
£3,200–3,800 *H&H*

LANCIA

After beginning his working career as a book-keeper, Vincenzo Lancia went to work for Fiat, leaving to set up his own car company late in 1906. The company's reputation was truly established in the 1920s with the technically advanced unitary-construction Lambda, and enhanced further in the 1930s with the splendidly packaged and very modern Aprilia. In the post-war era, the Aurelia fixed-head coupés have often been heralded as the first of the modern GTs. In the 1960s, the company made a brave attempt to move towards the mass market, but was taken over by Fiat in 1969.

1957 Lancia Aurelia B20 GT 6th Series Two-Door Coupé, coachwork by Pininfarina, floor-mounted gearchange, bonnet air intake, restored, engine rebuilt, good condition throughout.
£17,000–20,000 *BKS*

A year after launching its revolutionary V6-engined Aurelia saloon in 1950, Lancia followed with the Pinin Farina-styled B20 GT Coupé, which combined sports car performance with saloon car practicality. The car's competition potential was immediately obvious, and it achieved 19 major class victories in 1951 alone. The B20 GT Coupé was built in six series over seven years, the third, introduced in 1953, being the first to use the new 2451cc V6.

LANCIA Model	ENGINE cc/cyl	DATES	CONDITION 1	2	3
Theta	4940/4	1913-19	£24,000	£16,500	£8,000
Kappa	4940/4	1919-22	£24,000	£16,000	£8,000
Dikappa	4940/4	1921-22	£24,000	£16,000	£8,000
Trikappa	4590/4	1922-26	£25,000	£18,000	£10,000
Lambda	2120/4	1923-28	£40,000	£20,000	£12,000
Dilambda	3960/8	1928-32	£35,000	£16,000	£10,000
Astura	2604/8	1931-39	£30,000	£20,000	£10,000
Artena	1925/4	1931-36	£9,000	£5,000	£2,000
Augusta	1196/4	1933-36	£9,000	£4,000	£2,000
Aprilia 238	1352/4	1937-39	£10,000	£5,000	£3,000

Coachbuilt bodywork is more desirable and can upwardly affect prices.

1955 Lancia Aurelia B24 Spyder America, coachwork by Pinin
Farina, 118bhp, top speed 115mph, engine and floor-mounted
gearchange rebuilt, non-original cut-off switch in boot, Kenlowe fan
and temperature gauge under dashboard, completely restored,
6,000km covered since.
£42,000–48,000 *BKS*

*The Lancia Aurelia B24 Spyder derives from Vittorio Jano's Aurelia
saloon, which was the most advanced production car of its day, with
the world's first production V6 engine, a 4-speed synchromesh transaxle
and, by 1955, a De Dion rear axle. Pinin Farina not only designed the
sleek new body, but also built the whole car. It was made in two forms:
the Spyder America and the Convertible, which had quarter-lights and
wind-up windows. Total production of both (1955-58) was only 761
units, mainly because Pinin Farina was not geared up to make more.
They were the first left-hand drive Lancias to be built.*

1957 Lancia Aurelia B24S Convertible, 2451cc,
V6, 112bhp at 5,000rpm, 4-speed manual gearbox,
left-hand drive, restored, new paint and upholstery,
Wilton wool carpets and covers, tonneau, shoulder
harness/lap belts, new weatherstrips and seals,
original top, 32,000 recorded miles, excellent condition.
£49,000–54,000 *C*

1967 Lancia Fulvia Coupé, 1215cc, 4 cylinders,
80bhp, top speed 100mph, original factory
demonstrator, mechanically overhauled, original
toolkit, keys and spare tyre.
£2,400–3,000 *COYS*

*In 1963, Lancia introduced a new small car, the
Fulvia. It enjoyed many novel features, most obvious
of which was its narrow-angle V4 engine, with a
single cylinder head covering both banks of cylinders.
This drove the front wheels through a four-speed
gearbox. In 1965, a coupé version was introduced.*

Lancia Aurelia B20 GT Coupé and B24 Convertible and Spyder

Construction: Monocoque with pressed-steel
and box-section chassis.
Engine: 2451cc, overhead-valve aluminium
alloy V6.
Power output: 110–118bhp at 5,000rpm.
Transmission: Four-speed manual.
Suspension: Sliding pillar with beam axle
and coil springs at front; De Dion rear axle on
parallel leaf springs.
Brakes: Hydraulic, finned alloy drums,
inboard at rear.
Top speed: 112mph.
0–60mph: 14.3 seconds.

Beauty's more than skin deep on this lovely
Lancia, for underneath those lean Pininfarina
loins, the Aurelia's innards bristle with
technically dazzling and innovative
engineering. The compact free-revving alloy
V6, designed under Vittorio Jano (the man
responsible for the great racing Alfa Romeos of
the 1920s and 1930s), was the first mass-
produced V6; the clutch and gearbox are at the
back, housed in the transaxle, to endow the
Aurelia with near-perfect weight distribution.
The result: although the Aurelia was never the
most accelerative machine, its handling was so
impeccable that 40 years on, it still impresses
with its masterly cornering poise. All of these
innovations were mated with the Pininfarina
body in 1951 to produce the Aurelia B20 GT
Coupé, which is often credited as the first of
the new breed of modern post-war GTs. With
the B24 Convertible and Spyder, you got all
this and fresh air, too. Today, this rare and
charismatic roadster is the most prized of the
illustrious family.

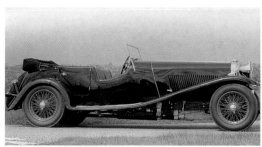

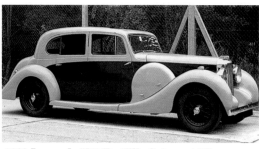

1935 Lagonda M45, 6 cylinders, 4453cc, black double-duck weather equipment, ground-up restoration costing £55,000, new ash frame, new panels, interior retrim, mechanical overhaul, pre-war Alvis gearbox with synchromesh, excellent condition.
£72,000–80,000 *COYS*

1939 Lagonda V12 De Ville Saloon, 4479cc, 12 cylinders, mechanical overhaul including engine, rewired, body rebuilt, repainted from bare metal, new upholstery and interior trim, very good condition throughout.
£16,000–20,000 *S*

In 1938, the prototype V12 model made history on the Brooklands concrete as the irst production saloon to cover 100 miles in one hour.

1954 Lagonda 3 Litre Drophead Coupé, coachwork by Tickford, leather upholstery, polished walnut fascia and garnish rail, resprayed, new carpets, radiator recored, restored, handbook, comprehensive file of workshop bills, very good condition.
£14,000–16,000 *S*

1968 Lamborghini 400GT 2+2, coachwork by Scaglione, 12 cylinders, 3939cc, 320hp at 6,500rpm, maximum speed 150+mph, recently resprayed, good condition.
£31,000–35,000 *Pou*

With its 150+mph performance, the Lamborghini 400GT aimed straight at Ferrari's heartland.

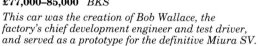

1971 Lamborghini Miura SV Prototype, coachwork by Bertone, chassis No. 4856, complete restoration costing £100,000, little used since, excellent condition throughout.
£77,000–85,000 *BKS*

This car was the creation of Bob Wallace, the factory's chief development engineer and test driver, and served as a prototype for the definitive Miura SV.

1969 Lamborghini Miura SV Jota, 3.9 litres, 418bhp at 8,800rpm, new engine fitted by the factory, original supplied, chrome racing-style mirrors on both wings, excellent restored condition.
£125,000–140,000 *S*

l. **1974 Lamborghini Countach LP400,** 3929cc, V12 engine, excellent condition.
£42,000–48,000 *EPP*

In 1974, when the Countach appeared, there really was nothing that approached its blend of brutal styling, 170+mph performance and near race-standard road holding.

r. **1952 Lancia Aurelia B20 GT 2nd Series,** coachwork by Pinin Farina, aluminium bonnet and boot, Nardi gearbox and tuning kit, original Landi exhaust system, restored, good condition.
£25,000–28,000 *BKS*

The Aurelia is a landmark car and today features in the 'All Time Top Ten' list. A production four-seater coupé that could finish 1-2-3 in the Targa Florio, and 2nd and 3rd in successive Mille Miglia, plus win its class at Le Mans is a little out of the ordinary.

l. **1957 Lancia Aurelia B24S Two-Door Convertible,** coachwork by Pininfarina, 2451cc, only moderate use since restoration in 1995, excellent condition.
£32,000--38,000 *BKS*

The B24 Spyder and convertible models were launched in 1955, differing only in the degree of weather protection offered.

r. **1967 Lancia Fulvia 1.3 Sport Two-Door Coupé,** coachwork by Zagato, 1298cc, 90bhp, 175km/h, ASI homologated in Italy, very original condition throughout.
£2,400–3,000 *BKS*

Arguably the most desirable of all the production Fulvias, the Zagato Sport was undeniably one of the most striking designs of its day.

1938 Lincoln K V12 Coupé, coachwork by Le Baron, 12 cylinders, 6785cc, 150bhp at 3,400rpm, 3-speed gearbox with freewheel and overdrive, excellent condition.
£47,500–55,000 *COYS*

l. **1961 Lotus Elite S2,** 1216cc Coventry-Climax PWE overhead-camshaft 4-cylinder engine, BMC 4-speed gearbox, 80bhp at 6,100rpm, excellent condition.
£22,500–27,500 *COYS*

1954 Maserati A6G/54 Zagato Coupé, coachwork by Zagato, 6 cylinders, 1986cc, double overhead-camshaft engine, 150bhp at 6,000rpm, triple choke sidedraught Weber carburettors, repainted with a central red stripe, very original example.
£160,000–180,000 *COYS*

Of the Maserati sports racing cars that took part in competition during the late 1940s/early 1950s, one of the most successful was the A6G/CS of 1947. A series of related A6G models, soon followed, this example being the seventh A6G/54 produced and the third built with Zagato coachwork.

1960 Maserati 3500GT Coupé,
coachwork by Touring, 6 cylinders,
3485cc, 220hp at 5,500rpm, 230km/h, disc
brakes all-round, excellent condition.
£16,500–18,000 *Pou*

1972 Maserati Ghibli Spyder Conversion,
8 cylinders, 4930cc, 355hp at 5,500rpm, converted
from fixed-head to convertible, excellent condition.
£18,000–22,000 *Pou*

*Only 125 original Ghibli Spyders were built
compared with 1,149 fixed-head coupés.*

l. **1935 Mercedes-Benz 500K
Cabriolet,** 4-seater coachwork by
Ferdinand Keible, Vienna, chassis
No. 113697, chassis, drive-train and
supercharger restored, panelling and
wood framing repaired, new hood,
carpets and leather trim, rewired,
excellent condition.
£145,000–165,000 *BKS*

r. **1956 Mercedes-Benz 300Sc
Roadster,** 6-cylinder in-line single-
overhead-camshaft engine, 2996cc,
175bhp at 5,400rpm, 4-speed manual
all-synchromesh gearbox, 1,000 miles
in past 17 years, Becker radio, tinted
sun visors, good condition.
£115,000–130,000 *C*

Only 53 roadsters were produced.

l. **1960 Mercedes-Benz 300SL Roadster,** 6-cylinder in-line engine, 2996cc, 4-speed manual gearbox, original engine, drum brakes, soft top only, excellent overall condition. **£100,000–115,000** *C*

Production of the 300SL began in 1954 in Gullwing coupé form only. In 1957, a roadster was finally offered as a companion model, and the Gullwing was soon phased out.

r. **1960 Mercedes-Benz 190SL Two-Door Roadster with Factory Hardtop,** 1897cc, twin Solex downdraught carburettors, 4-speed manual gearbox, 0–60mph in 13 seconds, front suspension and steering, restored, excellent condition. **£28,000–32,000** *BKS*

Announced early in 1954, the 190SL did not enter production until January 1955, owing to design alterations aimed at strengthening the saloon's shortened platform to compensate for the open-topped body's reduced stiffness.

l. **1967 Mercedes-Benz 250SL Coupé,** 6 cylinders, 2500cc, stripped to bare metal and resprayed, cylinder head, brakes and suspension rebuilt, extensive history file, good condition. **£13,000–16,000** *COYS*

The 250SL was introduced in 1966, and was an uprated version of the 230SL, fitted with a slightly bigger engine producing 150bhp.

r. **1971 Mercedes-Benz 280SE 3.5 Litre Cabriolet,** V8 engine, 200hp at 5,800rpm, electronic fuel injection, column-shift 4-speed automatic gearbox, hydraulic disc brakes all-round, repainted, original interior, bumpers rechromed, factory-installed air conditioning, very good condition. **£35,000–40,000** *C*

The performance of the 280SE is quite remarkable for a 4–5-seater car, with a 0–60mph time of under 10 seconds and a top speed of 125mph. Only 1,232 genuine convertibles were produced between 1969 and 1971.

l. **1973 Mercedes-Benz 600 Pullman Four-Door Saloon,** overhead-camshaft fuel-injected V8 engine, 6.3 litres, air suspension with variable ride control, 4-speed automatic transmission, all-round disc brakes, power-assisted steering, central locking, separate heating/ventilation systems for front and rear, hydraulically operated sunroof to rear, meticulously maintained. **£57,000–64,000** *BKS*

l. **1930 MG 18/100 MkIII Tigress Four-Seater Sports Tourer,** 2468cc, 6 cylinders, chassis No. 4B/0255, 96bhp at 4,300rpm, remote-control gearchange mechanism, redesigned crankshaft, pistons and camshaft, dry-sump lubrication, crossflow alloy cylinder head with twin sparking plugs per cylinder, excellent condition.
£115,000–130,000 *BKS*

Of all pre-war MGs, this Tigress model is the most powerful, and the most rare. From only five made only two survive intact, with the remains of two more in New Zealand.

r. **1933 MG J2,** cream interior, full chassis-up restoration, excellent condition.
£18,500–19,500 *BC*

This is an example of the desirable swept-wing model. Many consider the J2 the archetypal pre-war Midget. It gave at least 65mph for a cost of £199.10s.

l. **1934 MG PA Midget Two-Seater Sports,** 847cc, 4 cylinders, crossflow cylinder head, inwardly-inclined valves, oval combustion chambers, close-ratio top and 3rd gears, extra-low bottom gear, very good condition.
£11,500–13,500 *BKS*

Launched in March 1934 to replace the J-Type Midget, this is one of the best-loved small sports cars of the early 1930s. Some 2,000 examples were built during its two-year production span.

r. **1949 MG TC,** 4 cylinders, 1250cc, complete professional restoration, excellent condition.
£13,000–15,000 *COYS*

The TC, while being fundamentally the same as the TA, incorporated myriad detail changes, including a more flexible and powerful engine. It was popular with American servicemen, which led to an increase in sports car racing in the USA.

1950 MG TD MkI, fully restored.
£15,000–16,000 *SJR*
The TD continued the progression of the T-Series Midgets, adding rack-and-pinion steering, more power from the 1250cc engine and coil-sprung independent front suspension.

1955 MG TF, 1500cc, rebuilt, excellent condition.
£21,000–23,000 *SJR*
The TF is immediately distinguishable from its predecessors by the headlights, which are cowled into the wings.

l. **1953 MG TD Roadster,** 4-cylinder overhead-valve engine, 1250cc, 45bhp at 5,500rpm, 4-speed manual gearbox, fewer than 500 miles since complete restoration, left-hand drive. **£14,500–16,500** *C*

Almost 30,000 Midgets were built between 1950 and 1953, and the vast majority were exported. Unlike the TC, which was only available in right-hand drive form, the TD was available in left-hand drive. It was successful because it had classic good looks, good performance, drove well and handled smartly.

r. **1954 MG TF,** 1250cc, 4 cylinders, good mechanical condition, new brown leather interior, fully serviceable sidescreens and brown vynide hood, detailed record of work carried out, excellent condition. **£12,750–14,500** *BRIT*

Production of the TF ran to just 9,600 between 1953 and 1955, most going for export. It had a somewhat cool reception at its launch, as the styling was seen to be far too old fashioned in the face of sleek newcomers such as the Austin Healey 100 and Triumph TR2.

1958 MGA 1500 MkI Roadster, complete body-off restoration, leather retrimmed, full history, good condition. **£10,000–11,000** *Mot*

1960 MGA Twin Cam Roadster, 108bhp, top speed in excess of 110mph, disc brakes all-round, centre-lock wire wheels, restored, very good condition. **£14,500–16,500** *BKS*

1966 MGB Roadster, wire wheels, overdrive, completely rebuilt in 1991, 4,000 miles since, good condition. **£6,000–6,500** *Mot*

1958 MGA Roadster, 1500cc, restored, good condition. **£10,000–11,000** *SJR*

By the time the MGA ceased production in 1962, 100,000 examples had left the Abingdon factory.

1965 MGB Roadster, 1798cc, 4 cylinders, 4-speed
manual gearbox with overdrive, 48,071 recorded
miles, excellent original condition.
£8,500–9,000   *H&H*

1968 MGB Roadster, wire wheels,
overdrive, extensively restored.
£7,250–7,750   *UMC*

1969 MGC Roadster, 3 litres, 6 cylinders,
Downton engine conversion, torsion-bar
front suspension, rack-and-pinion steering
with 16in spring-spoked steering wheel,
very good condition.
£8,750–9,500   *BKS*

*Output of the MGC was far more modest
than that of the MGB, with fewer than
10,000 units completed. In its day, the
MGC was regarded as a replacement for
the Austin-Healey 3000 sports car.*

1970 MGB Roadster, completely restored,
excellent condition.
£10,500–11,000   *SJR*

1971 MGB Roadster, overdrive, Minilite wheels,
restored, excellent condition throughout.
£5,800–6,500   *PA*

1972 MG Midget, 1275cc, 4 cylinders,
4-speed manual gearbox, black interior,
hardtop, roll-over bar, very good condition.
£2,000–2,400   *H&H*

1974 MG Midget, 1275cc, completely restored,
very good condition.
£5,500–6,500   *SJR*

l. **1979 MGB GT,** new front
wings, resprayed, restored
new rear tyres, brakes,
callipers and carpets,
reconditioned engine,
new clutch and exhaust, new
chrome trims, overdrive switch
and wiring loom, history file,
excellent original condition.
£2,750–3,250   *H&H*

1973 MGB GT, 1798cc,
4 cylinders, 4-speed manual
gearbox with overdrive, fully
restored, good condition.
£3,000–3,500   *H&H*

r. **1963 Porsche 356B Two-Door Coupé,** coachwork by Reutter, air-cooled rear-mounted horizontally-opposed 4 cylinder overhead-valve engine, 1966cc, good mechanical condition, restored, new shock absorbers, tyres and clutch, engine overhauled, very good condition.
£10,000–12,000 *BKS*

For many, the 356 is the archetypal Porsche, representative of the first production series built at Stuttgart from 1950.

1955 Porsche 356A Super Spezial, coachwork by Laudari, 1582cc, 75bhp, 468 recorded miles from new, museum-stored in Florida for 40 years, original in every detail, mint condition throughout.
£14,000–17,000 *BKS*

Porsche 356

The Porsche 356 is so named because it was the 356th design from the Porsche design studio. Production started in 1948, and the model endured until 1965, when it was replaced by the immortal 911, which still owed much to the original 356 design and concept.

1973 Porsche 911 RS, 6 cylinders, 2687cc, 210hp at 6,300rpm, good condition.
£23,000–26,000 *Pou*

1963 Porsche 356C Cabriolet, air-cooled flat 4 overhead-valve engine, 4-speed gearbox, overhauled in 1994 including new starter and brakes, under 3,750 recorded miles, excellent condition.
£30,000–35,000 *S*

1972 Porsche 911E, 6 cylinders, 2200cc, ground-up restoration, 10 coats of paint, black hide upholstery, concours condition.
£12,000–14,000 *COYS*

1994 Porsche 911RS Lightweight, 3.8 litres, 12,000 recorded miles, leather interior, full service history, original condition.
£65,000–75,000 *DEV*

1990 Porsche 959, 6 cylinders, 2849cc, 450hp at 6,500rpm, 22,300km recorded, excellent condition.
£140,000–160,000 *Pou*

1913 Renault Type DG 12CV Open Drive Town Car, coachwork by Brewster, chassis No. 43446, engine No. 51789, Majestic headlamps, Powell & Hanmer oil sidelights, patent leather wings, button-quilted black leather driver's seat, fawn cloth interior trim with foldaway occasional seats.
£30,000–35,000 *BKS*

1954 Riley RME, 1½ litres, 3 owners, good history, very good condition.
£5,000–5,500 *UMC*

The 1½ litre RM Rileys were good for 75mph. The 2½ litre RMS nudged 95mph.

r. **1954 Riley RME,** 1½ litres, full history, very good condition.
£4,400–4,600 *UMC*

RM Rileys were designated RMA to RMF. The RMA and RME were 1½ litre models, while RMB, C, D and F were 2½ litre cars. Rarest are the RMC three-abreast roadster and RMD four-seater drophead.

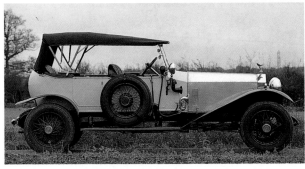

l. **1920 Rolls-Royce 40/50 Silver Ghost Alpine Eagle Four-Seater Sports Torpedo by Kellner, Paris,** chassis No. 32AE, engine No. 129, light alloy body, nickeled brightwork, 1,000 miles since restoration in 1989, excellent condition.
£85,000–100,000 *BKS*

When the Germans occupied France, the original owner of this car ordered the tyres to be removed and burnt to prevent the Germans from requisitioning it when they occupied his château. The ruse worked, and the car survived the war.

1925 Rolls-Royce 40/50 Silver Ghost Springfield, 7428cc, 85hp at 2,250rpm, fully restored, excellent condition.
£120,000–130,000 *Pou*

From 1907 until 1925, when the New Phantom was introduced, the Rolls-Royce 40/50 Silver Ghost was the only car offered by the company.

l. **1926 Rolls-Royce Silver Ghost Stratford Drophead Coupé,** coachwork by Brewster, chassis No. S348RL, engine No. 22485, 6 cylinders, 7428cc, 65bhp at 1,250rpm, 3-speed manual gearbox, 6,000 miles covered since 1978, restored, modified with 4-wheel brakes and overdrive, excellent condition.
£75,000–85,000 *C*

The Stratford Convertible Coupé body style on this car is rare – only seven were produced and it is thought that only two exist. This is one of the last examples built. It won several significant awards during the late 1950s and throughout the 1960s.

1927 Rolls-Royce Phantom I Brougham de Ville, coachwork by Henri Binder, chassis No. 61RF, engine No. FV15, veneered marquetry interior, meticulously restored, excellent condition.
£70,000–80,000 *S*

l. **1929 Rolls-Royce Phantom II Pullman Limousine de Ville,** coachwork by Barker, chassis No. 16WJ, engine No. X185, black leather interior to front, fawn cloth to rear, blinds all-round, 2 occasional seats, Lucas headlights, Brooks trunk at rear, original undertrays, good condition.
£44,000–50,000 *S*

This car dates from the first year of Phantom II production, and was the 16th production chassis constructed.

r. **1933 Rolls-Royce Phantom II Formal Town Car,** coachwork by Brewster, chassis No. 218AMS, engine No. U45J, aluminium and wood-veneered dashboard, original upholstery, gold handles, vanity cases and indirect lighting inside, German silver fittings to chauffeur's compartment, original lambswool carpet, covers for chauffeur's area, excellent condition.
£250,000+ *S*

l. **1948 Rolls-Royce Silver Wraith Four-Light Sports Saloon,** coachwork by Park Ward, chassis No. WAB45, engine No. W109B, 6 cylinder in-line overhead-inlet engine, side exhaust valves, 4257cc, dual-choke Stromberg carburettor, 4-speed manual gearbox with synchromesh, sliding sunroof, radio, full service history, excellent condition throughout.
£23,000–26,000 *C*

r. **1949 Rolls-Royce Silver Wraith Limousine,** by H. J. Mulliner, chassis No. LWFC65, tan leather interior front and rear, P100 headlamps, new exhaust system, left-hand drive, good overall condition.
£26,000–28,500 *RCC*

This car was the first left-hand drive Rolls-Royce manufactured in Crewe.

l. **1962 Rolls-Royce Long Wheelbase Silver Cloud II with Division,** coachwork by Rolls-Royce with Radford conversions, chassis No. LLCD224, V8 engine, 6230cc, twin SU carburettors, 4-speed automatic gearbox, rear compartment console/cowl with speedometer and other gauges, 2 writing desks with crystal glassware and sterling silver decanters, air conditioning, burr walnut dashboard, excellent condition throughout.
£43,000–50,000 *C*

1964 Rolls-Royce Phantom V Sedanca, coachwork by James Young, chassis No. 5VD25, electric division, occasional seats, footrests, twin rear reading lamps, drinks cabinet, vanity set, stereo, TV and video system with remote control, air conditioning, new wiring and stainless steel exhaust system, correct jack and tools, extensively restored to highest standards, concours condition.
£97,500–112,500 *S*

Announced in 1959, the Phantom V attracted buyers such as the British Royal family.

1966 Rolls-Royce Silver Cloud III Saloon,
chassis No. LSJR391, V8 pushrod-operated
overhead-valve engine, 6230cc, 4-speed
automatic gearbox, restored, bare metal respray,
retrimmed, sliding metal sunroof, modern air
conditioning, very good condition.
£36,000–40,000 *C*

*The Rolls-Royce Silver Cloud III was the last
of its series and, indeed, the last production
Rolls-Royce to retain a conventional chassis.*

1971 Rolls-Royce Phantom VI Limousine, coachwork
by H. J. Mulliner Park Ward, dual air conditioning,
electric division and windows, cocktail cabinet,
occasional seats, excellent condition throughout.
£42,500–47,500 *S*

1976 Rolls-Royce Silver Shadow,
V8 overhead-valve engine, 6750cc,
220bhp, 3-speed automatic gearbox,
20,000 recorded miles, full service history,
slight damage to one wing, cream leather
interior, excellent condition.
£35,000–40,000 *C*

*This car was given by Frank Sinatra to
his wife Barbara as a wedding present.
The colour is said to be the same blue as
her eyes.*

1986 Rolls-Royce Hooper Silver Wing Landaulette,
one owner until 1996, owner's manual, service book and
papers, excellent condition.
£29,000–34,000 *S*

1979 Rolls-Royce Silver Shadow II,
80,000 miles recorded, full service history,
excellent condition.
£10,000–12,000 *VIC*

1975 Rolls-Royce Corniche Convertible,
coachwork by H. J. Mulliner, alloy doors, boot
lid and bonnet, resprayed, beige hide interior
and trim, full tool kit, restoration bills
totalling over £40,000, burr walnut dashboard
and window trims, excellent condition.
£28,000–33,000 *S*

1985 Rolls-Royce Hooper Emperor Sports Saloon,
coachwork by Hooper, electric sunroof, upholstered in
burgundy leather to the front and burgundy velvet to the
rear, 2 handmade cabinets with 2 crystal decanters and
glasses, excellent condition throughout.
£17,500–20,000 *S*

This is the only Emperor sports saloon made by Hooper.

1975 Rolls-Royce Corniche Coupé,
6750cc, automatic transmission, resprayed,
very good condition.
£7,500–8,500 *H&H*

r. **1961 Rover 100 P4,** 2625cc, 6 cylinders, original tool kit, very good condition. **£5,000–5,500** *BC*

The P4's styling was initially considered controversial when launched in 1950 with an additional 'cyclops' front headlamp. Over the years, traditional Rover buyers came to love the P4 as the design mellowed, and the car that many affectionately call 'the Auntie Rover' soldiered on until 1964.

l. **1936 Singer Nine Four-Seater Sports,** 972cc, 4 cylinders, headlamp stone guards, twin Lucas 'Altette' horns on badge bar, period spot lamps, black weather equipment, hood, sidescreens and biscuit interior trim in excellent condition, completely rebuilt, very good condition throughout. **£9,350–10,000** *BRIT*

This car has won concours awards at Singer Owners' Club and other local events.

r. **1962 Studebaker Hawk Six Gran Turismo,** 6 cylinder overhead valve engine, 3-speed manual gearbox with column-mounted gearshift, white leather upholstery and off-white carpets, left-hand drive, excellent condition. **£3,750–4,500** *S*

Studebaker merged with Packard in 1954, one outcome being the Hawk coupé, powered by Packard's V8 engine.

1965 Sunbeam Tiger Harrington Sports Coupé, Webasto sunroof, alloy wheels, new gearbox, rear hatch, occasional seats, good condition. **£4,000–5,000** *BKS*

1955 Swallow Doretti, coachwork by Panelcraft, resprayed, requires slight attention. **£6,750–7,750** *BKS*

1968 Rover 3.5 Litre Coupé, light alloy V8 power unit, top speed 110mph, 39,366 recorded miles, Hydrosteer variable-ratio power steering, 3-speed Borg-Warner automatic transmission, leatherwork recoloured, very good condition. **£3,700–4,500** *BKS*

l. **1949 Talbot Lago Record T26 Sport,** chassis No. 100392, engine No. 26383, 4482cc, Wilson pre-selector transmission, re-upholstered, sunroof, sun visors, pull-down blind, Jaeger instruments, 64,000km, good all-round condition. **£20,000–23,000** *S*

1949 Triumph 2000 Roadster, 2088cc, all-synchromesh gearbox with column-lever change, one owner from new, original purchase receipt and all bills, notebooks detailing journeys travelled, mileage and maintenance, very good condition.
£15,500–17,000 *S*

r. **1963 Triumph TR3 Two-Door Roadster,** 1991cc, 4 cylinder wet-liner engine, larger-bore SU carburettors, 14,000km since restoration, left-hand drive, excellent condition.
£9,000–11,000 *BKS*

1971 Triumph Stag, 8 cylinders, 2997cc, black trim, new black canvas hood, extensive service history, original handbook, garaged and kept under covers, excellent condition.
£6,500–7,000 *BRIT*

This Stag has won a number of concours awards.

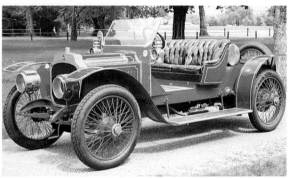

1973 Triumph TR6, 125bhp, excellent condition.
£9,500–10,000 *BLE*

1912 Vauxhall A-Type 20hp Two-Seater, 4 cylinders, 18hp, sidevalve engine, restored, well equipped with period accessories, excellent condition.
£17,000–20,000 *BKS*

This car has been campaigned in VSCC events, making respectable ascents at Prescott, and is well prepared for active Edwardian motoring.

1981 Triumph TR8 Convertible, 3628cc, V8 engine, excellent condition.
£4,500–5,000 *EPP*

1975 Triumph Stag, 2997cc, V8 engine, very good condition.
£6,500–7,000 *EPP*
25,877 Triumph Stags were produced from 1970 to 1977.

1949 Triumph 1800 Saloon, 1776cc, 4 cylinders, excellent original condition.
£6,000–7,000 *UMC*
The 1800 Saloon was the first Triumph produced after Standard took control of the company.

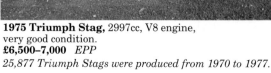

1936 Bentley Park Ward Saloon,
3½ litres, in 'as found' condition.
£8,000–8,500 *DB*

1929 Austin Heavy 12/4 Saloon, largely
original, dry-stored in barn for 30 years,
manual and log book, spares.
£4,750–5,500 *S*

1933 Austin 7 Saloon, to Longbridge
specification, dry-stored since 1981, interior
retrimmed, engine rebuilt some time ago.
£1,000–1,200 *S*

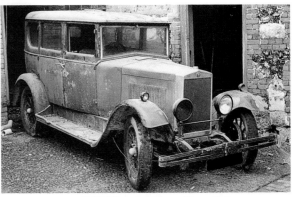

1929 Morris 6 Four-Door Saloon,
2468cc, 6 cylinder overhead-camshaft
engine, 17.7hp, spare engine partly
restored, quantity of spares including
exhaust manifold, dash panel, interior
light, speedometer, 2 Auto-Vacs, log book.
£2,900–3,400 *BKS*

1932 Crossley Four-Door Saloon, 125in-wheelbase
chassis, right-hand change 4-speed gearbox, 20.9hp,
partially disassembled for restoration, many parts.
£2,300–2,700 *BKS*

1921 Ford Model T Tourer, basically
complete, requires total restoration.
£3,500–4,000 *S*

**1968 Ferrari 330GT Series II 2+2
Two-Door Berlina,** coachwork by
Pininfarina, overhauled engine and
gearbox, blue leather interior.
£9,000–11,500 *BKS*

r. **1938 Ford 7W Shooting Brake,**
coachwork by Southgates, Fakenham,
substantially original condition.
£2,100–2,500 *S*
*This is believed to be one of only
two examples surviving.*

1937 Renault 12hp Touring Saloon, 1463cc,
3-speed synchromesh gearbox, Solex downdraught
carburettors, barn discovery, original and complete,
interior in good condition, bodywork sound.
£4,200–4,800 *S*

1932 Morris Major Saloon, 6 cylinder
engine, requires total restoration.
£1,200–1,500 *DB*

l. **1931 Rolls-Royce 20/25 Two-Door Coupé,**
chassis No. GNS 51, later body, stripped,
engine runs very well, correct early
instruments and radiator, excellent potential
for rebodying.
£9,000–9,750 *RCC*

r. **1928 Rolls-Royce Phantom I Saloon,**
chassis No. S408FL, later steel saloon body
probably by Inskip, largely complete,
engine runs well, stored for many years,
left-hand drive.
£12,000–12,500 *RCC*

l. **1927 Rolls-Royce 40/50
Rolling Chassis,** chassis No.
109NC, engine No. OJ55, believed
complete and in good order,
engine, transmission, and
electrical equipment sound,
original overall condition.
£11,500–14,000 *S*

1936 Rover 10 Shooting Brake,
1389cc, 4 cylinders, believed to have
been orderd in chassis form and
bodied with this coachwork, some
work already carried out, off the road
for some years, sound condition.
£2,000–2,500 *BRIT*

r. **1934 Talbot AX65 Light
Saloon,** coachwork by
Darracq, stored since 1962,
in-line 6 cylinder engine,
original handbook and
Wilson pre-selector self-
changing manual gearbox,
rear axle jacks, fitted front
jacking system, very original
unrestored condition.
£4,650–5,250 *CGC*

*This example is one of
2,080 cars made of this
particular model.*

l. **1968 Lancia Fulvia Sport Coupé,** coachwork by Zagato, 1298cc, V4, 4-speed manual gearbox, right-hand drive, excellent condition.
£4,750–5,250 *BKS*

Introduced in 1967 with a 1298cc, 87bhp engine, the Zagato was later offered with the 1.6 litre, 114bhp HF unit. Production ceased in 1972 after Zagato had manufactured around 7,000 cars.

1969 Lancia Fulvia 1.3 Sport Coupé, coachwork by Zagato, 1298cc, V4, restored, good condition throughout.
£2,600–2,800 *BKS*

Lancia Beta Monte Carlo

The Lancia Beta Monte Carlo was an automotive may-be, so right in concept, sadly lacking in execution. The concept was pure Fiat: a mid-engined enlargement of the X1/9. In fact, it was even going to be called the X1/20. A chunky, tough-looking car with plenty of attitude, it looked faster than it was, offering a top speed of only 120mph or so. The first series cars also had servo-assisted brakes, but only on the front, and that spelled heart-stopping front lock-up in the wet. The Monte Carlo was suspended from 1978, but came back in 1980 as a revised and improved model with better braking. And it's these models that fetch a premium. Sadly, there aren't many to be found – some say as few as 200 in the UK.

1982 Lancia Beta 2000 HPE, 1995cc, 4 cylinders, optional automatic transmission, stored for past 7 years, 1,000 miles since 1987, good condition.
£2,200–2,600 *BRIT*

The Beta HPE (High Performance Estate) offered an excellent combination of Lancia's sporting heritage with the practicality of a hatchback.

1982 Lancia Beta Monte Carlo.
£6,500–7,000 *EPP*
The Monte Carlo was suspended in 1978 but re-introduced with improvements in 1982. These later models command a premium.

> **Miller's is a price GUIDE
> not a price LIST**

1989 Lancia Integrale Four-Door Saloon,
4-wheel drive, 5-speed manual gearbox, power steering, air conditioning, regularly maintained, 74,985km recorded.
£6,400–7,000 *BKS*

With the Integrale model, Lancia of Turin underlined their reputation for high performance and sophisticated design.

Miller's
Starter Marque

Starter Lancias: *Beta Coupé and Spyder, Beta HPE, 1972–84.*

- There are lots of lovely Lancias, and many models are affordable. However, some only came to the UK in small numbers, and this relative rarity makes them harder to keep on the road than more populous late-era classics. In other cases, their innovative engineering, which is one of their joys, can also stretch the resources and patience of a DIY enthusiast.

- A good all-round introduction to classic Lancia ownership is the lively Lancia Beta Coupé, Spyder or HPE – the high-performance estate. For a start, they've had less time to rust than older models, and unfortunately that's an important consideration with many Lancias. The Beta saloon, introduced in 1972, was the first 'Fiat-Lancia', and one of its chief virtues was the Fiat-derived double-overhead-camshaft engine, which had proved so successful in the Fiat 124. Over the model's life, customers were offered a choice that ran from 1300cc to 2000cc, and all of them, even when inserted in the humblest saloon, were good for a genuine 100+mph.

LANCIA Model	ENGINE cc/cyl	DATES	CONDITION 1	2	3
Aprilia 438	1486/4	1939-50	£11,000	£6,000	£3,000
Ardea	903/4	1939-53	£10,000	£5,000	£3,000
Aurelia B10	1754/6	1950-53	£9,000	£6,000	£3,000
Aurelia B15-20-22	1991/6	1951-53	£15,000	£10,000	£8,000
Aurelia B24-B24S	2451/6	1955-58	£35,000+	£17,000	£12,000
Aurelia GT	2451/6	1953-59	£18,000	£11,000	£9,000
Appia C10-C105	1090/4	1953-62	£6,000	£3,000	£2,000
Aurelia Ser II/IV	2266/6	1954-59	£11,000	£6,000	£4,000
Flaminia Zagato	2458/6	1957-63	£18,000	£10,000	£7,000
Flaminia Ser	2458/6	1957-63	£15,000	£10,000	£5,000
Flavia 1500	1500/4	1960-75	£6,000	£4,000	£2,000
Fulvia	1091/4	1963-70	£3,000	£2,000	£1,000
Fulvia S	1216/4	1964-70	£5,000	£4,000	£1,500
Fulvia 1.3	1298/4	1967-75	£6,000	£4,000	£2,000
Stratos	2418/6	1969-71	£45,000	£20,000	£10,000
Flavia 2000	1991/6	1969-75	£3,000	£2,000	£1,000
Fulvia HF/1.6	1584/4	1969-75	£7,000	£4,000	£2,000
Beta HPE	1585/4	1976-82	£3,000	£1,500	£500
Beta Spyder	1995/4	1977-82	£4,000	£1,500	£800
Monte Carlo	1995/4	1976-81	£6,000	£3,000	£1,000
Gamma Coupé	2484/4	1977-84	£2,500	£1,500	£500
Gamma Berlina	2484/4	1977-84	£2,500	£1,200	£300

Competition history and convertible coachwork could cause prices to vary.

LAND ROVER

1956 Land Rover Series 1 Station Wagon, 1198cc, 4 cylinders, 4-speed gearbox, good original condition. **£2,200–2,600** *H&H*

1949 Land Rover Series 1, original specification, small headlamps behind full grille, narrow front springs, flat-topped hood-sticks, rear D-lamps, 'ring-pull' type free-wheel mechanism to gearbox, deep bronze green, very good condition. **£5,200–6,000** *S*

Maurice Wilks, technical director of Rover, conceived the idea of a 'go-anywhere' vehicle that became known as the Land Rover. He had acquired two war-surplus Jeeps and, clearly impressed by their performance, proceeded to exploit the potential of an all-purpose design. The original Land Rover prototype was essentially a Jeep equipped with a Rover gearbox and powered by the Rover 60's four cylinder engine.

LAND ROVER Model	ENGINE cc/cyl	DATES	CONDITION		
			1	2	3
Ser 1	1595/4	1948-51	£6,000	£3,000	£1,500
Ser 1	1995/4	1951-53	£4,500	£2,500	£1,000
Ser 1	1995/4	1953-58	£4,000	£2,000	£500
Ser 1	1995/4	1953-58	£3,000	£1,800	£800
Ser 2	1995/4	1958-59	£2,000	£950	£500
Ser 2	1995/4	1958-59	£2,800	£1,200	£500
Ser 2	2286/4	1959-71	£2,000	£950	£500
Ser 2	2286/4	1959-71	£2,500	£1,200	£500
Range Rover	3528/V8	1970-	£5,000	£1,200	£600

Series 1 Land Rovers are very sought after.

LEA-FRANCIS

In 1895, Richard Henry Lea and Graham Ingoldsby Francis formed a partnership to make bicycles. In 1904, they produced a car design, but it was 1920 before production really got going. During the vintage era, they produced some fine small sports cars. After financial setbacks, a new company produced a range of more modern sporting cars in 1937, and these provided the basis of machines built until 1952. A revival was attempted in 1960 with the unhappy-looking Lynx, but only three prototypes were made.

l. **1948 Lea-Francis Two-Seater Sports,** rebodied original Lea-Francis chassis, running gear and 1767cc engine, finished in cream with tan hide interior, very good condition throughout. **£12,000–14,000** *H&H*

This car was sold in the USA a few years ago for £45,000.

LEA-FRANCIS Model	ENGINE cc/cyl	DATES	CONDITION		
			1	2	3
12hp	1944/4	1923-24	£10,000	£5,000	£3,000
14hp	2297/4	1923-24	£10,000	£5,000	£3,000
9hp	1074/4	1923-24	£7,000	£4,000	£2,000
10hp	1247/4	1947-54	£10,000	£5,500	£3,000
12hp	1496/4	1926-34	£12,000	£6,000	£4,000
Various 6 cylinder models	1696/6	1927-29	£13,500	£9,500	£5,000
Various 6 cylinder models	1991/6	1928-36	£10,500	£8,750	£5,000
14hp	1767/4	1946-54	£7,000	£4,000	£2,000
1.5 litre	1499/4	1949-51	£11,000	£6,000	£3,000
2.5 litre	2496/4	1950-52	£14,000	£8,000	£4,000

LINCOLN

In 1917, Henry Leland left Cadillac to form his own company, which he named after his long-time hero, Abraham Lincoln. The early Lincoln cars had sidevalve V8 engines and boasted pressure lubrication. Their smoothness and reliability is legendary. However, despite their excellence, the company ran into financial troubles early on, but was rescued by Henry Ford in 1922. Ford developed the V8 formula further, while the quality and design of the coachwork received much needed attention. The elegant styling of the later Lincolns is rated highly among American classics, being closely associated with US presidential transport.

1931 Lincoln Model K Seven-Seater Tourer, dual-cowl design, quarter-round roll-up windows, dual side-mounted spares, beige livery, completely restored to correct original specification.
£37,000–42,000 *S*

Lincoln's famous greyhound mascot first appeared in 1929 and, in many ways, symbolised the new Model K, a low, sleek car launched for 1931. It adopted its predecessor's successful V8 engine, but had a larger bonnet and new peaked radiator shell, which gave the car a fresh appeal. Mechanical improvements included a Bendix Duo-Servo braking system, better shock absorbers and synchromesh on second and third gears.

1964 Lincoln Continental Convertible, V8, automatic transmission, radio, power seats and windows, power brakes and steering, electrically-operated hood, repainted in black, light tan leather interior trim, fawn carpets, original.
£22,000–26,000 *S*

President John F. Kennedy followed a tradition when he acquired a Continental in 1961 – Calvin Coolidge, F. D. Roosevelt and Harry S. Trueman had all owned Lincoln cars. The 1961 Lincoln Continental retained the same basic styling until 1969.

1988 Lincoln-Continental Town Car Four-Door Limousine, 5 litre, fuel-injected V8, automatic transmission, power-assisted steering, left-hand drive, 64in stretch, air conditioning, stereo system, cocktail cabinet, TV, glass division and roof panel, 60,000 recorded miles.
£4,600–6,000 *BKS*

LINCOLN Model	ENGINE cu in/cyl	DATES	CONDITION 1	2	3
Première Coupé	368/8	1956-57	£6,000	£4,000	£2,000
Première Convertible	368/8	1956-57	£14,000	£8,000	£5,000
Continental Mk II	368/8	1956-57	£10,000	£6,000	£4,000
Continental 2 door	430/8	1958-60	£6,000	£4,000	£2,000
Continental Convertible	430/8	1958-60	£18,000	£10,000	£7,000

LIVER

l. **1900 Liver 3½hp Phæton,** 1045cc, Benz horizontal single-cylinder engine, 2-speed belt transmission, 'Crypto' extra low gear, final drive by side chains, foot-operated rear hub brakes, handbrake 'spoon' acting on rear tyres, tiller steering, solid rubber tyres, good condition, needs small amount of recommissing.
£52,500–58,000 *C*

William Lea was the Benz agent for the Merseyside area of Britain at the turn of the century. In 1900, he decided to build a British version of the Benz, using the Benz engine.

LOCOMOBILE

One of the great early American car manufacturers, Locomobile, as the name suggests, began by producing steam cars in the pioneering days of motoring. By the end of the first decade of the 20th century, they had become renowned for building high-powered quality vehicles. Indeed, during the 1920s, their offerings were among the finest cars available in America. Unfortunately, as with many fine makes, production of Locomobiles succumbed to the stock market crash of 1929.

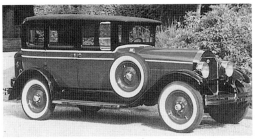

1928 Locomobile 8/70 Sedan, 3254cc, Lycoming straight 8 engine, restored, excellent condition. **£15,000–17,500** *BRIT*

LORRAINE-DIETRICH

r. **1912 Lorraine-Dietrich Type SLF Torpedo,** coachwork by G. Chesnot, 2116cc, 4 cylinders, acetylene headlamps, running board-mounted toolbox and spare tyres, body and mechanical components in good condition. **£42,000–48,000** *Pou*

The French industrial company Lorraine-Dietrich built their first cars in 1905 and went on to produce some fine touring cars in the 1920s. The 15CV model won at Le Mans in 1925 and 1926. However, car production came to an end in 1934 as the company concentrated on railway rolling stock.

LOTUS

When one-time second-hand car dealer Colin Chapman created the first Lotus from a left-over Austin, few could have imagined that the marque would survive to celebrate its 50th anniversary in 1998. Fewer still could have predicted that the company, which started out in a North London lock-up, would have risen to the very pinnacle of motor racing and produced a memorable string of truly innovative road cars. Chapman died in 1982, but today's splendid Elise is very much a hallmark Lotus, a pert little machine so well poised that it easily matches and can embarrass more powerful rivals.

R. E. Renold, Lotus Elite – Le Mans, depicting the works Lotus Elite No. 42 passing the pits tribunes, oil on canvas, c1962, 18 x 28in (45.5 x 71cm). **£345–375** *C*

l. **1967 Lotus Elan +2,** 1558cc, 4 cylinders, new chassis, restored. **£6,500–7,000** *WILM*

LOTUS Model	ENGINE cc/cyl	DATES	CONDITION 1	2	3
Six		1953-56	£13,000	£7,000	£5,000
Seven S1 Sports	1172/4	1957-64	£12,000	£9,000	£5,000
Seven S2 Sports	1498/4	1961-66	£10,000	£8,000	£5,000
Seven S3 Sports	1558/4	1961-66	£10,000	£8,000	£5,000
Seven S4	1598/4	1969-72	£8,000	£5,000	£3,000
Elan S1 Convertible	1558/4	1962-64	£12,000+	£8,000	£4,500
Elan S2 Convertible	1558/4	1964-66	£12,000	£7,000	£4,000
Elan S3 Convertible	1558/4	1966-69	£12,000+	£8,000	£5,000
Elan S3 FHC	1558/4	1966-69	£13,000	£7,000	£5,000
Elan S4 Convertible	1558/4	1968-71	£12,000+	£9,500	£7,000
Elan S4 FHC	1558/4	1968-71	£10,000	£7,500	£5,000
Elan Sprint Convertible	1558/4	1971-73	£13,000+	£8,500	£7,000
Elan Sprint FHC	1558/4	1971-73	£10,000	£7,000	£6,000
Europa S1 FHC	1470/4	1966-69	£4,000	£3,500	£2,000
Europa S2 FHC	1470/4	1969-71	£5,500	£3,000	£2,000
Europa Twin Cam	1558/4	1971-75	£8,000	£6,000	£4,000
Elan +2S 130	1558/4	1971-74	£8,000	£5,000	£4,000
Elite S1 FHC	1261/4	1974-80	£3,500	£2,500	£1,500
Eclat S1	1973/4	1975-82	£3,500	£3,000	£1,500
Esprit 1	1973/4	1977-81	£6,500	£5,000	£3,000
Esprit 2	1973/4	1976-81	£7,000	£4,000	£2,500
Esprit S2.2	2174/4	1980-81	£7,000	£5,500	£3,000
Esprit Turbo	2174/4	1980-90	£9,000	£7,000	£4,000
Excel	2174/4	1983-85	£5,000	£3,000	£2,500

Prices vary with some limited edition Lotus models.

1968 Lotus Elan S4, finished in white, very original.
£12,000–14,000 *VIC*

1969 Lotus Elan S3, 1558cc, 4 cylinders, 105bhp, good mechanical condition.
£5,000–6,000 *Pou*

1971 Lotus Elan +2S 130, 1558cc,
4-speed gearbox, chassis and engine
rebuilt, original Philips radio,
knock-off wheels.
£5,000–6,000 *H&H*

**Miller's is a price GUIDE
not a price LIST**

Did You Know?

Emma Peel, played by Diana Rigg in the TV series, *The Avengers*, drove a Lotus Elan. Patrick McGoohan was also supposed to drive one in *The Prisoner* cult 1960s TV series, but when he visited the factory and saw a cycle-winged Lotus Seven he decided the spartan sportster was more in keeping with his on-screen character.

Lotus Elan (1962–73)

Engine: 1588cc, double-overhead-camshaft, Ford in-line four.
Power output: Up to 126bhp (Elan Sprint).
Transmission: 4/5 speed manual.
Brakes: Discs all-round.
Top speed: 121mph (Elan Sprint).
0–60mph: 6.7 seconds (Elan Sprint).
Production: 12,224.

Colin Chapman's original Lotus Elite was an exquisite delicacy enjoyed by a very lucky few, but its successor, the Elan, was the small company's first really practical road-going package. Little larger than a half-sucked boiled sweet and just as sticky when it came to gripping the road, the lithe fibreglass-bodied Elan could embarrass and bait much bigger-engined sports rivals on the road and track, thanks to its superb dynamics and inbuilt race breeding. From 1962 to 1973, the little Lotus evolved into a very accelerative machine, culminating in the Elan Sprint, a 126bhp banshee. In the 1980s, there was much talk of how the Mazda MX-5 recreated the spirit of the original Elan. Well, any Elan offered stronger acceleration than the latter-day pastiche.

1973 Lotus Elan +2 130/5, 1558cc, 5-speed manual gearbox, new clutch, starter motor and front brake pistons, 10,000 miles since 1981, very good condition.
£4,750–5,250 *LF*

1971 Lotus Elan +2S 130, restored, new galvanised chassis, engine rebuilt, brakes and suspension overhauled, partially rewired, new radiator, brake servo and head lining, retrimmed Webasto sunroof.
£7,000–8,000 *BKS*

One of the most important of the Lotus Elan +2 developments was the +2S 130 model, with its 126bhp 'big-valve' engine. This particular car was specially built for the 1971 Earl's Court Motor Show. Uniquely, it was given a white interior (production models were available in black or oatmeal) and a bonnet bulge, which did not appear on any subsequent cars.

1979 Lotus Eclat 521, 1973cc, original corrosion-proofed chassis, finished in yellow with black and grey interior, Kenwood stereo system and amplifier, very well maintained using Lotus parts.
£2,900–3,400 *H&H*

1980 Lotus Eclat S2.2, galvanised chassis, hide upholstery, power-assisted steering, air conditioning, stainless steel exhaust, genuine 78,000 miles, history, good condition.
£3,250–3,750 *BKS*

The introduction of the four-seat Elite in 1974 signalled a move upmarket by Lotus. The newcomer's backbone chassis, all-independent suspension and brilliant handling were already Lotus hallmarks, but the 2 litre 16-valve engine was new. Its looks, though, were not to everyone's taste, and in 1975 it was joined by a restyled version – the Eclat. The latter's fastback shape raised top speed to 129mph, all-round performance receiving a further boost in 1980 with the launch of the 2.2 litre model with 5-speed Getrag gearbox. Only 223 examples of the S2.2 were built.

MARCOS

1971 Marcos, 3 litres, completely restored, excellent condition.
£8,500–9,500 *WILM*

MARCOS Model	ENGINE cc/cyl	DATES	CONDITION 1	2	3
1500/1600/1800	1500/1600/ 1800/4	1964-69	£8,000	£5,000	£2,500
Mini-Marcos	848/4	1965-74	£3,500	£2,500	£1,500
Marcos 3 litre	3000/6	1969-71	£9,000	£6,000	£4,000
Mantis	2498	1970/71	£10,000	£4,500	£1,500

MARMON

1930 Marmon Big Eight Dual-Cowl Phæton, coachwork by Briggs, 315.2cu in, straight 8, 125hp at 3,400rpm, 4-speed gearbox, mahogany cabinet for rear tonneau, full discs on all wheels, original.
£29,000–34,000 *C*

By 1930, Marmon had abandoned its long-standing six-cylinder models and was producing small-engined and larger-displacement eight-cylinder cars. The Big Eight, which arrived in 1930, was offered on two wheelbases: 136 and 130in. The engine was sensational, and the first in the company's history to combine dual carburettors with a dual downdraught manifold. The Big Eight also offered four-wheel mechanical brakes with a Bendix booster for superior braking capability. The majority of bodies for the Big Eight were designed by LeBaron and finished in white, but this car bears a Briggs emblem. Ralph Roberts had sold LeBaron to Briggs in 1928, and LeBaron production was moved to Detroit, after which the Briggs name was seldom, if ever, used.

MASERATI

The first car to bear the Maserati name was the 1926 Tipo 26 Grand Prix car, but the origins of the marque go back to 1912, when the five Maserati brothers formed the company, first producing spark plugs, then, after WWI, building racing cars for Isotta-Fraschini and Diatto. By 1937, the company was no longer under family control. The first road car, the A6, appeared at the 1947 Geneva show and was produced in small numbers, but it was not until Maserati abandoned racing in 1957 that the company could concentrate on true series-production road cars. The first of these was the 3500GT, and plenty of memorable cars have followed, but for many enthusiasts the ultimate Maserati is the gorgeous Ghibli.

1959 Maserati 3500GT, 3485cc, 6 cylinders, 5-speed gearbox, triple Weber carburettors, mechanics restored, little used since, good overall condition.
£15,000–17,000   COYS

Richard Crump and Rob de la Rive Box, *Maserati, Sports, Racing & GT Cars from 1926,* second edition, 1983.
£25–30   GPCC

1958 Maserati 3500GT, coachwork by Touring, completely restored 1994–96, engine rebuilt, braking and fuel systems overhauled, new clutch, engine mounts and stainless steel exhaust, bare metal respray in Maserati Gladis, brightwork rechromed, new rubber seals to windows and doors, new head lining and carpets, reupholstered in beige Connolly leather, 750 miles since restoration.
£21,000–23,000   BKS

Maserati's survival strategy for the 1960s centred on establishing the company as a producer of road cars. The marque's new era began in 1957 with the launch of the Touring-bodied 3500GT, a luxury 2+2 that drew on competition experience, employing a tubular chassis and an engine derived from the 350S twin-cam six of 1956.

1963 Maserati 3500GT, 3486cc, fuel injection, good condition.
£20,000–22,000   EPP

r. **1963 Maserati 3500 Vignale Spyder,** 3485cc, 6 cylinders, rebuilt engine and 5-speed ZF gearbox, bare metal respray, brightwork replated, optional Borrani wire wheels, interior retrimmed in Connolly hide, new black mohair hood, black leather hood bag, 1,500 recorded miles.
£51,000–56,000   COYS

This car is No. 237 of the 242 Spyders built, and one of approximately six right-hand drive examples.

MASERATI Model	ENGINE cc/cyl	DATES	CONDITION 1	2	3
AG-1500	1488/6	1946-50	£30,000	£20,000	£10,000
A6G	1954/6	1951-53	£50,000	£35,000	£22,000
A6G-2000	1985/6	1954-57	£45,000	£35,000	£20,000
3500GT fhc	3485/6	1957-64	£25,000	£15,000	£12,000
3500GT Spyder	3485/6	1957-64	£35,000	£22,000	£15,000
5000GT	4935/8	1960-65	£60,000	£20,000	£15,000
Sebring	3694/6	1962-66	£20,000	£15,000	£10,000
Quattroporte	4136/8	1963-74	£11,000	£9,000	£7,000
Mistral	4014/6	1964-70	£15,000	£11,000	£9,000
Mistral Spyder	4014/6	1964-70	£30,000	£18,000	£12,000
Mexico	4719/8	1965-68	£15,000	£12,000	£9,000
Ghibli	4719/8	1967-73	£20,000	£15,000	£12,000
Ghibli-Spyder/SS	4136/8	1969-74	£50,000	£40,000	£25,000
Indy	4136/8	1969-74	£18,000	£13,000	£10,000
Bora	4719/8	1971-80	£25,000	£18,000	£11,000
Merak/SS	2965/6	1972-81	£16,000	£14,000	£9,000
Khamsin	4930/8	1974-81	£16,000	£11,000	£9,000

Early cars with competition/Berlinetta coachwork eg. Zagato command a premium.

1966 Maserati Sebring MkII Coupé, coachwork by Vignale, engine noisy, Lucas fuel injection replaced by carburettors, manual gearbox, good condition.
£16,000–18,000 *BKS*

The 2+2 Sebring Coupé arrived in 1962. By then, a five-speed gearbox, four-wheel disc brakes and fuel injection had become standard equipment; automatic transmission, air conditioning and a limited-slip differential were options. Introduced in 1965, the Sebring Series II came with a 3.7 litre, 245bhp engine. Some cars left the factory with 4 litre units towards the end of production in 1966, by which time 96 Series IIs had been built.

1967 Maserati Mistral Spyder, 4014cc, 6 cylinders, engine rebuilt, right-hand drive, excellent condition.
£30,000–35,000 *COYS*

The Mistral was the last Maserati to use the straight-six layout, as subsequent models adopted V8 or V6 engines. Coachwork was designed by Frua and built in steel, with the exception of doors, bonnet and boot lid, which were in aluminium. Two attractive body styles were offered, a Coupé and a Spyder. The Mistral was produced from 1963 until 1970, a total of 948 cars being built; only 120 were Spyders. Of these, 20 or so had 4 litre engines, and only three or four of them were right-hand drive models.

1969 Maserati Ghibli, 4719cc, V8, manual gearbox, new clutch, left-hand drive, excellent engine, good condition throughout.
£13,000–16,000 *COYS*

Introduced at the 1966 Turin Show, the Ghibli displayed dramatic purposeful lines, drawn by Giorgietto Giugiaro while still at Ghia's design studio. Under the bonnet was Maserati's magnificent all-alloy, 4.7 litre four-cam V8, derived from the company's sports racing powerplants and mated to a five-speed gearbox. Claimed top speed was 174mph.

r. **1975 Maserati Indy,** 4930cc, V8, 320bhp at 5,500rpm, 5-speed manual gearbox.
£10,000–12,000 *Pou*

This particular car was one of the last examples built.

1975 Maserati Khamsin, 4930cc, V8, manual gearbox, right-hand drive, slight rust to boot, otherwise good condition.
£8,750–10,250 *BRIT*

First seen as a prototype at the 1972 Turin show, the Khamsin was designed to replace the Indy and was the first Maserati road car by Bertone, who built the body/chassis unit ready for completion by the factory. The race-proven V8 engine was retained, but displaced 4.9 litres and produced 320bhp at 5,500rpm. Performance was impressive, with 0–60mph in 7.5 seconds, and a 130mph top speed.

1976 Maserati Merak, 2965cc, V6, restored 1989–91, air conditioning needs attention, 45,000 miles, good condition throughout.
£8,500–10,000 *BRIT*

In the early 1970s, Maserati offered not one, but two mid-engined machines built on the same basic design: the sensational Bora, introduced in 1971, and its little sister, the Merak, which followed in 1972. The Merak was powered by the same engine that was utilised in the Citroën SM, a 3 litre 90° V6. This engine was smaller than that used in the Bora, allowing the cabin to be extended and small rear seats to be installed. The result was an attractive and well balanced machine.

l. **1989 Maserati Biturbo Spyder,** coachwork by Zagato, manual gearbox, clutch needs attention, service history, 6,900 recorded miles, good condition.
£13,000–15,000 *BKS*

The first series-production road car to employ a twin-turbocharger engine, Maserati's Biturbo saloon, debuted in 1982. Produced initially with a 2 litre, four-cam, three-valves/cylinder V6 developing 180bhp, the Biturbo gained 2.5 and 2.8 litre units as the model range expanded to include four-door and open variants. The 2 litre Spyder appeared in 1984 and was considerably faster than the saloon. In three-valve form, it had a top speed of around 140mph, but this was improved slightly with the four-valve engine.

MAYBACH

1933 Maybach 12 Cylinder 'Zeppelin' Touring Sedan.
£210,000–230,000 *S*

The Maybach car first appeared in 1921, and the first example of the chassis designed around the giant V12 Zeppelin engine, the DS-7, was introduced in 7 litre form in 1929. The name 'Zeppelin' was reserved for the fabled DS-8, shown in Paris in 1930. This 8 litre, 200bhp version was equipped with a new pre-selector transmission with steering-column change and no clutch. It featured servo-assisted pneumatic braking, after the Bosch-Dewandre system. This particular car was presented to His Highness, The Maharajah of Patiala and Raj Pramukh by Adolf Hitler, in expectation of neutrality, or favour for the German cause. The gift was accepted graciously, but with the coming of war, and given its origin, it was hidden for the duration. The Maharajah pledged his support to the Allies during the hostilities.

MERCEDES-BENZ

The company's origins date back to the dawn of motoring, to 1886 when Karl Benz and Gottleib Daimler, working independently of each other, both produced petrol-engined road vehicles. In 1894, Benz's Velo became the world's first true production automobile. The name Mercedes was first used on a Daimler in 1899. In 1926, the two concerns merged to form Daimler-Benz, the cars being called Mercedes-Benz. Today, the company is Germany's largest industrial concern, the cornerstone of which for many decades has been the superb build quality and engineering of its cars.

Nicholas Watts, Summer of 54, limited-edition print, signed by Mercedes works drivers Juan Fangio, Karl Kling and Hans Herrmann, and Ferrari driver José Gonzalez, 25 x 33in (63 x 84cm).
£275–295   *MPG*

The return of Mercedes to Grand Prix racing at the 1954 French Grand Prix at Rheims caused a sensation. Two of their cars, under the control of the legendary Alfred Neubauer, took the first two places. The eventual winner, Juan Fangio, is depicted leading his team-mate Karl Kling, who is overtaking the Ferrari 553 Squalo of José Gonzalez. In the background, the third Mercedes team car of Hans Herrmann negotiates the Thillois corner.

Nicholas Watts, Sicilian Magic, limited-edition print, signed by Stirling Moss, 25 x 33in (63 x 84cm).
£90–95   *MPG*

The Targa Florio of 1955 was the final event for Mercedes before their withdrawal from competition. The image depicts Stirling Moss in the battered Mercedes 300SLR, which he shared with Peter Collins, rushing to victory through the town of Campofelice.

r. A Mercedes-Benz Car Club badge, c1960, 3½in (9cm) diam.
£100–120   *LE*

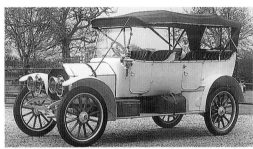

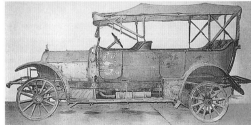

1912 Mercedes-Benz 40hp Phæton Tourer, 5.7 litres, 4 cylinders, 4-speed gearbox with reverse, Mercedes-Maybach carburettor, original coachwork, restored, limited mileage.
£90,000–100,000   *C*

By 1912, Mercedes were offering a range of eight models, from a comparatively small 15hp four of 1.8 litres, which sold in Britain for £350, to an 80/90hp 9½ litre that, at £1,275, was £300 more expensive than a Rolls-Royce Silver Ghost. Near the middle of the range was the 40hp, with bi-bloc engine, that sold in chassis form for £725. Two versions were offered: the standard example had shaft drive, 895 x 135mm tyres and an 8½in ground clearance; the 'Colonial' model had a side-chain final drive, 1020 x 120mm tyres and a 12in ground clearance.

1928 Mercedes-Benz Stuttgart 200 Cabriolet, 2 litres, 6 cylinders, older restoration, new hood, engine and transmission in working order, fitted with flashing indicators.
£32,000–36,000   *BKS*

From the time of the merger of Daimler and Benz in 1926, until the advent of technical director Hans Nibel's advanced 170 in 1931, the Stuttgart comprised the bulk of Mercedes-Benz production. Built in 2 litre (200) and 2.6 litre (260) forms, it was a well-engineered car that represented the last of the old technology. The gearbox was a three-speed unit with floor-change, the radiator was flat-fronted, and the steel wheels were of the artillery type. Top speed was about 50mph. Total production of the Stuttgart 200 amounted to 6,450 cars when it was superseded in 1933.

1935 Mercedes-Benz 200 Cabriolet C,
coachwork by Sindelfingen, 4/5 seater, left-hand
drive, red with tan upholstery, restored.
£22,000–25,000 *BKS*

*Launched in 1932, the Mercedes 200 was an
uprated 2 litre derivative of the six-cylinder 170 –
the first Mercedes model with all-independent
suspension. Designed by the gifted Hans Nibel, the
200 boasted twin parallel leaf-spring assemblies
with hydraulic shock absorbers acting as radius
arms at the front, and swing-axles at the rear
suspended by twin coil springs. The idea was to
ensure maximum road contact with minimum
unsprung weight, giving an exceptionally smooth
ride for the period.*

1937 Mercedes-Benz 320 Saloon, 51,000km,
original condition.
£30,000–35,000 *FHF*

1952 Mercedes-Benz 220 Cabriolet A, coachwork by Sindelfingen, 2.2 litres, 6-cylinder overhead-
camshaft engine, all-synchromesh 4-speed gearbox with steering-column shift lever, restored,
fitted with c1960 Mercedes air conditioning.
£32,000–36,000 *BKS*

*This variant of the 220 is fitted with the most sporting of Mercedes' in-house cabriolet body styles, the 2+2
Cabriolet A, with blind rear quarters and landau irons.*

MERCEDES-BENZ Model	ENGINE cc/cyl	DATES	CONDITION 1	2	3
300ABCD	2996/6	1951-62	£15,000	£10,000	£8,000
220A/S/SE Ponton	2195/6	1952-60	£10,000	£5,000	£3,000
220S/SEB Coupé	2915/6	1956-59	£11,000	£7,000	£5,000
220S/SEB Cabriolet	2195/6	1958-59	£25,000	£18,000	£7,000
190SL	1897/4	1955-63	£20,000	£15,000	£10,000
300SL 'Gullwing'	2996/6	1954-57	£120,000+	£100,000	£70,000
300SL Roadster	2996/6	1957-63	£110,000	£90,000	£70,000
230/250SL	2306/ 2496/6	1963-68	£14,000	£10,000	£7,000
280SL	2778/6	1961-71	£16,000	£12,000	£9,000
220/250SE	2195/ 2496/6	1960-68	£10,000	£7,000	£4,000
300SE	2996/6	1961-65	£11,000	£8,000	£6,000
280SE Convertible	2778/6	1965-69	£25,000	£18,000	£12,000
280SE V8 Convertible	3499/8	1969-71	£30,000+	£20,000	£15,000
280SE Coupé	2496/6	1965-72	£12,000	£8,000	£5,000
300SEL 6.3	6330/8	1968-72	£12,000	£7,000	£3,500
600 & 600 Pullman	6332/8	1964-81	£40,000+	£15,000	£8,000

1953 Mercedes-Benz 300S Cabriolet, 2996cc,
6 cylinders, 150bhp at 5,000rpm, 4-speed manual
gearbox, fitted luggage in boot, complete tool kit,
fully restored at a cost of over $200,000, little used
since, very good condition.
£135,000–145,000   C

*Despite the effects of wartime bombing, by the early
1950s, Mercedes was producing trucks and a full range
of cars, including the successful upmarket 300 sedan.
In 1952, this provided the basis for a luxury two-door
sports model, the short-chassis 'S' series. Built for the
rich and famous, they were the pinnacle of the Mercedes
range. Unfortunately, they were so labour-intensive
that the company lost money on every car built, and
production ceased in 1957. Only 560 were made.*

1963 Mercedes-Benz 300SL Roadster, 2996cc,
6 cylinders, 215bhp, fuel-injected, dry-sump
lubrication, factory paint, 69,000km recorded,
original, unrestored.
£125,000–140,000   COYS

1955 Mercedes-Benz 300SL Gullwing, 2996cc,
6 cylinders, completely restored, 3,000 miles since,
31,000 miles since new, excellent condition.
£135,000–150,000   COYS

*Originally conceived as a competition car, the SL
had a fuel-injected straight-six engine, with dry-
sump lubrication, in a space-frame chassis. It was
clothed with startlingly advanced coupé bodywork
featuring gullwing doors. It cost a fortune in 1954
(£5,600 compared to £1,400 for a Jaguar XK120),
but the SLs were magnificent – solid, handsome
and very fast. Racing 300 SLR versions won the
Le Mans 24-hour race and the gruelling Carrera
Panamericana road race.*

*Several important developments occurred during
the lifetime of the 300SL Roadster. In 1961,
Dunlop four-wheel disc brakes were fitted,
allowing the performance of the magnificent engine
to be exploited in safety and with confidence.
Today, these disc-brake Roadsters are highly
prized. The ultimate 300SL, however, arrived
late in 1962, when the Roadster was given a new
aluminium engine. Only 200 cars were produced
with this powerplant.*

r. **1956 Mercedes-Benz 190SL Two-Seater
Roadster,** 1897cc, 4-cylinder overhead-
camshaft engine, 105bhp at 5,800rpm,
left-hand drive, completely restored.
£26,500–30,000   BKS

*For those who could not afford the expensive,
race-bred 300SL, Mercedes-Benz offered the more
modest 190, based on the floorpan and running
gear of the 180/220 saloons. It was powered by
a 1.9 litre overhead-camshaft four and had a
four-speed manual gearbox. The 105bhp on tap
was sufficient to propel the 190SL to 60mph in
13 seconds, and to a top speed of 107mph.
Fuel consumption was 24mpg.*

l. **1961 Mercedes-Benz 190SL Roadster,** 1897cc, restored late 1980s to original condition, Solex carburettors, original dealer's chrome badge, 44,000 miles from new, full history, excellent condition.
£22,000–25,000 *H&H*

1957 Mercedes-Benz 220S Cabriolet, 2195cc, 6 cylinders, 106bhp at 5,200rpm, 4-speed manual gearbox, restored, engine, drive-train and suspension rebuilt, resprayed, brightwork rechromed, new leather upholstery.
£35,000–39,000 *C*

Introduced in 1956, the 220S was the first Mercedes to utilise unitary construction. It was offered as a four-door saloon, a cabriolet and two-door coupé. All shared the same slab-sided, smooth coachwork with rounded roof, plenty of chrome and a large distinctive radiator grille. They were powered by a new 2.2-litre, six-cylinder, overhead-camshaft engine with twin Solex carburettors, which would survive unchanged into the 1970s. Its 106bhp could propel the 220S to a top speed of 100mph, with acceleration to match. Production ceased in 1959. In total, only 2,178 cabriolets were built.

1959 Mercedes-Benz 220S Four-Door Saloon, 2195cc, 6 cylinders, right-hand drive. restored 1991/92, zinc-treated bodyshell, resprayed.
£6,500–8,000 *BKS*

The 220S saloon debuted at the 1956 Frankfurt show. It featured unitary construction, all-independent suspension and drum brakes. Power came from a 100bhp, 2195cc, overhead-camshaft six, which was good for a top speed of around 99mph. Apart from a power increase to 106bhp in 1957, the 220S changed little in the course of its comparatively short life, production ceasing in 1959.

1972 Mercedes-Benz 220, 2198cc, new exhaust, new wings, resprayed, original tools, 79,000 miles recorded, excellent condition throughout.
£2,250–2,750 *H&H*

r. **1966 Mercedes-Benz 230SL,** 2306cc, 6 cylinders, manual gearbox, 52,000 miles.
£11,250–12,250 *BRIT*

Introduced in 1963 as a replacement for the 190SL, the 230SL was an altogether more modern machine with square-cut lines and distinctive pagoda-style hardtop.

1967 Mercedes-Benz 250SL, 2496cc, 6 cylinders, automatic transmission, unused tool kit, 59,650 miles from new, very good condition throughout.
£14,000–16,000 *H&H*

1969 Mercedes-Benz 280SL Cabriolet, 6 cylinder overhead-camshaft engine, 4-speed automatic transmission, right-hand drive, green with matching factory hardtop, black upholstery, partially restored and repainted, sections of floorpan replaced, good condition.
£16,000–19,000 *BKS*

The last of a popular and extremely successful line, the 280SL was introduced in 1967. Power output of the Bosch fuel-injected M130 engine was 180bhp, and while the 280's 120+mph top speed was no greater, it was significantly quicker off the mark than the 250SL.

1969 Mercedes-Benz 250 Saloon, 170bhp, very good condition throughout.
£2,200–2,700 *S*

1973 Mercedes-Benz 280CE, 2778cc, 6 cylinders, central locking, electric sunroof, good condition throughout.
£3,250–3,750 *BRIT*

1985 Mercedes-Benz 280CE, ABS, alloy wheels, cruise control, electric sunroof, velour trim, 104,000 miles recorded, full service history, excellent condition.
£6,750–7,500 *PA*

l. **1975 Mercedes-Benz 280CE,** extensively restored, unused for some years, full service history.
£3,500–4,000 *PA*

Mercedes-Benz 280SL (1968–1971)

Body style: Two-door, two-seater convertible with detachable hard-top.
Construction: Pressed-steel monocoque.
Engine: 2778cc in-line six; two valves per cylinder operated by a single, chain-driven overhead camshaft; Bosch mechanical fuel injection system.
Power output: 170bhp at 5,750rpm.
Transmission: Four- or five-speed ZF manual, or four-speed automatic.
Suspension: Front: independent with twin transverse wishbones, coil springs, telescopic gas-filled dampers and anti-roll bar. Rear: single-joint, low-pivot swing axle with coil springs, gas-filled telescopic dampers and compensating spring.
Brakes: Servo-assisted front discs and rear drums; dual hydraulic circuits.
Top speed: 121mph (automatic).
0–60mph: 9.3 seconds (automatic).
0–100mph: 30.6 seconds (automatic).
Production: 23,885 (plus 19,831 230SLs and 5,196 250SLs).

The Mercedes 280SL has mellowed magnificently. In 1963, the new SLs took over the sporting mantle of the ageing 190SL. Named W113 in Mercedes parlance, they evolved from the original 230SL, through the 250SL, and on to the 280SL. But the most remarkable thing about them is how incredibly modern they appear, for with their uncluttered, clean-shaven good looks, it's hard to believe that the last one was made in 1971. Underneath the timelessly elegant sheet metal, they were based closely on the earlier 'fintail saloons,' sharing even the decidedly unsporting recirculating-ball steering. Suspension, too, was on the soft side for string-backed glove types. Yet the looks and all-round quality really mark this Merc as something special, and that enduring design, with its distinctive so-called 'pagoda roof', is down to Frenchman Paul Bracq. This well-manicured Merc is a beautifully built boulevardier that will induce a sense of supreme self-satisfaction on any journey.

1967 Mercedes-Benz 300SE Convertible, 2996cc, 6 cylinders, 160bhp at 5,000rpm, 4-speed manual gearbox, all-independent suspension, air suspension at rear, partially restored, good condition.
£29,000–34,000 *C*

r. **1969 Mercedes-Benz 300SEL Saloon**, 6.3 litres, V8, automatic transmission, Pale Antelope metallic livery and interior, extensively restored, new engine, some electrical attention required.
£5,250–6,500 *BKS*

Mercedes-Benz S-class cars of the 1960s made serious inroads on the luxury market which, for almost two decades, had been the exclusive domain of Rolls-Royce and Bentley. The superbly-engineered 300SEL was the flagship of the range, being designed for absolute reliability and high-speed cruising, accommodating 4–5 passengers in great comfort.

l. **1972 Mercedes-Benz 280SE Four-Door Saloon**, 3.5 litres, V8, automatic transmission, right-hand drive, electric windows, central locking, stereo radio/cassette, electric aerial, full service history, original tool kit and handbooks, excellent condition throughout.
£6,000–7,000 *BKS*

From 1971, Mercedes-Benz's overhead-camshaft V8 was available in the 280SE, the marriage resulting in a fast and well-equipped saloon that combined 125mph performance with considerable luxury. A little over 11,000 were built between 1971 and 1972.

1972 Mercedes-Benz 300SEL Saloon, 6.3 litres, automatic transmission, finished in blue with matching interior, wood cappings to fascia, dry-stored since 1993, good condition throughout.
£5,250–6,000 *S*

The 300SEL, designed for fast touring and powered by a 6.3-litre V8 engine, was capable of 137mph. Power-assisted steering, automatic transmission and air conditioning were standard features.

1971 Mercedes-Benz 300SEL, 6300cc, good condition.
£10,000–12,000 *H&H*

l. **1981 Mercedes-Benz 350SL Two-Door Convertible**, automatic transmission, partially restored, hood torn, interior fair, well maintained.
£6,500–7,500 *BKS*

Introduced in 1971 as a replacement for the popular 230/250/280SL family, the 350SL was larger and heavier, but its 200bhp, 3.5 litre V8 more than offset the increase in bulk, providing a top speed of 130mph. More sports tourer than sports car, the 350SL was equipped with all-independent suspension and four-wheel disc brakes, ventilated at the front.

1986 Mercedes-Benz 380SL, very good condition.
£17,000–19,000 *BLE*

1979 Mercedes-Benz 450SL, V8, engine and gearbox overhauled, bodywork restored, new mohair hood and hardtop, excellent original interior, good condition.
£10,000–11,000 *Mot*

1975 Mercedes-Benz 450SL Two-Door Convertible, automatic transmission, bodywork restored, very good condition.
£8,000–9,000 *BKS*

The 450SL Roadster and 450SLC Coupé were outwardly identical to their 350 (3.5 litre) sister models, but they offered superior performance from a more powerful 4.5 litre V8. With the option of either four-speed manual or automatic transmission, top speed was over 130mph. Considerably more popular than its coupé sibling, the 450SL sold in excess of 66,000 units before production ceased in 1980.

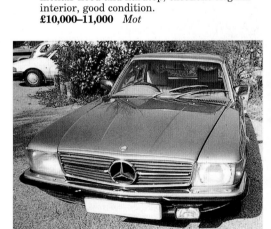

1979 Mercedes-Benz 450SLC, 99,822 miles recorded, full service history.
£4,000–5,000 *H&H*

l. **1979 Mercedes-Benz 450SLC,** 4520cc, V8, good condition throughout.
£4,750–5,250 *BRIT*

1979 Mercedes-Benz 450SEL, 6834cc, 3-speed
automatic transmission, stainless steel exhaust,
resprayed 1993, 81,000 miles recorded,
very good condition.
£5,500–6,500 *H&H*

1978 Mercedes-Benz 450SEL, 4520cc,
V8, interior showing signs of slight wear,
otherwise good condition throughout.
£2,000–2,500 *BRIT*

**1966 Mercedes-Benz 600 SWB Four-Door
Saloon,** restored 1994/95, engine replaced,
20,000 miles covered since, interior and brakes
require attention.
£8,500–12,000 *BKS*

*Introduced in 1963, the 600 saloon featured an
overhead-camshaft, fuel-injected, 6.3 litre V8
engine, air suspension with variable ride control,
four-speed automatic transmission, four-wheel disc
brakes, power-assisted steering, central locking and
separate heating/ventilating systems for front and
rear compartments. Built in saloon and nine-seater
limousine forms, the imposing heavyweight 600
was endowed with respectable performance,
reaching 60mph in a little under 10 seconds, and
exceeding 125mph flat-out.*

l. **1979 Mercedes-Benz 450SEL Saloon,** 6834cc,
V8, 3-speed automatic transmission, 113,000 miles
recorded, good condition throughout.
£4,500–5,000 *H&H*

1981 Mercedes-Benz 500SE Four-Door Saloon, AMG enhancement kit, left-hand drive, very good condition.
£1,500–1,800 *BKS*

*Introduced in 1979, the top-of-the-range 500SE and SEL (long-wheelbase) saloons used the 4973cc
overhead-camshaft V8 from the 450SLC of 1977. In saloon trim, the all-alloy motor produced 240bhp at
4,750rpm on Bosch mechanical fuel injection, and drove through a new four-speed automatic transmission.
Both the SE and SEL could accelerate to 60mph in around 7 seconds and reach 140mph.*

MG

The origins of MG date back to 1923, when Cecil Kimber, general manager of Morris Garages in Oxford, attached a stylish two-seater sporting body to a standard Morris chassis to create the first MG. Until the outbreak of war, MG remained a specialist marque, rather than a volume producer, creating a string of cars that offered the sporting driver affordable performance. In 1935, the company was incorporated into Morris, later to become part of BMC and British Leyland, which had an increasing influence on MG

products. Nevertheless, MG managed to keep its distinct sporting identity for many years, producing memorable cars such as the T-Series Midgets, the pretty MGA, the world-beating MGB and the Midget. The low point was the 1980s, when the MG octagon badge was debased by being tacked on to Montegos and Maestros, and for a while it looked as if the marque would fade away. Yet in 1992, its renaissance began with the RV8, an update of the original MGB, and has now gathered real momentum with the capable little MGF.

An enamel MG Magnette K-Series advertising sign, 'Safety Fast', 1933, 9in (23cm) square.
£20–30 *CGC*

1929 MG M-Type Midget, correct specification, show-standard restoration.
£9,000–9,500 *Mot*

The mighty Midget was launched to an enthusiastic public at the 1928 London Motor Show. Based on the 847cc Morris Minor, with its overhead-camshaft, four-cylinder engine producing 20bhp and lowered leaf-spring suspension, the diminutive fabric-bodied, boat-tail two-seater was capable of 65mph and lively acceleration via its three-speed gearbox.

1932 MG J2 Midget, completely restored, balanced crankshaft, 12in brakes, Collingham interior, complete history, concours condition.
£21,000–22,500 *BaW*

Derived from the first M-Type Midget, and introduced for 1933, the two-seater J2 established the look that would characterise MG sports cars into the 1950s. The 847cc overhead-camshaft engine was coupled to a four-speed gearbox. The lightweight J2 possessed exemplary handling and steering by the standards of the day, and was good for 65mph.

r. **1933 MG J2 Midget,** comprehensive rebuild in 1996, mildly-tuned engine, hydraulic brakes, finished in red with matching interior.
£12,250–14,000 *BKS*

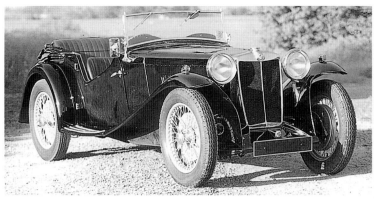

l. **1933 MG K1 Magnette Four-Seater Tourer,** 1086cc KB engine, restored, slight paint cracking on bonnet, new red leather interior, Art Deco sunburst pleating on front door pockets and rear body sides, good overall condition.
£16,500–18,000 *BKS*

The open four-seater model was deservedly popular, representing approximately 47 per cent of the total K1 production of 206 cars.

1933 MG K-Type Magnette/K3 Replica, 1271cc, 6 cylinders, completely overhauled, 1,000 miles covered since, rebuilt Marshall supercharger, uprated half-shafts, hubs and wheels, Dunlop racing tyres, new dynamo and distributor, very good condition.
£51,000–56,000 *COYS*

In essence, the K3 was a supercharged 1087cc K2 with two-seat racing bodywork. Initially supplied with an 1100cc engine, this particular car was returned to the works in January 1934, when it was fitted with a KD 1271cc engine and ENV perfected gearbox. It is worth noting that it is not a new replica, but that the chassis and mechanics, down to the magnesium brake drums and backplates, have remained together since 1934.

1934 MG PA Midget, 847cc, 4-cylinder overhead-camshaft engine, 4-speed manual gearbox, mostly restored, engine stripped and crank reground, new front and rear wings, new door frames, woodwork replaced, interior retrimmed, new carpets, door trim and seats, new tonneau, requires completing.
£8,000–9,000 *C*

Forebears of the PA Midget included the M- and J-Types, while its best-known successor was the T-Type. This appeared in 1936 and, in TC form, survived WWII to become one of Britain's most successful early post-war car exports to the USA.

MG Model	ENGINE cc/cyl	DATES	CONDITION 1	2	3
14/28	1802/4	1924-27	£26,000	£18,000	£10,000
14/40	1802/4	1927-29	£25,000	£18,000	£10,000
18/80 Mk I/Mk II/Mk III	2468/6	1927-33	£40,000	£28,000	£20,000
M-Type Midget	847/4	1928-32	£11,000	£9,000	£7,000
J-Type Midget	847/4	1932-34	£15,000	£12,000	£10,000
J3 Midget	847/4	1932-33	£18,000	£14,000	£12,000
PA Midget	847/4	1934-36	£13,000	£10,000	£8,000
PB Midget	936/4	1935-36	£15,000	£10,000	£8,000
F-Type Magna	1271/6	1931-33	£22,000	£18,000	£12,000
L-Type Magna	1087/6	1933-34	£26,000	£18,000	£12,000
K1/K2 Magnette	1087/6	1932-33	£45,000	£40,000	£35,000
N Series Magnette	1271/6	1934-36	£35,000	£30,000	£20,000
TA Midget	1292/4	1936-39	£13,000+	£12,000	£9,000
SA 2 litre	2288/6	1936-39	£22,000+	£18,000	£15,000
VA	1548/4	1936-39	£12,000	£8,000	£5,000
TB	1250/4	1939-40	£15,000	£11,000	£9,000

Value will depend on body style, history, completeness, racing history, the addition of a supercharger and originality.

1938 MG TA Two-Seater,
very good condition throughout.
£8,000–8,750 *DB*

1934 MG NA Magnette Four-seater, restored,
two-tone paintwork in dark brown and tan,
tan hood, rigid side curtains, good condition.
£17,000–20,000 *BKS*

*Launched in March 1934, the N-Type Magnette
was intended to fill the gap left by the end of
production of the L-Type Magna. It had a new,
stronger chassis, underslung at the rear, with
no fewer than eight tubular crossmembers. An
unorthodox feature was the use of a four-point
flexibly-mounted subframe to insulate the body
from road shocks, while the six-cylinder 1271cc
power unit was also flexibly mounted.*

r. **1939 MG TA Tickford Drophead Coupé,**
1250cc, 4 cylinders, red with Biscuit leather
interior, walnut dash and door cappings, new
double-duck hood, very good original condition.
£13,000–15,000 *BRIT*

1946 MG TC Midget, 1250cc, very good original condition.
£10,500–12,000 *BKS*

MG TC/TD/TF Midgets (1945–1955)

Engine: 1250 or 1466cc (TF1500), in-line four.
Power output: 1250cc, 54–57bhp;
1466cc, 63bhp.
Top speed: 1250cc, 75+mph; 1466cc, 85+mph.
0–60mph: 1250cc, 19–22 seconds; 1466cc,
18+ seconds.

Even at the launch of the TC in September 1945, MG's Midget theme was pretty well matured, if not pushing middle age. The two-seater TC was a make-over of the pre-war TB, itself an update of the 1935 TA, which carried genes dating back to the original M-Type Midget of 1929. In effect, the post-war TC Midget was a brand-new vintage sports car. Yet it took off, spearheading MG's export trail across the world, and particularly to the USA.

The TC sold in greater numbers than any previous MG, and two-thirds of the 10,000 built went abroad, even though they were only produced with right-hand drive. In 1950, the winning formula was warmed over slightly to make the TD, with rack-and-pinion steering, a few extra bhp from the 1250cc engine and independent front suspension. The TD, the first MG available in left-hand drive, sold 29,664, most going abroad. The final fling was the restyled TF, which paid passing lip service to modernity with a lower bonnet line, raked grille and headlamps blended into the wings. In its last years, the TF received a 1500cc engine, but with falling sales – 9,600 TFs were built – the theme was played out as a volume product.

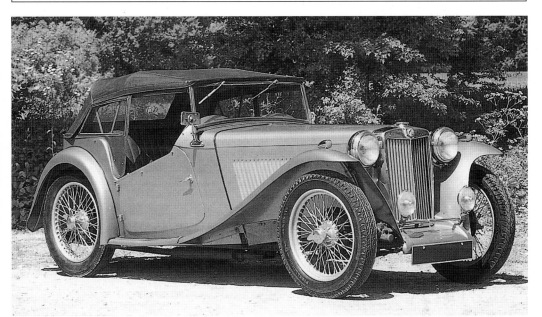

1949 MG TC Midget, 1250cc, restored, dry-stored, excellent condition.
£11,500–13,000 *BKS*

Make the most of Miller's

Condition is absolutely vital when assessing the value of a vehicle. Top class vehicles on the whole appreciate much more than less perfect examples. Rare, desirable cars may command higher prices even when in need of restoration.

1950 MG TD Midget, 1250cc, 4 cylinders, optional Lucas fog lamps, wire wheels, original disc wheels included, restored, engine rebored, new crank, Lumenition electronic ignition, radiator recored, stainless steel exhaust, new body panels, running boards and fuel tank, original green leather seats, excellent condition.
£10,500–12,000 *BRIT*

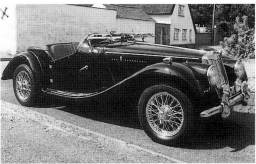

1953 MG TF Midget, restored, bare metal respray, chrome wire wheels, headlamp stone guards, aero screens, Lucas SLR and SFT auxiliary lamps, luggage rack, original red leather trim, good condition.
£13,000–15,000 *BRIT*

By 1953, the TD Midget was looking decidedly archaic, and the TF was hurried into production late that year. Its revised front-end styling featured faired-in headlamps and an inclined radiator grille. However, the mechanical specification was largely unchanged, the XPAG type engine developing 57bhp at 5,500rpm, as in the TDII.

1954 MG TF 1500 Midget, restored, 7,638 miles since, well maintained, very good condition.
£10,250–11,500 *BKS*

The TF initially used the TD's 57bhp, 1250cc XPAG engine, but the need for more power prompted the swift introduction of the TF 1500, with 63bhp, 1466cc XPEG engine. The latter accounted for more than half of total TF production. With the 1500's introduction, top speed improved from 80 to 85mph, and the standing quarter-mile time was reduced by one second.

1950 MG YA Saloon, 1250cc, 4 cylinders, 4-speed manual gearbox, restored, original green leather interior, sliding sunroof, very good condition.
£5,500–6,000 *H&H*

1958 MG ZB Magnette, 1500cc, restored, 100 miles covered since, excellent condition throughout.
£3,500–4,000 *H&H*

1959 MG Magnette MkI, 1489cc, finished in black and white with red trim, 23,000 miles from new, stored for past 17 years, good condition throughout.
£1,700–2,000 *LF*

BMC called in Farina to redesign their mid-range cars in the late 1950s, and the result was a crisp-looking family car. The sporting version wore MG's octagon badge and retained the Magnette designation.

Miller's Starter Marque

Starter MGs: *MGA, MGB, MGB GT, MG Midget 1961 onwards.*

- MGB: In its long life, the MGB became the best-selling British sports car ever, notching up just over 500,000 sales. These days, it's still hard to beat as a great-value and practical everyday classic that's perfectly usable in the cut and thrust of modern traffic.

- The fact that you could, if you had the inclination, build a brand-new MGB from scratch says it all. Parts availability, club support and professional services for the MGB are unrivalled.

- **Pick of the bunch:** Purists prefer the models produced before 1974, when the styling and handling were compromised with rubber bumpers and a higher ride height – both introduced to meet US regulations.

- MGA: Many liken the lovely MGA to a scaled-down Jaguar XK120, yet despite its slightly exotic looks, it's pretty rugged and has the benefit of being based largely on readily available mechanicals from the Morris-BMC-Nuffield parts bins. With just a few more than 100,000 made, it also stands out a lot more than the MGB.

- MG Midget: The Midget is a compelling classic cocktail for the cost conscious. With more than 200,000 built up to 1979, there's tremendous club support, a well-established and competitive spares and remanufacturing industry, and a network of marque specialists and restorers. Once again, it's a BMC parts-bin special, based on the mechanicals and running gear from the likes of the million-selling Morris Minor and the Austin A35. If classic looks matter most, go for a pre-1974 car with chrome bumpers. The best performer from this era is the 1966–74 Midget MkIII with its 1275cc engine. For performance alone, the 1500cc Triumph Spitfire-engined Midgets from 1974 onwards are the fastest, being capable of 100mph.

1959 MGA 1500, imported from USA, red with black upholstery and trim, restored, converted to right-hand drive, wire wheels, new weather equipment, sidescreens, full tonneau, 1,600 miles since restoration, very good condition.
£9,000–10,000 *BKS*

Launched in 1955 as a replacement for the TF Midget, the MGA took the American and British markets by storm, breaking all MG sales records during its production, which lasted until 1962. The design was based on a new box-section chassis, which featured the TF coil-sprung independent front suspension and a leaf-sprung live rear axle. The bodyshell was built entirely of pressed steel panels. The BMC B-Series overhead-valve engine, with twin SU carburettors, initially produced 68bhp (later 72bhp) at 5,500rpm, giving the car a top speed of almost 100mph.

1960 MGA 1500, 1.5 litres, Powder Blue with blue leather interior, fully restored, excellent condition.
£12,000–14,000 *VIC*

1960 MGA Fixed-Head Coupé, 1600cc, resprayed, new screen rubbers and head lining, very good condition throughout.
£4,750–5,250 *H&H*

1962 MGA 1600 MkII, specially built with wind-up windows, locking doors, stored for 20 years, excellent unrestored condition.
£13,000–14,000 *THOR*

1963 MGB Roadster, 1798cc, restored, original pull handles, chrome luggage rack, wire wheels, very good condition.
£8,500–10,000 *H&H*

1964 MGB Roadster, 3-bearing engine, original pull handles, extensively restored, 700 miles covered since.
£8,500–10,000 *Mot*

MG Model	ENGINE cc/cyl	DATES	CONDITION 1	2	3
TC	1250/4	1946-49	£13,000	£11,000	£7,000
TD	1250/4	1950-52	£13,000	£9,000	£5,000
TF	1250/4	1953-55	£15,000	£13,000	£8,000
TF 1500	1466/4	1954-55	£16,000	£14,000	£9,000
YA/YB	1250/4	1947-53	£5,500	£2,750	£1,500
Magnette ZA/ZB	1489/4	1953-58	£3,500	£2,000	£500
Magnette Mk III/IV	1489/4	1958-68	£3,500	£1,200	£350
MGA 1500 Roadster	1489/4	1955-59	£12,000	£7,000	£4,000
MGA 1500 FHC	1489/4	1956-59	£8,000	£6,000	£3,000
MGA 1600 Roadster	1588/4	1959-61	£11,000	£9,000	£4,500
MGA 1600 FHC	1588/4	1959-61	£7,000	£5,000	£3,000
MGA Twin Cam Roadster	1588/4	1958-60	£18,000	£12,000	£9,000
MGA Twin Cam FHC	1588/4	1958-60	£14,000	£9,000	£7,000
MGA 1600 Mk II Roadster	1622/4	1961-62	£13,000	£10,000	£4,000
MGA 1600 Mk II FHC	1622/4	1961-62	£9,000	£7,000	£3,000
MGB Mk I	1798/4	1962-67	£7,000	£4,000	£1,200
MGB GT Mk I	1798/4	1965-67	£5,000	£3,500	£1,000
MGB Mk II	1798/4	1967-69	£7,500	£4,000	£1,500
MGB GT Mk II	1798/4	1969	£4,500	£2,500	£850
MGB Mk III	1798/4	1969-74	£6,500	£4,000	£1,100
MGB GT Mk III	1798/4	1969-74	£4,500	£2,500	£1,000
MGB Roadster (rubber bumper)	1798/4	1975-80	£6,000	£4,500	£1,200
MGB GT	1798/4	1975-80	£5,000	£3,000	£1,000
MGB Jubilee	1798/4	1975	£5,000	£3,000	£1,200
MGB LE	1798/4	1980	£8,500	£4,750	£2,250
MGB GT LE	1798/4	1980	£6,000	£3,750	£2,000
MGC	2912/6	1967-69	£8,000	£6,500	£4,000
MGC GT	2912/6	1967-69	£7,000	£5,000	£2,000
MGB GT V8	3528/8	1973-76	£9,000	£6,000	£3,000
Midget Mk I	948/4	1961-62	£4,000	£2,000	£850
Midget Mk II	1098/4	1962-66	£3,000	£2,000	£850
Midget Mk III	1275/4	1966-74	£3,200	£2,000	£850
Midget 1500	1491/4	1975-79	£3,000	£2,000	£850

All prices are for British right-hand drive cars. Deduct 10–15 per cent for left-hand drive varieties, even if converted to right-hand drive.

l. **1971 MGB Roadster,** restored, full mechanical overhaul, new sills, castle rails and inner stepsills, new floor panels, new doors and wings, bare metal respray, good condition throughout.
£7,500–8,000 *PA*

1974 MGB Roadster, optional overdrive, chrome bumpers, leather upholstery, restored, new Heritage bodyshell, drive train overhauled, all worn components replaced, new interior, hood, full tonneau, wheels, exhaust and wiring harness, 100 miles since restoration, as-new condition.
£15,000–17,000 *BKS*

1978 MGB Roadster, 1798cc, 4 cylinders, 4-speed gearbox with overdrive, orange-striped seating, black trim, 73,000 miles recorded, very good condition.
£4,500–5,000 *H&H*

l. **1967 MGB GT,** left-hand drive, recently restored, engine rebuilt, chromework replated, centre-lock chromed wire wheels, finished in Dark Ocean Blue, red upholstery and matching carpets.
£3,500–4,000 *S*

1977 MGB GT, 1798cc, manual overdrive gearbox, excellent condition.
£2,250–2,750 *H&H*

1972 MGB GT, new engine, rear axle and sills, 4-speed manual gearbox with overdrive, wire wheels, new leather seats and walnut dashboard, excellent condition.
£2,750–3,250 *H&H*

r. **1981 MGB GT,** 1798cc, 4 cylinders, engine rebuilt, stainless steel exhaust, well maintained, original unrestored condition.
£2,800–3,200 *BRIT*

1968 MGC Roadster, 2912cc, engine and bodywork rebuilt, 2,000 miles covered since, new cylinder head, camshaft and triple carburettors, 6 branch exhaust manifold, excellent condition throughout.
£8,500–9,500 *H&H*

r. **1968 MGC GT,** 3 litres, Borg-Warner 3-speed automatic transmission, 15,358 miles recorded, good condition.
£4,900–5,400 *BKS*

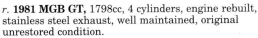

1969 MGC GT, 2912cc, 6 cylinders, optional overdrive, engine rebuilt, new front brake calipers and discs, good condition throughout.
£2,200–2,800 *BRIT*

The MGC was introduced in 1967 and, although outwardly very similar to the MGB, it was powered by a 2912cc engine similar to that used in the contemporary Austin 3 Litre. To accommodate this engine, the bonnet was restyled and torsion-bar front suspension was utilised. Available in GT and Roadster form, the MGC continued in production until 1969, by which time 8,999 examples had been built, production being split almost equally between the two body styles. It is likely that this particular car is one of a number of C GTs marketed by University Motors, under the guise 'University Special', as it is fitted with the horizontally-slatted grille and vinyl roof associated with these cars, several of which had Downton triple-carburettor cylinder heads.

MGB GT V8 (1973–76)

Body style: 2+2 fixed-head coupé.
Construction: Unitary.
Engine: 3528cc alloy V8.
Power output: 137bhp at 5,000rpm.
Suspension: Front, coil springs and wishbones; rear, semi- elliptic parallel leaf springs.
Brakes: Servo-assisted front discs, rear drums.
Steering: Rack-and-pinion.
Top speed: 125mph.
0–60mph: 8.5 seconds.
Fuel consumption: 20–27mpg.
Production: 2,591.

1976 MGB GT V8, 3.5 litres, 137bhp at 5,000rpm, 4-speed manual gearbox with synchromesh and overdrive, restored c1988, well maintained and garaged.
£4,400–5,000 *C*

r. **1994 MG RV8,** Le Mans Green pearlescent metallic with tan leather interior, maple dashboard and door cappings, air conditioning, CD/stereo, full and half tonneau, spoked alloy wheels, 11,000 miles from new, excellent condition.
£19,500–22,000 *CARS*

The MG RV8 was built as a limited edition of about 2,000, most of which were exported to the Far East, mainly Japan. With the 1997 financial crisis in the Pacific Rim, some of these MGs found their way back to the UK, causing prices to fall.

1974 MGB GT V8, concours winner, excellent condition.
£13,000–15,000 *Mot*

1975 MGB GT V8, 3528cc, new wings and sills, cream leather interior, excellent condition throughout.
£5,800–6,500 *BRIT*

With a production run of only 2,591 units, between 1973 and 1976, the V8-engined MGB's performance was particularly impressive, despite the use of the low-compression Rover V8 engine. Its 137bhp equated to a 0–60mph time of around 8 seconds, while maximum speed was in excess of 125mph. This example was registered during 1975 and is one of the last chrome-bumpered models.

1968 MG Midget MkIII, 1275cc, very good condition.
£2,750–3,250 *LF*

MINERVA

1931 Minerva Type AL Convertible Limousine, coachwork by Rollston, Apricot over brown livery, side-mounted spares, black hood, well-appointed interior, upholstered in brown leather and broadcloth, Jaeger instrumentation, Scintilla electrics, excellent condition.
£100,000–120,000 S

Minerva Motors SA, the foremost Belgian manufacturer, was associated with large, luxurious motor cars, and although never common, Minervas could be seen in front of some of the smartest houses in major cities around the world. Production of the 'goddess of automobiles' ceased in 1939. The company's aim with the Type AL, introduced in 1929, was to 'design the finest car in the world'. The chassis was a mammoth, its 153½in wheelbase being exceeded only by the Bugatti Royale and 8 litre Bentley. It was powered by a gigantic 6.6 litre straight-eight engine. Type AL Minervas carried a variety of majestic and exotic coachwork. The number of chassis built before production ceased in 1934 is not known, but only eight are known to have survived.

MINI

The remarkable Mini is the car they couldn't kill off. In the early 1980s, the mediocre Austin Metro was intended as its replacement, but merely demonstrated the brilliance of the original Mini package. And it looks as if the 1959 wonder-car will make it to the millenium – just – before it is replaced for good. One thing's for sure: millions will mourn its passing, because millions have owned and fallen in love with Minis over the years. To some, it's been a commuter runabout, to others – in hot Mini Cooper form – a racing and rallying giant killer. It was a chic fashion accessory in the swinging sixties, and a film star, most notably in the 1960s caper movie *The Italian Job*, starring Michael Caine and Noel Coward. It's all down to designer Sir Alec Arnold Constantine Issigonis, who created the revolutionary, front-wheel-drive Mini with its east-west engine layout and brilliant compact packaging. Since its launch, this cheeky little cherub of a car has found more than five million friends.

1963 Morris Mini Estate, 848cc, full retrim and new carpets, body restored but restoration incomplete, engine not running.
£1,500–1,900 H&H

Mini designer Alec Issigonis showed an uncanny prophetic talent when he quipped to Italian automobile couturier Sergio Farina: 'Look at your cars, they're like women's clothes – they're out of date in two years. My cars will still be in fashion after I've gone.'

1960 Austin 7 Mini Saloon, 850cc, floor start, black fleck upholstery, 56,000 miles recorded, excellent condition.
£1,600–2,000 H&H

Offered originally as an Austin 7 Mini or Morris Mini Minor, this pocket-sized wonder car achieved its own identity by 1970, becoming simply the Mini.

l. **1978 Mini 1340 Turbo,** 1340cc, completely rebuilt, turbocharger with adjustable waste gate, high-pressure fuel pump, oil cooler, Cooper S brakes with braided pipes, 13in Revolution alloy wheels, bare metal respray, roll cage, harnesses, excellent condition.
£2,500–3,000 *H&H*

1985 Mini 1000 City F, 15,000 miles recorded, very good condition.
£1,200–1,700 *PA*

1993 Mini British Open Classic, electric sunroof, one of 2,000, excellent condition.
£3,500–4,000 *CARS*

Ford was one of several companies to take fright when the Mini appeared, but when production engineers took one apart they conclued that BMC could not make money on the Mini's asking price. Ford was right: BMC lost money on each one it sold for the first 10 years but was too badly organised to realise.

Miller's Starter Marque

Starter Minis: *All models.*

- The Mini was so right at its launch in 1959 that it's been left pretty much unmolested over the years, but for many the subtle little touches give early cars an extra charm – the cord door pulls, external hinges and those sliding windows that encourage herbaceous borders to grow in the grooves. Whichever model you choose, once you're behind the wheel, the agility and handling will amaze you, and you'll begin to understand what made the Mini Cooper the definitive rally car of the 1960s.

- The A-Series BMC engines are generally trouble-free, but the Mini's bugbear is rust, and when you're looking at a Mini to buy, the rule of thumb is that wherever there's metal, there's the potential for rust, so pore over it and pay particular attention to the roof panel, guttering and pillars supporting the roof. Rust or filler in these areas suggests worse to come. Examine floorpans from above and below, joints with the inner sill, front and rear bulkheads, crossmember and jacking points. If the subframe has welded plates, check they've been properly attached. Look inside the parcel compartment on each side of the rear seat, beneath the rear seat, all corners of the boot, spare-wheel well and battery container. These are all common areas for rust.

- With a Mini Cooper, you want to be absolutely certain it's the real thing, as their relatively high prices compared to ordinary Minis have encouraged cynical fakers. The best move is to join the club or take professional advice. It's not just a question of checking the uprated specification – twin carbs, disc brakes, badges and the like – but unravelling engine and chassis numbers.

- Of the original generation of Coopers, the best all-round performer is the 1275 S, with 60mph coming up in 10.9 seconds, and the puff running out just shy of the ton.

l. **1966 Mini Moke,** resprayed and reupholstered, 25,000 miles recorded, dry stored, original, requires recommissioning.
£5,750–6,250 *S*

MINI	ENGINE	DATES	CONDITION		
Model	cc/cyl		1	2	3
Mini	848/4	1959-67	£3,500	£1,200	-
Mini Countryman	848/4	1961-67	£2,500	£1,200	-
Cooper Mk I	997/4	1961-67	£8,000	£5,000	£2,500
Cooper Mk II	998/4	1967-69	£6,000	£4,000	£1,500
Cooper S Mk I	var/4	1963-67	£7,000	£5,000	£2,000
Cooper S Mk II	1275/4	1967-71	£6,000	£5,000	£2,000
Innocenti Mini Cooper	998/4	1966-75	£4,500	£2,000	£1,000

1968 Mini Moke, 44,000 miles recorded, original condition.
£3,700–4,000 *WILM*

1970 Mini Hustler, all-wooden bodywork.
£800–950 *DB*

1972 Mini Pick-up, restored, 42,000 miles recorded.
£3,500–4,000 *WILM*

1963 Austin Mini Cooper, oil cooler, Revolution alloy wheels, good condition.
£1,300–1,500 *H&H*

1967 Austin Mini Cooper S, 1275cc, green with white roof and grey interior, right-hand drive, completely restored to original condition.
£5,200–5,800 *BKS*

The record books show three Monte Carlo Rally wins for the Mini Cooper – in 1964, 1965 and 1967, but Coopers actually filled the first three spots in 1966 only to be disqualified by the miffed Monegasque organisers on trumped up technicalities.

1968 Morris Mini Cooper MkII, 998cc, blue with white roof, black interior, 71,000 miles from new, very good condition.
£1,250–1,400   *H&H*

1968 Austin Mini Cooper,
very good condition throughout.
£2,500–3,000   *H&H*

1968 Morris Mini Cooper, 998cc, 4-speed manual gearbox, new sills, floors and sub-frame, fully restored, excellent condition.
£2,000–2,500   *H&H*

1973 Innocenti Mini Cooper 1300, 1275cc, 4 cylinders, twin fuel tanks, front quarter-lights, Cooper bonnet stripes, good condition throughout.
£3,000–3,500   *BRIT*

Probably best known for the Lambretta scooter, Innocenti moved into car production in 1961 by assembling the Farina-designed Austin A40. Throughout the 1970s, all Innocentis were BMC-based, often with unique styling. The Innocenti Mini Cooper was built between 1972 and 1975 and had a level of trim that was far better than any Mini model produced before. The principal exterior differences were the quarter-light windows, the radiator grille, square number plate recessed on the boot lid, side repeater indicators and a sump guard. The engine was unique to this car, the 1275cc Cooper S 11-stud head being used on the Leyland 1300cc 4-cylinder engine, because of its thicker block walls. The power output was similar to the Cooper S at 75bhp.

1971 Austin Mini Cooper S MkIII, 1275cc, Wood & Pickett conversion, twin fuel tanks, additional carpets, tinted windows, roll-back sunroof, good condition.
£4,500–5,000   *S*

Sir Alec Issigonis died in 1988 when the Mini was poised for a renaissance as a fully-catalysed enviro-friendly car for the nineties and beyond.

r. **1975 Innocenti Mini Cooper,** 1300cc, extensively restored, Minilite alloy wheels, fabric sunroof, quadoptic halogen headlights with chrome grilles, interior trimmed in Connolly hide, Wilton carpets, walnut door cappings, Motolita woodrim steering wheel, very good condition.
£3,200–3,700   *H&H*

l. **1946 Cisitalia D46 Monoposto,** completely restored, new space-frame, original supplied, race-ready condition. **£27,000–32,000** *BKS*

The D46 was the first series-built racing car with a space-frame. Over the years, this car has become well-known in Historic events and at venues such as the Nürburgring, Mont Ventoux, Monte Carlo and Bern.

r. **1953 Cooper-Bristol MkII,** 6 cylinders, 1971cc, chassis No. CB12, engine No. 1100644, tubular space-frame chassis, good condition. **£35,000–38,000** *COYS*

This car has been campaigned in VSCC and GHPCA events.

l. **1952 2 Litre Connaught A-Type Formula 2 Single-Seater,** chassis No. A4, Lea-Francis-based 4 cylinder engine, full FIA Historic paperwork and VSCC Blue Form, completely restored, bills for over £31,000, excellent condition. **£165,000–185,000** *BKS*

This car has had an active and prolonged racing career.

1952 HWM-Alta Formula 2, 4 cylinders, 2500cc, 2-stage supercharger, excellent condition. **£88,000–98,000** *COYS*

Tony Gaze raced this car in New Zealand, taking fourth in the New Zealand Grand Prix and second to Peter Whitehead's blown Ferrari in the Lady Wigram Trophy. The car's entire history is known and fully documented.

r. **1955 Indy Car Streamliner,** ID No. 270-302-1, light alloy in-line 4 engine, double overhead camshafts, 2700cc, 385bhp at 5,250rpm, 4-speed manual gearbox, numerous spares including an original 2-speed gearbox, excellent condition. **£78,000–88,000** *C*

l. **1956 2½ Litre Maserati 250F Formula 1 Grand Prix Single-Seater,** completely restored, in running order. **£500,000+** *BKS*

This is thought to be one of the best presented and potentially most competitive Historic racing Maserati 250Fs to have been seen in recent years.

l. **1970 8 Litre McLaren-Chevrolet M8D,** excellent condition.
£145,000–160,000 *BKS*

This magnificently presented CanAm McLaren was John Foulston's favourite racing car, and is a glittering reminder of the Gulf-McLaren works team's success from 1967 to 1971.

r. **1971 5 Litre Repco-Brabham BT36X Competition Single-Seater,** V8 engine, Hewland DG300 5-speed transaxle gearbox, restored, good condition.
£32,000–36,000 *BKS*

l. **1971 3 Litre McLaren-Cosworth Ford M19A Formula 1 Single-Seater,** chassis No. M19A-1, restored, 889 miles since last rebuild, excellent condition.
£145,000–160,000 *BKS*

Built for the 1971 Formula 1 World Championship season, this car made its debut in the opening South African Grand Prix, driven by former World Champion, Denny Hulme.

r. **1989 Reynard 893-Alfa Romeo Formula 3 Single-Seater,** chassis No. 074, newly rebuilt, excellent condition.
£17,500–20,000 *BKS*

Jacques Villeneuve drove this car in 1989 mostly in Italy, but also in Monte Carlo.

l. **1980 5 Litre Lola-Chevrolet T530 CanAm Single-Seater,** chassis No. HU4-10, 180+mph, 10.9in diam ventilated front disc brakes, 11.97in rears, excellent condition.
£52,000–58,000 *BKS*

Only 10 of these cars were built, and they were among the world's most potent racing cars.

1988 1½ Litre Turbocharged Ferrari F187/88C Formula 1 Single-Seater, chassis No. 102, well preserved.
£200,000+ *BKS*

This is the Ferrari F187/88C in which Gerhard Berger secured the marque's first Formula 1 race win after the death of Enzo Ferrari.

1939 Midget Racer, 2229cc, Ford V8 92A engine, good condition.
£900–1,200 *BKS*

1948 Iota P1-JAP Wasp, race-ready condition.
£7,000–9,000 *BKS*

This car first appeared as the Wasp at the 1949 British Grand Prix meeting at Silverstone, driven by its original owner/builder, Jack Moor.

1994 3½ Litre Lotus-Honda Type 109 Formula 1 Single-Seater, chassis No. 109/03, no engine.
£36,000–40,000 *BKS*

This is the last Formula 1 car made by the legendary Lotus company before its withdrawal from Formula 1 competition at the end of the 1994 World Championship season.

l. **1959 Elva 100 Formula Junior,**
998cc, BMC engine, fully restored,
race-ready for VSCC and FIA events.
£20,000–21,000 *Car*

r. **1959 Gemini Formula Junior
MkII,** 1100cc, Ford engine, all-alloy
body, FIA papers, eligible for VSCC,
excellent condition.
£23,000–25,000 *Car*

*From the Tolhurst Collection, this
famous car was driven in the 1960
Monaco Formula Junior Race by
Geoff Duke.*

l. **1960 Lotus 18,** F1 Alfa Romeo
1500cc engine, Colotti 5-speed
gearbox, Conraro tuning parts,
restored in 1992.
£100,000–110,000 *Car*

*This car won the South African
Formula 1 Championship in 1961,
driven by Syd van der Vvyer. It is
the only Lotus 18 fitted with an
Alfa Romeo engine.*

r. **1960 Lancia Volpini FJ,**
1000cc, Lancia V4 rear-
mounted engine, ready-to-
race condition.
£18,000–20,000 *Car*

*Unfortunately, this car was
not competitive in its day.
It is unique as it is the only
one made with a rear-
mounted engine.*

1962 Cooper T59 Formula Junior, 1100cc, Ford MAE engine, Cooper ERSA gearbox, excellent condition.
£23,000–25,000 *Car*

This was one of Cooper's best Formula Juniors. Its first owner was Kurt Lincoln, Jochen Rindt's father-in-law.

1961 Lotus 20/22 Formula Junior, 1100cc, restored, excellent condition.
£25,000–27,500 *Car*

This car has raced successfully in HSCC events.

r. **1967 Austin-Healey 3000 MkIII BJ8,** 3000cc, photographic record of restoration costing over £40,000, hard core radiator, oil cooler, fully balanced engine, triple Weber carburettors, Tulip gearbox, competition overdrive, limited-slip differential, twin coils, twin petrol pumps, 4 disc brakes, competition seats, inbuilt fire system, foam-filled petrol tank, full roll-over cage, full harness, louvred bonnet, rally boot, works replica hardtop, sump guard, chrome wire wheels, new steel panels all round, excellent condition.
£21,000–25,000 *H&H*

This car has competed in the Pyrenees, Alsace and Irish rallies with total reliability and good results.

l. **1965 Alfa Romeo Giulia Tubolare TZ1,** styling by Zagato, chassis No. 750 069, full FIA specification restoration, Plexiglass windows, racing mirrors, roll-cage, full racing harnesses to bucket seats, excellent condition.
£70,000–75,000 *S*

This model was designed for racing, but was available in street and competition trim. TZ1s came first and second in class at Le Mans in 1964. It is believed that only 124 closed coupé examples were produced.

r. **1952 RGS Atalanta-Jaguar,** 6 cylinders, 3442cc, double overhead camshafts, C-Type cylinder head, 250bhp, fibreglass shell, good condition.
£25,000–28,000 *COYS*

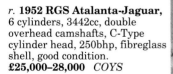

l. **1965 Elva MkVII BMW,** chassis No. 70/064, 4 cylinders, 1997cc, 210bhp, FIA papers, race-prepared condition.
£41,000–45,000 *COYS*

Driven by Lanfranchi, this car had considerable success in sprint races.

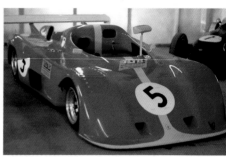

1957 1.1 Litre Lotus-Climax Type 11 'Club' Road/ Race Sports Two-Seater, chassis No. 287, engine No. 601ST, 4 cylinders, 75bhp, single overhead camshaft.
£22,500–26,000 *BKS*

1973 Osella PA3 Group Six, 2000cc, BMW M12 Formula 2 engine, race-ready condition.
£67,000–70,000 *Car*

l. **1971 Porsche 908/3,** 8 cyinders, 350hp at 8,400rpm, excellent condition.
£470,000+ *Pou*

Only 13 of these 200+mph cars were built between 1968 and 1971.

1954 Lister-Bristol Open Sports, coachwork by Williams & Pritchard, 6 cylinders, 1971cc, 140bhp at 6,000rpm, triple downdraught Solex carburettors, 4-speed synchromesh Bristol gearbox, history file, comprehensively restored, excellent condition.
£69,000–76,000 *COYS*

With this car is a 1987 letter from Brian Lister, in which it is described as 'one of the most original of the genuine Lister cars in existence today'. There are also copies of race results, technical drawings and specifications, the original buff log book and current registration document.

l. **1966 Fiat Abarth 1000SP,** 4 cylinders, 982cc, restored, right-hand drive, very good condition.
£45,000–50,000 *COYS*

Between 1965 and 1970 this car competed in events throughout Italy, including the Trento Bondone hill climb, Mugello and the famous Targa Florio.

r. **1961 Alfa Romeo Giulietta SZ Coupé by Zagato,** 4 cylinders, 1600cc, roll-over bar, competition bucket seats, Halda timing equipment, fully rebuilt original engine, restoration costing £30,000, excellent condition.
£45,000–50,000 *COYS*

l. **1955 Alfa Romeo 1900 C SS Two-Seater Coupé,** coachwork by Touring, double-overhead-camshaft engine, race-prepared at great expense, unused for 4 years, good condition throughout.
£19,000–24,000 *BKS*

This car was raced at Misano, Monza and the Nürburgring, and won its class in the 1992 Targa Florio.

r. **1953 Scuderia Ferrari 340/375 Mille Miglia Spyder,** coachwork by Scaglietti, chassis and engine No. 02934AM, V12 engine, 4.4 litres, 360bhp at 6,600rpm, 4-speed manual gearbox, 2 owners from new, restored, documented history, excellent condition.
£675,000+ *C*

Introduced in 1953, the 340 Mille Miglia coincided with the inauguration of the World Sports Car Championship, a series for which it will forever be remembered. Most recently it was accepted in the 1997 Mille Miglia Retro and raced at the 1997 Sears Point Wine Country Classics.

l. **1956 Alfa Romeo 1900 Super,** 4 cylinders, 1975cc, 5-point roll-cage, Fusina racing seats, Koni dampers, twin Weber sidedraught carburettors, aluminium bonnet, special vintage instruments, 2 owners, completely restored, excellent condition.
£12,000–14,000 *COYS*

In 1995, this car was prepared for competition in the gruelling historic Carrera Panamericana with the Squadra Corse del Portello.

r. **1965 Ford GT40,** chassis No. 1013, 8 cylinders, 4727cc, Weber carburettors, fully restored to race specification, documented history, excellent condition.
£200,000+ *COYS*

l. **1964 Ferrari 250 Le Mans,** 12 cylinders, 3286cc, 360bhp at 7,500rpm, 5-speed non-synchromesh gearbox, restored, excellent condition.
£600,000+ *COYS*

This is the ninth of 32 examples.

l. **1962 Jaguar MkII,** 3.8 litres, manual gearbox with overdrive, race-modified, racing history, left-hand drive, excellent condition.
£11,000–12,000 *WILM*

MkII Jaguars were a mainstay of British 1960s saloon car racing, although less commonly employed as rally cars.

r. **1956 Jaguar D-Type Sports Racing Car,** chassis No. XKD537, engine No. E2047-9, 6 cylinders, 3444cc, double overhead camshafts, 275bhp at 6,000rpm, 4-speed manual gearbox, 4-wheel brakes, less than 20,000 miles from new, excellent condition.
£640,000+ *C*

There are probably fewer than 10 D-Types intact that still retain their original monocoque, sub-frame, engine, gearbox, bodywork and all major components. This car even has the original shock absorbers.

l. **1954 Kieft-Climax Sports Racing Two-Seater,** fully road equipped with hood and tonneau cover, very good condition.
£17,000–20,000 *BKS*

These were the first cars to use the Coventry Climax FWA engine. It was shown at the 1954 Earl's Court Motor Shows, repainted red and shown in full touring guise, having previously also run in the Tourist Trophy at Dundrod.

r. **1957 Lotus Eleven Sport,** chassis No. 271, BMC Sprite engine, BMC A-Series close-ratio gearbox, stored from 1972, completely restored in 1995, excellent condition.
£21,000–25,000 *COYS*

The Lotus Eleven, created in 1956, was one of the company's most successful competition cars. All four Lotus Elevens that entered the 1956 Le Mans 24-Hour Race finished, one taking first in class and 9th overall.

l. **1967 Ford Team Lotus Cortina Two-Door Saloon,** Formula 2 Cosworth FVA 16-valve 1598cc engine, 218bhp, fuel injection, excellent condition.
£25,000–30,000 *BKS*

Raced by the late, great Graham Hill during 1967, this competition saloon, with many light-alloy panels, may be the only survivor of the most exclusive variant of the much-loved Lotus Cortina, specially built for track racing by Ford's Competition Department at Boreham, under the direction of competition

l. **1964 MGB,** 4 cylinders, 1840cc, 135bhp, competition bearings, forged pistons, gas-flowed head, lightened flywheel, 3-speed close-ratio gearbox with competition uprated overdrive, brakes uprated to competition specification with braided stainless steel hoses, competition springs and shock absorbers, full harnesses, 6-point roll-cage, matching Swiss SINN watches, Halda Twin Master, Halda Speed Pilot, rebuilt at cost of £30,000, 5,000 miles since, excellent condition.
£17,500–20,000 *COYS*

1946 Lancia Aprilia Barchetta Corsa 1500, by Luigi Berretta, 4 cylinders, 1486cc, 85hp at 6,000rpm, aluminium body, restored, excellent condition.
£48,000–55,000 *Pou*

1970 Mini Cooper Saloon, 998cc, in rally trim, Corbeau seats, full safety harness, competition steering wheel, spotlights, Don Barrow navigation light and roll-over bar, rebuilt in early 1980s, good condition.
£4,000–4,500 *S*

Racing & Rallying – Getting Started

From Peking to Paris, Edinburgh to Monte Carlo, Land's End to John O'Groats, or the entire width of the United States, these are just a few of the epic adventures tackled by classic cars in recent years as they re-enact some of the great motoring challenges.

Perhaps the most extreme classic endurance event ever was 1997's 10,000 mile Peking to Paris Motor Challenge, an epic re-creation of the 1907 race, won by Prince Scipio Borghese aboard an Itala. The 1997 race was won not by a hugely valuable exotic, but by a humble 1942 Willys Jeep, which ably demonstrates that whatever you own there's a whole world of opportunities for friendly classic competition. At the other end of the scale and closer to home, each year at the end of May over 1,000 classic cars enjoy the Guardian Insurance RAC Classic road run. Enthusiasts from start points all over the country converge on Silverstone race circuit at the end of the day. All you need is a 20-year-old car and a friend to read the map. Many who have taken part have caught the rallying bug and have gone on to tackle serious competitive events.

It you feel like having a go on a racing circuit, you can whet your appetite without building or buying a fully race-prepared machine. For example, each year the magazine *Classic and Sports Car* organises a series of track days that allow owners of standard, road-going classic cars to taste the thrill of circuit driving. For some, that fulfills their need for speed, but whatever you drive you can find a way to participate that suits your car, your pocket and your competitive instincts, from cross-continent epics to countryside meanders, from race track capers in Citroën 2CVs to serious single-seater racing in valuable and historic Grand Prix cars, such as the fabled Maserati 250F. It is refreshing and thrilling for spectators that there are people out there who consider there is no such thing as a car too valuable to race. At the other end of the scale, gentle exercise and competition keeps cars alive rather than lying unused in lock-ups.

l. **1962 MGA MkII Coupé,** 4 cylinders, 1622cc, rebuilt into a Sebring replica with alloy opening panels, Perspex windows, additional brake cooling ducts, twin SU carburettors, close-ratio gearbox, excellent condition.
£10,000–12,000 *COYS*

The 1992 Lotus 107 rear wing end plate from Mika Hakkinen's race car, with Goodyear and Whionogi decals, signed by the driver and inscribed 'The Finn 1992'.
£350–400 *BKS*

A Camel Lotus Honda 99T front wing end plate from Ayrton Senna's racing car, used in the 1987 San Marino Grand Prix, where he came second, signed.
£800–1,000 *BKS*

A photograph of the 1994 Formula 1 drivers, signed by Nigel Mansell, framed and glazed.
£150–175 *BKS*

A signed photograph of Ayrton Senna, by John Toscano, dated '1993', 5 x 7in (13 x 18cm).
£675–725 *S*

A photograph of Graham Hill in his car, signed.
£420–450 *BKS*

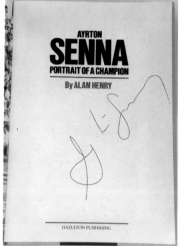

Alan Henry, *Ayrton Senna, Portrait of a Champion*, signed by Senna, 1988.
£75–100 *GPCC*

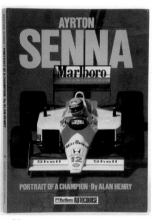

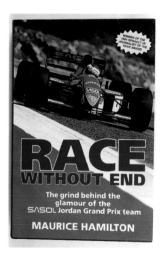

Maurice Hamilton, *Race Without End*, signed by Barrichello, Irvine and Eddie Jordan, 1994, 9½ x 6½in (24 x 16.5cm).
£45–50 *GPCC*

Alan Henry, *Brabham, The Grand Prix Cars*, 1985.
£22–25 *GPCC*

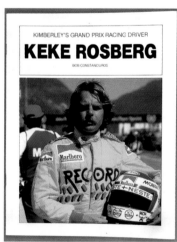

Bob Constanduros, *Keke Rosberg, Kimberley's Grand Prix Racing Driver*, signed by Rosberg, 1984, 11 x 8½in (28 x 21.5cm).
£40–45 *GPCC*

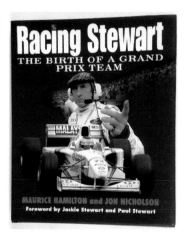

Maurice Hamilton and Jon Nicholson, *Racing Steward, The Birth of a Grand Prix Team*, signed, 1997, 11½ x 9in (29 x 23cm).
£70–75 *GPCC*

Bernd Rosemeyer's Castrol presentation silver helmet, lining repaired and replaced, inscribed and dated '1934',.
£10,350–11,350 *C*

Juan Fangio's leather helmet, used at the Belgian Grand Prix, 1950, signed.
£1,800–2,000 *BKS*

Emerson Fittipaldi's race-worn McLaren Bell visor and helmet, used for the 1974 World Championship racing season.
6,300–6,700 *BKS*

James Hunt's race-worn McLaren Bell visor and helmet, used in the 1976 World Championship racing season.
£11,500–14,500 *BKS*

Keke Rosberg's race-worn Bell helmet and visor, with a letter, book and photograph, c1980.
£2,000–2,300 *BKS*

Denny Hulme's Bell helmet, visor missing, c1972.
£3,500–4,000 *S*

Michael Schumacher's race-worn Bell helmet, worn during the 1992 racing season, with original box and manual.
£2,600–2,900 *BKS*

Martin Brundle's race-worn Bell helmet and tinted visor, used during the 1996 Canadian Grand Prix, signed and dated.
£3,000–3,300 *BKS*

Nigel Mansell's race-worn Arai helmet and visor, used during the 1992 Grand Prix season.
£3,750–4,250 *BKS*

Ayrton Senna's race-worn helmet, used in 2 Grands Prix in 1992, signed, with original visor and certificate of authenticity.
£33,000–37,000 *BKS*

A special edition Ferrari helmet, painted by Bieffe, signed by 13 Ferrari drivers, with helmet bag and box, and letter of provenance.
£2,150–2,400 *S*

David Coulthard's race-worn Bell helmet and tinted visor, used during 1995 racing season, with a photograph and carrying bag.
£5,750–6,250 *BKS*

A pair of James Hunt's racing overalls, used in his 1976 World Championship-winning season, mounted with a photograph, in a display case.
£5,750–6,250 *S*

A Parmalat Formula 1 baseball cap, signed on the peak by triple World Champion, Niki Lauda, with 2 pictures of Lauda.
£460–500 *S*

A racing suit, worn by James Hunt, Marlboro McLaren World Champion 1976, oil-stained and well-worn.
£7,000–8,000 *C*

A pair of Simpson race overalls, used by 1979 World Champion Jody Scheckter, March 1980.
£4,000–4,500 *S*

A pair of Emerson Fittipaldi's racing overalls, by Stand 21, used during the 1993 Indy Car Championship season for the Penske team, signed.
£8,000–10,000 *S*

l. A pair of Damon Hill's Sparco racing overalls, used during the 1996 World Championship season.
£3,400–3,700 *S*

Michael Schumacher's Ferrari OMP race suit, used during the qualifying rounds for the British Grand Prix of 1996.
£5,200–5,600 *BKS*

Gerhard Berger's Nomex race-worn Sparco/Benetton racing suit, used during the 1996 Grand Prix season.
£1,800–2,100 *BKS*

The sponsors' logos include Mild Seven, Autogrill, Elf, Renault, Kickers etc. The driver's name is embroidered on the belt and it also comes with a certificate of authenticity from Benetton.

A pair of Rubens Barrichello's Sparco overalls, used at the Japanese Grand Prix of 1996, signed.
£1,100–1,300 *S*

Eddie Irvine's race-worn Momo Corse Ferrari race suit, used in the Melbourne Grand Prix of 1997, signed.
£1,500–1,700 *BKS*

The steering wheel from Ayrton Senna's Formula 1 car, suede covered, signed and dated 'Brasil '84'.
£6,200–6,600 *S*

Senna's first Grand Prix appearance was at Brazil in the Toleman Group Motorsport 1.5 litre turbocharged TG183B.

A Momo Ferrari steering wheel, signed by Alain Prost and Jean Alesi, 1991, and a photograph depicting Prost in his 1991 Ferrari racing overalls.
£1,150–1,350 *S*

A collection depicting the history of the Land and Waterspeed records, with 70 cars and boats, by Rod Holland, together with related signed photographs, copy posters and press cuttings.
£10,350–10,750 *C*

The steering wheel from Innes Ireland's Seattle crash in the Lotus 19 Team Rosebud car, September 1963, together with letters and cards.
£5,200–5,500 *S*

Nelson Piquet's Momo flat-base steering wheel, from his Lotus-Judd type 101 driven in the 1989 Japanese Grand Prix, signed and inscribed 'Suzuka 89'.
£700–750 *BKS*

A Momo red suede Team Lotus Ford 107B steering wheel, from a Lotus Formula 1 car, hub drilled ready to accept boss switch gear, 1993.
£250–300 *BKS*

l. A model of the Williams FWO8, driven by Keke Rosberg, winner of the 1982 World Championship.
£150–180 *PC*

l. A model of the Le Mans-winning 1993 Peugeot 905.
£200–250 *PC*

r. A Toschi Ferrari model, with steering wheel, flyscreen, exhaust vents and transfers.
£950–1,150 *BKS*

Normally made as a rubber-band driven toy, this model was supplied as a spirit decanter holder. Now without its original bottle, the liquid would have been dispensed from a funnel in the front grille.

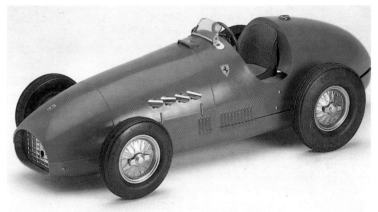

Ferrari 375 MM Spyder Corsa, a model by Jacques Catti of the famous Mille Miglia and Le Mans team car, with detachable bonnet, boot and metal tonneau cover, with a similar scale model of the full running-chassis, 13in (33cm) long.
£11,000–12,000 *C*

l. A model of the German Grand Prix-winning Mercedes SSK 2-seater car, wire-spoked wheels, bright chromework, outside exhaust, black leather trim, drilled chassis, triple-stud racing tyres, stoneguard, mounted on a polished wood base, 16in (40.5cm) long.
£4,400–4,800 *C*

Nicholas Watts, Monaco Grand Prix 1930, depicting René Dreyfus in a Bugatti Type 35, limited edition print, 33 x 25in (84 x 63cm).
£120–140 *MPG*

Nicholas Watts, Nürburgring German Grand Prix 1937, depicting Caracciola in Mercedes W125, oil on board, signed and dated '1985', 20½ x 28¾in (52 x 73cm).
£1,700–1,900 *BKS*

Nicholas Watts, Nürburgring German Grand Prix 1939, depicting Caracciola in Mercedes W154, oil on board, signed, 20½ x 29in (52 x 74cm).
£1,350–1,550 *BKS*

Nicholas Watts, Mille Miglia 1955, depicting Stirling Moss and Denis Jenkinson in their Mercedes 300SLR, limited edition print, 33 x 25in (84 x 63cm).
£110–125 *MPG*

Nicholas Watts, Le Mans 1954, Gonzalez and Trintignant in their Ferrari 375, leading the Bristol 450 of Fairman and Wisdom, and the Gordini of Pollet and Guelfi, limited edition print, 33 x 25in (84 x 63cm).
£135–150 *MPG*

r. Nicholas Watts, Monte Carlo Rally 1964, depicting the Mini Cooper S of Paddy Hopkirk and Henry Lidden en route to Monte Carlo in the 1964 event, signed by Hopkirk and John Cooper, limited edition print, 33 x 25in (84 x 63cm).
£90–110 *MPG*

l. Nicholas Watts, Targa Florio 1970, depicting Brian Redman and Jo Siffert in their Porsche 908-3, climbing into the mountains from Cerda with Vaccarella's Ferrari 512 behind, signed by Redman, Hans Mezger and Manfred Bantle, 33 x 25in (84 x 63cm).
£100–110 *MPG*

Viejo Santamarta, San Sebastian Gran Premio de España, September 1935, poster, 39 x 27in (100 x 70cm).
£1,150–1,450 S

E. A. Hermans, Grosse Preis von Belgien, original poster for the RAC Belgium, 20 June 1952, 22 x 28in (56 x 71cm).
£400–450 C

Brooklands, Weybridge, British Trophy Race poster, on plywood, 1936, 30 x 20in (76 x 51cm).
£400–450 LE

Le Mans, original film poster featuring Steve McQueen.
£750–800 C

L'Amour en Quatrième Vitesse, original film poster featuring Elvis Presley and Ann-Margret.
£625–675 C

r. Aintree, RAC British Grand Prix 1955, advertising poster, 30 x 19½in (12 x 49.5cm).
£300–350 LE

After Meinhold, a Dunlop poster depicting Donald Campbell's Bluebird record run in July 1964, fitted with Dunlop tyres.
£500–550 BKS

Tudor, Votre Batterie, by P. Rayez, original artwork for poster design, charcoal and watercolour, c1950, framed and glazed, 20 x 40in (51 x 101.5cm).
£520–580 C

MORGAN

Without doubt, Morgan is stuck in a time-warp. Today's products display a direct lineage to the company's original pre-war four-wheeler, the 1935 4/4 model. Until then, from its foundation in 1910 by H. F. S. Morgan, the company's output had been purely three-wheelers, which actually soldiered on until 1952. The four-wheeled Morgans have evolved ever so gently over the years, being powered by a wide variety of proprietary four-cylinder engines. One of the biggest changes was the Plus 8 of 1968, for which Morgan adopted the 161bhp Rover 3.5 litre V8 to create a thrilling 125mph charger.

l. A Morgan 4/4 Club member's badge, pressed steel and chrome with coloured glass enamels, limited edition, c1990.
£35–40 *CARS*

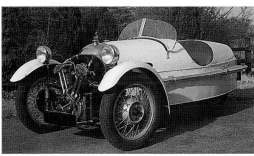

1934 Morgan Super Sports, restored, little use since, finished in ivory with maroon upholstery, tonneau cover, modified with hydraulic brakes.
£13,500–15,000 *S*

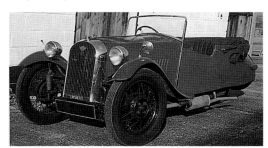

1952 Morgan F4 Tourer, finished in red with black upholstery, correct dashboard, black double-duck hood, good condition.
£3,000–3,500 *S*

1951 Morgan Plus 4 Two-Seater,
2 litres, good condition.
£20,000–23,000 *FHD*

1927 Morgan Aero Two-Seater Sports, 1000cc, air-cooled V-twin JAP engine, twin-exhaust-port cylinder heads, electric starter, restored, new chassis tubes, good condition throughout.
£11,500–13,000 *BKS*

The first of the distinctive three-wheeler Morgans emerged from Malvern College workshops in 1909, a lightweight V-twin-engined machine with chain final drive and independent front suspension. Series production of a three-wheeler began in 1910, and it was not until 1936 that Morgan offered a four-wheel option. This was not surprising, as the three-wheel formula was remarkably successful, not only as a family runabout, but also in Aero and Grand Prix form as a competition machine. A choice of Blackburne, JAP and Matchless engines was offered.

1927 Morgan Aero Anzani.
£18,000–23,000 *FHF*

MORGAN Model	ENGINE cc/cyl	DATES	CONDITION 1	2	3
4/4 Series I	1098/4	1936-50	£10,000	£7,000	£6,000
Plus 4	2088/4	1950-53	£15,000	£10,000	£7,000
Plus 4	1991/4	1954-68	£14,000	£11,000	£7,000
4/4 Series II/III/IV	997/4	1954-68	£10,000+	£7,000	£5,000
4/4 1600	1599/4	1960 on	£14,000	£9,000	£6,000
Plus 8	3528/8	1969 on	£17,000+	£13,500	£10,000

1982 Morgan 4/4, alloy body, sports seats, luggage rack, good condition.
£11,000–12,000 *UMC*

1997 Morgan 4/4, 1800cc, Ford Zetec engine, good condition.
£19,500–21,000 *BHM*

1976 Morgan Plus 8, 3528cc, V8, alloy wheels, Lucas fog lamps, weather equipment in good condition, mohair hood, right-hand drive, good condition.
£12,000–14,000 *BRIT*

The Plus 8, which first saw the light of day in 1968, was the fastest Morgan of all time. Its Rover V8 engine provided a sensational power-to-weight ratio, delivering ferocious acceleration and a top speed in excess of 125mph.

1980 Morgan Plus 8, 3528cc, V8, very well maintained, 47,000 miles recorded, excellent condition throughout.
£13,000–15,000 *BRIT*

1985 Morgan Plus 8, 3500cc, Rover V8 engine, twin carburettors, 5-speed gearbox, twin exhaust, good condition.
£18,000–19,000 *FHD*

l. **1992 Morgan Plus 8,** 3.9 litres.
£27,000–29,000 *BHM*

MORRIS

William Richard Morris was born the son of a farm manager in 1877 near Oxford, the oldest of seven children. A fine athlete and trophy winning cyclist, he bought his first car in 1905 and built up a service and sales operation, but soon had ambitions to make his own car. By 1910, he had laid down what he called 'principles of first importance' for the car he would build: 'The ability to start at any time at a moment's notice; simplicity of control when driving; absolute freedom from trouble.' By 1913, his first car, the one litre 'Bullnose' Morris Oxford was ready, followed two years later by the 1.5 litre Cowley. Both were stout, commendable cars, and they formed the cornerstone of Morris's early reputation. In 1925, with record production of 54,000, Bullnose Morrises accounted for 40 per cent of all British cars made that year.

In later years, the best Morrises still embodied those sound early principles, perhaps none more so than the 1948 Morris Minor. In 1952, Morris and Austin merged to form the British Motor Corporation, and seven years later, in 1959, the Mini – or Morris Mini Minor – appeared. Through the 1960s and 1970s, other Morris offerings were little more than alternately badged Austins, and the name disappeared for good in 1984.

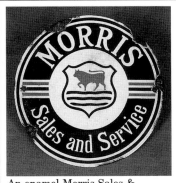

An enamel Morris Sales & Service sign.
£80–90   *CGC*

1913 Morris Oxford Bullnose, 1018cc, 4 cylinder, 10hp White & Poppe engine, 3-speed gearbox, worm-driven rear axle, restored in mid-1980s, dry-stored since.
£9,500–11,000   *COYS*

1923 Morris Oxford Bullnose Tourer,
£8,250–8,750   *DB*

1929 Morris Cowley Wide Track, coachwork by Holden, 2 seater with dickey, built to drive on roads or railways in Australia, restored.
£15,000–16,000   *UMC*

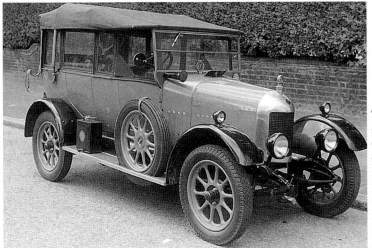

l. **1925 Morris Cowley 11.9hp Bullnose Four-Seater Tourer,** restored to correct original specification, grey livery, dash-mounted petrol gauge, Lucas windscreen-mounted bulb horn, lighting and driving mirror, scuttle ventilator, running board-mounted tool box and spare wheel, full weather protection.
£10,400–12,000   *S*

MORRIS Model	ENGINE cc/cyl	DATES	CONDITION 1	2	3
Prices given are for saloons					
Cowley (Bullnose)	1550/4	1913-26	£12,000	£8,000	£6,000
Cowley	1550/4	1927-39	£10,000	£6,000	£4,000
Oxford (Bullnose)	1803/4	1924-27	£14,000	£10,000	£6,000
Oxford	1803/4	1927-33	£10,000	£8,000	£6,000
16/40	2513/4	1928-33	£8,000	£7,000	£6,000
18	2468/6	1928-35	£9,000	£7,000	£5,000
8 Minor	847/4	1929-34	£5,500	£4,000	£2,000
10/4	1292/4	1933-35	£5,000	£3,000	£1,500
25	3485/6	1933-39	£10,000	£8,000	£5,000
Eight	918/4	1935-39	£4,000	£3,000	£1,500
10hp	1140/4	1939-47	£4,500	£3,000	£1,500
16hp	2062/6	1936-38	£5,000	£3,500	£2,000
18hp	2288/6	1935-37	£5,000	£3,500	£2,500
21hp	2916/6	1935-36	£6,000	£4,000	£2,500

A touring version of the above is worth approximately 30 per cent more and value is very dependent on body type and has an increased value if coachbuilt.

1933 Morris Oxford Four-Door Saloon, 2062cc, 4-speed gearbox, original, dry-stored, requires recommissioning.
£5,300–6,300   *BKS*

Launched in August 1929, the Oxford-Six remained in production until 1933 and was the company's bestseller of the early 1930s. It was always traditionally styled, for Morris had conservative taste in body design and was averse to making change for its own sake. The Autocar described the Oxford-Six as being 'a handsome four-door six-light body of modern lines, with deep sides, eddy-free head, valanced swept wings and louvres over all windows'. The body was mounted on a strong channel-steel chassis. Lockheed hydraulic brakes were fitted, while the clutch was a traditional Morris design with cork inserts in a single plate running in oil.

1937 Morris 14/6 Series III, 1818cc, 6 cylinders, Lockheed hydraulic brakes, black with brown leather interior, good original condition.
£2,600–3,200   *BRIT*

The larger Morris offerings of the late 1930s, powered by six-cylinder engines, represented exceptional value and boasted a particularly high level of equipment. From late 1937, the Morris 14/6 Series III was introduced and was immediately recognisable by its painted radiator shell instead of the earlier chromed surround. Also new were the 'Easiclene' wheels. Due to their great strength and integrity, many of these vehicles remained in service as provincial hire cars well into the 1950s.

1935 Morris 8 Saloon, 918cc, body-off restoration, engine and chassis overhauled, rewired, retrimmed, resprayed, 1,300 miles since rebuild.
£2,900–3,500   *H&H*

l. **1953 Morris Oxford MO,** partially restored, needs completing. **£330–380** *CGC*

1953 Morris Minor Tourer, 1000cc reconditioned engine, completely restored, only 3,480 miles since, resprayed in original Empire Green, new beige hood, interior reupholstered in green, corrosion-proofed every year, excellent condition. **£3,200–3,800** *H&H*

1954 Morris Minor Tourer, 803cc. **£2,700–3,200** *H&H*

Miller's Starter Marque

Starter Morris: *Minor (1948–71).*

- Designed by Alec Issigonis, the genius who later created the Mini, the 1948 Morris Minor became Britain's first million-seller, a feat marked in 1960 with a series of 349 livid lilac-hued Morris 'Millions'. The Minor featured advanced unitary chassis-body construction, and its handling finesse and ride comfort more than made up for the lack of power. The combination proved to be just what ordinary people needed from a car, and the Morris Minor soldiered on until 1971.

- Any model is affordable, and almost as practical to own now as when in production, owing to ready availability and a growing cottage industry that can provide everything you need to keep your Minor in good shape. Generally long-lived, the Minor is one of the easiest cars for DIY maintenance. Its wings are bolted on and may appear sound while concealing horrors beneath. The wood framing of Travellers plays a structural role and should be inspected very carefully.

- The best choice are the first split-screen 'low-light' models, especially convertibles, built before the headlights were raised to the tops of the wings to conform to US regulations.

- Beware 'rogue rag-tops'. Convertibles are more prized, and although there's a legitimate industry converting saloons to open tops, there are also fast-buck cowboys and inept DIY bodgers. Bodged convertibles are potential killers.

Body styles: Saloon, Tourer convertible, Traveller estate.
Engine: 803–1098cc in-line four.
Power output: 28–48bhp.
Top speed: 62–75mph.
Production: 1,619,958.

l. **1956 Morris Minor Saloon,** 948cc engine in place of original 803cc unit, split windscreen, 38,000 miles recorded. **£3,000–3,250** *ESM*

MORRIS Model	ENGINE cc/cyl	DATES	CONDITION 1	2	3
Minor Series MM	918/4	1948-52	£3,000	£1,600	£800
Minor Series MM Conv	918/4	1948-52	£4,500	£2,200	£1,200
Minor Series II	803/4	1953-56	£2,000	£1,000	£500
Minor Series II Conv	803/4	1953-56	£5,500	£3,500	£1,500
Minor Series II Est	803/4	1953-56	£3,000	£1,250	£800
Minor 1000	948/4	1956-63	£1,750	£925	£250
Minor 1000 Conv	948/4	1956-63	£3,000	£2,000	£750
Minor 1000 Est	948/4	1956-63	£4,000	£2,200	£1,200
Minor 1000	1098/4	1963-71	£2,000	£950	£250
Minor 1000 Conv	1098/4	1963-71	£4,500	£3,000	£1,500
Minor 1000 Est	1098/4	1963-71	£4,000	£3,000	£1,500
Cowley 1200	1200/4	1954-56	£1,675	£1,000	£300
Cowley 1500	1489/4	1956-59	£1,750	£950	£350
Oxford MO	1476/4	1948-54	£2,000	£850	£250
Oxford MO Est	1476/4	1952-54	£3,000	£1,500	£350
Series II/III	1489/4	1954-59	£2,000	£1,200	£300
Series II/III/IV Est	1489/4	1954-60	£2,250	£1,350	£250
Oxford Series V Farina	1489/4	1959-61	£1,800	£800	£250
Oxford Series VI Farina	1622/4	1961-71	£1,750	£750	£200
Six Series MS	2215/6	1948-54	£2,500	£1,500	£500
Isis Series I/II	2639/6	1955-58	£2,500	£1,300	£450
Isis Series I/II Est	2639/6	1956-57	£2,600	£1,350	£500

1957 Morris Minor 1000 Saloon, 948cc, 4 cylinders, finished in grey with red interior, modified for unleaded fuel.
£1,100–1,400 *H&H*

1957 Morris Minor 1000 Tourer, 948cc, 4 cylinders, wing mirrors, front seat belts, tow bar, engine replaced in 1972, new exhaust, hood, bumpers and front wing, well maintained.
£2,250–2,750 *BRIT*

The Minor 1000 replaced the Series II model (recognised by its split windscreen) at the 1956 Motor Show. This particular example has had the same owner for the past 40 years.

1961 Morris Minor Four-Door Saloon, grey paintwork, original red leather interior, 50,000 miles, service history.
£2,100–2,400 *ESM*

When he first saw mock-ups of the Minor, Morris boss Lord Nuffield dismissed the design as an ugly 'poached egg'.

1962 Morris Minor 1000 Tourer, completely restored, very good condition.
£5,500–6,000 *WILM*

r. **1966 Morris Minor Two-Door Saloon,** restored, resprayed in Smoke Grey, blue interior, new chrome trim and carpets.
£2,700–3,000 *ESM*

1965 Morris Minor Traveller, original green livery, matching interior trim, 19,000 miles, good condition throughout.
£3,800–4,200 *S*

This particular car was formerly the property of J. Edward Sieff of Marks & Spencer. It has appeared in the television series Heartbeat *and* Darling Buds of May.

1965 Morris Minor 1000 Saloon, 1098cc, grey paintwork, red interior, restored, 45,000 miles, excellent condition.
£1,500–2,000 *H&H*

In 1950 a Minor even tempted the young Stirling Moss into high-speed cornering antics that lost him his licence for a month.

1967 Morris Minor 1000, 1098cc, 4 cylinders, new wings all-round, resprayed, brightwork replated or replaced, 95,000 miles, very good condition.
£2,150–2,650 *BRIT*

The final Minor Series, from 1962 to 1971, utilised the 1098cc version of the A-Series engine, which gave a top speed approaching 80mph, together with considerably improved acceleration.

1971 Morris Minor 1000 Traveller, 1098cc, 4 cylinders, completely restored, Old English White with dark blue interior, 51,000 miles, excellent condition.
£2,600–2,900 *BRIT*

> **Don't Forget!**
> ***If in doubt please refer to the 'How to Use' section at the beginning of this book.***

r. **1968 Morris Minor Traveller,** completely restored, new interior and wood, excellent condition.
£6,000–6,500 *WILM*

The Minor was originally to be called the Mosquito but the name was abandoned as several companies claimed rights to it.

1976 Morris Marina 1800TC Coupé, 1798cc, twin carburettors, bodywork requires some attention, 69,000 miles.
£300–350 *H&H*

NASH

1927 Nash Special Six Coupé, imported from
USA in 1980, finished in maroon and black,
black hide interior, restored.
£7,600–8,400 *CGC*

1929 Nash Six Coupé Series 420, 3107cc,
6 cylinders, restored, original specification,
unused for some time, requires recommissioning.
£5,700–6,400 *BRIT*

*The Nash Six became one of the most popular
American cars following its introduction in the
1920s. A variety of models was available, including
Cabriolet, Sedan, Coupé and Phæton. The overhead-
valve, six-cylinder engine performed well, being
reliable and long-lasting, while the coachwork was
tasteful and distinctive with handsome styling.*

r. **1941 Nash Street
Rod,** good condition.
£4,000–5,000 *PALM*

l. **1955 Nash Metropolitan
Convertible,** good condition.
£3,750–4,500 *PALM*

OGLE

1965 Ogle SX1000, original, green paintwork,
good running order.
£4,900–5,500 *BKS*

*This was the very last Ogle SX1000 to be made,
being built to a very high standard two years after
the last of the regular production run. It was made
for John Ogier and subsequently passed to his
daughter, Patricia.*

1963 Ogle SX1000, rebuilt, full history,
good condition.
£3,750–4,500 *BKS*

*The SX1000 was a high-quality, well-trimmed car
based on a strengthened Mini floorpan with Mini
suspension and a fibreglass body. It offered a choice
of 997cc or 1275cc Mini Cooper engines. Most
SX1000s, like this particular car, had the smaller
unit. Ogle made 66 of these handsome little coupés,
and this was one of the last to be registered.*

OLDSMOBILE

1971 Oldsmobile Cutlass Convertible, good condition.
£4,000–5,000 *PALM*

OLDSMOBILE Model	ENGINE cc/cyl	DATES	CONDITION 1	2	3
Curved Dash	1600/1	1901-04	£16,000	£14,000	£12,000
30	2771/6	1925-26	£9,000	£7,000	£4,000
Straight Eight	4213/8	1937-38	£14,000	£9,000	£5,000

OPEL

l. **1979 Opel Kadette De Luxe,** 16,800 miles recorded, as-new condition. **£1,700–1,900** *Mot*

PACKARD

1926 Packard Third Series Six Model 326 Rumble-Seat Roadster, 4730cc, in-line 6, 136in wheelbase, restored 1990.
£23,000–25,000 *BKS*

Packard sold 40,358 examples of this 'volume classic', more than four times the sales of the Second Series Six, and demand was so great that there was a four-month waiting list for delivery.

| PACKARD | ENGINE | DATES | CONDITION | | |
Model	cc/cyl		1	2	3
Twin Six	6946/12	1916-23	£30,000	£20,000	£15,000
6	3973/6	1921-24	£20,000	£15,000	£12,000
6, 7, 8 Series	5231/8	1929-39	£35,000+	£25,000+	£14,000+
12	7300/12	1936-39	£50,000+	£30,000+	£18,000+

1937 Packard Super Eight 15th Series Sedan, finished in light over dark silver, grey/green interior, right-hand drive, indicators, luggage rack, very good condition throughout.
£11,500–13,000 *S*

The Packard brothers, James Ward and William Dowd, produced uniformly superb motor cars, well made and very expensive. In 1915, they created one of the most outstanding engines of all time, the famous Twin Six, a pioneering 6.9 litre V12. The Twin Six Packard became a formidable rival to the Cadillac. One of the leaders in the American luxury-car market, Packard dominated the Vintage years. The company's management, headed primarily by engineers, spared nothing to produce an outstanding car, and sales outstripped their two rivals, Peerless and Pierce-Arrow.

PANHARD-LEVASSOR

l. **1897 Panhard-Levassor Type M2F Single Phæton with Hood,** 1.65 litre, twin-cylinder engine, 4-speed gearbox, restored, new wooden chassis, original engine, clutch, gearbox, axles, brakes and wheel hubs, new carburettor, burner box, lubricators and water-pump, new wooden bonnet, non-original period bodywork, water tank missing, tube-ignition burner-box incomplete, exhaust system requires silencer and piping, small amount of work needed to recommission.
£145,000–165,000 *C*

In the decade up to 1900, most motorists who wanted 'the best car in the world' would have been more than content with a Panhard-Levassor. The successes of the company's products in early motoring competitions, especially that of Émile Levassor in finishing first in the 1895 Paris-Bordeaux-Paris race, caught the public imagination and, for those who could afford one, a Panhard-Levassor was the car to have.

PANTHER

1976 Panther Rio Saloon, 1998cc, 4 cylinders, 3-speed automatic transmission, 31,544 miles, good condition throughout.
£1,400–2,000 *H&H*

1979 Panther Lima, 2.3 litres, finished in yellow and black, partially restored.
£5,000–6,000 *WILM*

PARAMOUNT

l. **1955 Paramount,** partially stripped for mechanical overhaul, engine rebuilt, original upholstery.
£3,300–4,000 *BKS*

PEUGEOT

l. **1966 Peugeot 404 Cabriolet,** originally imported from USA, completely restored, new floorpan, bare metal respray in white, black interior, concours condition.
£11,500–12,500 *CPUK*

1972 Peugeot 304 Cabriolet, 1288cc, 4 cylinders, 4-speed manual gearbox, restored, red with black interior and hood, 88,000 miles recorded, very good condition.
£3,750–4,250 *H&H*

1973 Peugeot 304 S Coupé, right-hand drive, rear wheel arches repaired, lower half resprayed, 97,000 miles recorded, very good original condition.
£3,000–3,500 *CPUK*

l. **1975 Peugeot 504 V6 Cabriolet,** body, hood and interior restored 10 years ago, 190,000km recorded, excellent condition.
£13,000–15,000 *CPUK*

The V6 Cabriolet was only built between 1975 and 1977 (970 models sold), while four-cylinder cars were available from 1969 to 1974, and 1978 to 1983. This particular car is one of only four V6 models in the UK.

PEUGEOT Model	ENGINE cc/cyl	DATES	CONDITION 1	2	3
Bebe	856/4	1912-14	£18,000	£12,000	£8,000
153	2951/4	1913-26	£9,000	£5,000	£3,000
163	1490/4	1920-24	£5,000	£4,000	£2,000
Bebe	676/4	1920-25	£7,000	£6,000	£3,000
156	5700/6	1922-24	£7,000	£5,000	£3,000
174	3828/4	1922-28	£7,500	£5,000	£2,000
172	714/4	1926-28	£4,000	£3,000	£1,500
183	1990/6	1929-30	£5,000	£3,000	£1,500
201	996/4	1930-36	£4,500	£3,000	£1,500
402	2140/4	1938-40	£4,500	£3,000	£1,000

Right-hand drive cars and tourers will always achieve more interest than left-hand drive. Good solid cars.

PIERCE-ARROW

The first Pierce cars appeared in 1902; by 1908, the company had become Pierce-Arrow and went on to produce some gorgeous and magnificent luxury machines. Studebaker took over in 1928, and the Pierce-Arrows made since then were probably the best, being serious rivals to Cadillac and Lincoln in the USA. The last Pierce-Arrow was built in 1938.

1916 Pierce-Arrow Model 38-C4 38hp Brougham, 7 litres, 6 cylinders, excellent condition throughout. **£23,000–25,000** *BKS*

The designer of the Pierce-Arrow was a Scot named David Fergusson, who had entered the British motor industry in 1897. In 1901, he became chief engineer at Pierce, where 'his brilliant mathematical mind . . . created motors that knew no equal'. A unique feature of the Pierce-Arrow was its cast-aluminium bodywork, which eliminated the difficulties inherent in traditional coachbuilding methods. This particular 38hp car is from the Fourth Series, current from 1916 to 1918. Despite the fact that the Pierce-Arrow was the costliest car on the American market, Fourth Series production totalled 4,900 cars, all made to the most exacting standards. Like most quality cars of the day, this example has right-hand drive. Pierce-Arrow did not build a left-hand-drive car until 1921, as Fergusson considered that it did not offer any advantage in touring.

PIPER

Piper's initial offerings comprised a range of sports racing, GT coupé and Formula 3 cars designed by Tony Hilder. The best-known and most populous Piper was the GTT, an ultra-low, race-bred coupé. Between 1968 and 1974, about 100 GTTs were produced, accounting for approximately two-thirds of total Piper production.

l. **1967 Piper GT Sports,** 1600cc, 4 cylinders, 4-speed gearbox, yellow with black trim, very good condition. **£5,500–6,500** *H&H*

PONTIAC

One of the few subsidiary US marques to have been created rather than acquired, Pontiac emerged as a General Motors brand in 1926, slotting in between Chevrolet and the flagship Cadillac. In the 1960s, however, Pontiac changed direction dramatically with the tyre-smoking 1964 GTO – the car that started the whole muscle-car movement – and followed it up with the joyfully excessive Trans-Am. The latter reigned in its full glory for only a few years, before the mid-1970s fuel crisis and American emission laws toned down its extravagant behaviour.

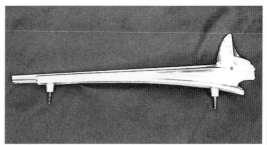

A Pontiac Chieftain mascot, 1946, 16¼in (41.5cm) long.
£120–150 *PC*

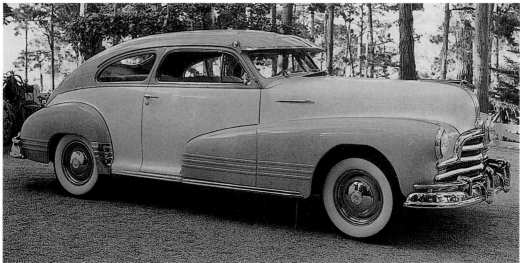

1947 Pontiac Torpedo Sedan, 222cu in, sidevalve, 6 cylinder in-line engine, 93.5bhp at 3,400rpm, 3-speed manual gearbox, restored 1986–87, new brake shoes, hoses and wheel cylinders, steering overhauled, seat belts, radio/tape deck in glove compartment, very good condition.
£6,500–8,000 *C*

General Motors introduced the Pontiac marque in 1925 to fill a price gap above the popular Chevrolet models. The first Pontiac was a six-cylinder model, and for the next 20 years the division's good-looking sixes and straight-eights fitted neatly into GM's line-up, always more exclusive than Chevrolet, but never competing with the Cadillac flagships. It was a successful policy. The Pontiac was ranked America's fourth best-selling make in 1935. With the introduction of the Streamliner in 1941, Pontiac's sales rose to record-breaking levels. After WWII, production began again in 1946 with Streamliner and Torpedo 8s and 6s.

1988 Pontiac Fiero, 'Testarossa' coachwork, 2800cc, MPFi V6 engine, 5-speed Getrag manual gearbox, fully adjustable front and rear suspension, resprayed, fewer than 30,000 miles.
£7,000–8,000 *BRIT*

Produced between 1984 and 1988, the Pontiac Fiero broke new ground for General Motors with its steel space-frame chassis and plastic panels, which were attached to the chassis at the very end of the assembly line. Bodywork specialists (such as AutoGraphic Design of North Carolina) saw the potential to replace selected panels with more exotic bodywork. This example, one of the last Fieros built, was converted with 'Testarossa' panels from new.

1956 Pontiac Starfire Convertible, completely restored, good condition.
£20,000–23,000 *PALM*

PONTIAC Model	ENGINE cc/cyl	DATES	CONDITION 1	2	3
Six-27	3048/6	1926-29	£9,000	£7,000	£4,000
Silver Streak	3654/8	1935-37	£12,000	£9,000	£5,500
6	3638/6	1937-49	£7,000	£4,000	£3,500
8	4078/8	1937-49	£7,000	£4,000	£3,500

PORSCHE
50th Year Celebration

In the spring of 1949, the beautiful, little jelly-mould 356 made its debut at the Geneva Motor Show, giving birth to the Porsche marque. It was also the beginning of a superlative sporting tradition that, to this day, displays the genes of the very first Porsche in the styling and layout of the most recent models.

However, the remarkable Porsche story did not begin with Ferry Porsche's post-WWII 356, but with his father, Ferdinand, born in 1875. By 1930, when he set up his own design studio, Porsche senior – by then titled Herr Doktor Ingenieur, with an honorary doctorate from the University of Vienna – already had a remarkable motoring history that dated back to the beginning of the century. Having worked his way up to become managing director of Austro-Daimler, he moved on to Daimler-Benz, then Steyr, before forming his own design firm in Stuttgart, Germany. His long-time associate, Karl Rabe, joined him in the new company, along with young Ferry, who had been born in 1909 and had already served apprenticeships at Steyr and Bosch.

The company's Project 60, which first saw the light of day in prototype form in 1936, is better known today as the Volkswagen Beetle, the world-beating people's car built at Adolf Hitler's request. For his efforts, Ferdinand Porsche was granted the additional title of Professor by Hitler.

Both father and son were arrested by American occupation forces after the war and imprisoned by the French, Ferry being released in 1946. While his father lingered in captivity for a further year, Ferry worked with Karl Rabe on developing a sporting variant of the Volkswagen Beetle, the 356, so named because it was the company's 356th design project.

The 356 actually went into very limited production – being virtually hand-assembled – in June 1948, powered initially by a tuned 1086cc version of the Beetle's air-cooled flat-four. Post-war expediency had forced a make-do reliance on the Volkswagen's underpinnings, but the 356 was much more than a bug in butterfly's clothing. Its concept, rear-engined layout and design descended directly from the parent car, but in the handsome, athletic offspring, the genes had mutated miraculously into a true sporting machine. In 1950, a Porsche 356 won its class at Le Mans to begin an impressive collection of trophies for the Stuttgart marque.

In fact, from 1948 to 1950, only about 47 cars were produced. Ferdinand Porsche died of a stroke a little over a year later as development of the 356 began to gain momentum, the Porsche distancing itself from its humble Beetle origins and gaining larger, more powerful engines. Finally, in late 1964, it was replaced by the 911 with a new 1991cc, flat-six engine, giving 130bhp and close to 130mph. Although, in many ways, the 911 was a brand-new model, it was also part of a direct evolutionary process that has continued unbroken to this day.

At the Frankfurt show of 1965, Porsche introduced the 912, which used the 911 body and running gear, but had a smaller, 1582cc engine. It was the first Porsche to feature a removable Targa top. In 1966, the 100,000th Porsche delivered was a 912.

However, it was the sizzling 911 that really made the world take notice, and many commentators reckon that Ferrari's Dino 246 GT was produced as a response to the threat posed by the Stuttgart company's upstart budget super-car. Neither did Porsche stand still, upping the performance stakes with the Carrera RS 2.7 in 1973, then two years later producing a Turbo version, which became one of the quickest-accelerating cars around.

Even so, for a period in the 1970s, Porsche's financial standing was faltering, before the low-cost 924 and super-car 928 helped trigger an impressive recovery. The 924, introduced in 1976, was the first front-engined and water-cooled Porsche. The 928 had the same configuration, but was powered by an all-aluminium, 4474cc V8 that pumped out 240bhp. A turbo-charged 924 came in 1978, and Porsche filled out the range in 1982 with the 944, essentially a revised 924 with a new 2479cc, overhead-camshaft, four-cylinder, 163bhp engine. For many, the defining late-era classic Porsche is the 1986 four-wheel-drive, 185mph 959 with its 450bhp, twin-turbo, 2850cc flat-six. Squint when you look at one and you can still see its lineage right back to the original 356.

1962 Porsche 356 Cabriolet, 1582cc, 4 cylinders, 102bhp at 5,500rpm, 4-speed manual gearbox, transmission rebuilt, front brakes overhauled, resprayed, new hood, reupholstered front seats, rear in original leather, little use since 1989, very good condition.
£11,500–13,000 *Pou*

Porsche 356

Although descended from the VW Beetle, the Porsche 356 is a true sporting machine, a peppy, pert piece of precision engineering available in myriad combinations from humble 'cooking' models, for less than Mondeo money, to the exotic and very precious Speedsters and quad-cam Carreras.

Pick of the bunch: Ultimate in performance and price is the 356C Carrera II. Some purists favour the early, split-windscreen, jelly-mould shape, but for all-round drivability and affordability, the last-of-the-line 1600cc 356C coupés, with four-wheel disc brakes, make most sense.

1965 Porsche 356 Coupé, 1600cc, left-hand drive, engine overhauled, resprayed in grey, new blue leather trim and carpets, good condition throughout.
£9,250–10,000 *BKS*

The 356 series established the Porsche marque, the first cars being built in Gmünd, Austria, before proper production facilities were established in Zuffenhausen, near Stuttgart, Germany, in 1949. By the time production ended, in September 1965, over 76,000 examples of the 356 had been produced, and the design had evolved from a spartan, drum-braked, 85mph, 1100cc model to a sophisticated 1600cc sportster with disc brakes all-round, capable of top speeds in the region of 115mph.

1973 Porsche 911 Carrera 2.7 RS Lightweight, right-hand drive, rebuilt, replacement factory engine, finished in white with blue decals, 61,000 miles recorded, good original condition.
£39,000–44,000 *BKS*

Announced in 1972, the lightweight Carrera RS was Porsche's motor sport variant of the perennial 911. Thinner body panels gave a 900kg dry weight, while its fuel-injected, 2.7 litre flat-six engine was tuned for 210bhp. The model immediately proved a winner in both rallies and circuit races, the resulting demand proving so great that the intended production run of 500 was extended to 1,000. This example is one of only 17 right-hand-drive models.

Porsche 356B 1959–63

Body styles: 2+2 Fixed-Head Coupé, Cabriolet and Speedster.
Construction: Unitary.
Engine: 1582cc, air-cooled, flat-four with twin carburettors.
Power output: 90bhp at 5,500rpm (Super 90).
Transmission: Four-speed manual, all-synchromesh, rear-wheel drive.
Suspension: Front: independent, trailing arms, transverse torsion bars and anti-roll bar. Rear: independent, swing half-axles, radius arms and transverse torsion bars. Telescopic shock absorbers all-round.
Brakes: Hydraulic drums all-round.
Top speed: 110mph.
0–60mph: 10 seconds.
Fuel consumption: 30–35mpg.
Production: 30,963.

1974 Porsche Carrera 3.0 RSR, 2993cc, 6 cylinders, 330bhp, uprated Fichtel & Sachs sintered clutch, titanium springs, light alloy dampers, 10½in wide front rims and 14in rear, restored, good condition.
£32,000–36,000 *COYS*

The Porsche Carrera RSR was one of the great long-distance sports racing cars of the early 1970s. Only 57 of these 330bhp 'evolution' versions of the already exciting Carrera RS were built, but they were successful beyond all expectations, winning every GT championship entered around the world. As much as 345bhp was achieved by some teams. This particular car was the last of the original batch built in 1974.

1976 Porsche 911 Carrera 3-Litre Targa, 5-speed manual gearbox, left-hand drive, engine overhauled, very good original condition.
£5,000–8,000 *BKS*

Porsche's 911 arrived in 1964 as a replacement for the 356. The latter's rear-engined layout was retained, but the 911 switched to unitary construction and dropped the 356's VW-based suspension in favour of a McPherson-strut and trailing-arm arrangement. The overhead-camshaft air-cooled flat-six displaced 1991cc and produced 130bhp; it would eventually grow to more than 3 litres and, in turbocharged form, put out over 300 horsepower. Porsche revived the Carrera name for its top-of-the-range 911 in 1973. Revised suspension and wider wheels helped improve handling, while the fuel-injected, 2.7 litre, 210bhp engine boosted top speed to around 155mph. Not merely a styling gimmick, the Carrera's tail spoiler made a vital contribution to high-speed stability. In 1973, the Carrera was enlarged to 3 litres and 230bhp, a move that further enhanced its smoothness and drivability.

l. **1974 Porsche 911 Carrera,** 2687cc, left-hand drive, air conditioning, electric windows, leather interior, Blaupunkt stereo and dictation facility, unused original tool kit, resprayed metallic red, leather bonnet cover, 28,000 miles from new, excellent condition.
£17,000–20,000 *H&H*

1979 Porsche 911SC, 2994cc, 6 cylinders, left-hand drive, optional Sport Package including front/rear spoilers and 16in Fuchs alloy wheels, new fuel injectors, turbo-type exhaust system, good condition.
£8,500–10,000 *BRIT*

1979 Porsche 928S Coupé, 4500cc, V8, 5-speed manual gearbox, service history, 28,000 miles from new, excellent condition.
£9,500–11,000 *H&H*

PORSCHE Model	ENGINE cc/cyl	DATES	CONDITION 1	2	3
356	var/4	1949-53	£15,000	£8,000	£5,000
356 Cabriolet	var/4	1951-53	£20,000	£14,000	£10,000
356A	1582/4	1955-59	£13,000	£9,000	£5,000
356A Cabriolet	1582/4	1956-59	£16,000	£10,000	£7,000
356A Speedster	1582/4	1955-58	£25,000	£19,000	£14,000
356B Carrera	1582/ 1966/4	1960-65	£40,000+	£30,000+	£18,000
356C	1582/4	1963-65	£15,000	£11,000+	£5,000
356C Cabriolet	1582/4	1963-64	£22,000+	£16,000	£10,000
911/911L/T/E	1991/6	1964-68	£10,000	£7,000	£5,000
912	1582/4	1965-68	£6,500	£5,000	£2,000
911S	1991/6	1966-69	£12,000	£8,000	£5,500
911S	2195/6	1969-71	£13,000	£9,000	£6,000
911T	2341/6	1971-73	£13,000	£8,000	£6,000
911E	2341/6	1971-73	£12,000	£8,000	£6,000
914/4	1679/4	1969-75	£4,000	£3,000	£1,000
914/6	1991/6	1969-71	£6,000	£3,500	£1,500
911S	2341/6	1971-73	£16,000	£10,000	£8,500
Carrera RS lightweight	2687/6	1973	£35,000+	£28,000+	£16,000
Carrera RS Touring	2687/6	1973	£30,000	£26,000	£17,000
Carrera 3	2994/6	1976-77	£14,000	£9,000	£7,000
924 Turbo	1984/4	1978-83	£5,000	£4,000	£2,000
928/928S	4474/4664/V8	1977-86	£10,000	£7,000	£4,000
911SC	2993/6	1977-83	£13,000	£8,000	£6,000

Sportomatic cars are less desirable.

1981 Porsche 924 Carrera GT, engine rebuilt, gearbox overhauled, finished in red with black interior, 85,000km recorded, excellent original condition.
£6,750–7,750 *BKS*

A road model with competition potential, the luxuriously-equipped Porsche 924 Carrera GT was launched in 1979. Built in limited numbers to gain homologation for rallying and Group 4 events, it offered 210bhp, but this could be boosted to well over 300bhp for racing. Three cars were entered by the works in the 1980 Le Mans 24-hour race, finishing 6th, 12th and 13th.

Don't Forget!

If in doubt please refer to the 'How to Use' section at the beginning of this book.

1982 Ruf Porsche BTR-1, engine and transmission rebuilt, resprayed, leather interior, roll bar, sunroof, stereo radio/cassette, 17in Ruf wheels.
£14,500–17,000 *BKS*

From tuner and modifier of Porsches, Alois Ruf graduated to automobile manufacture in 1981. The first Ruf cars, numbered BTR-1, -2 and -3, were constructed in 1982 on the Porsche 911. The engine was based on the 3.3 litre Turbo's, but displaced 3.4 litres and was fed by an oversize KKK turbocharger. The resulting 369bhp was transmitted to the road by a Ruf 5-speed gearbox. The suspension and brakes were also of Ruf design. This particular car made history in 1984 when, after a test conducted by Road & Track, it was pronounced the 'world's fastest'. Driven by ex-F1 World Champion Phil Hill, it clocked a staggering 186.2mph, later managing 188.98mph with Paul Frère at the wheel.

1982 Porsche 911SC, 3 litres, finished in Guards Red, 50,000 miles, service history, excellent original condition.
£16,500–18,000 *DEV*

1982 Porsche 911 Targa, finished in silver, whale tail, 90,000 miles recorded, some history, good condition.
£12,000–14,000 *VIC*

1983 Porsche 924, very good condition.
£3,000–3,300 *PA*

1985 Porsche 911 Sports Cabriolet, 3.2 litres, Guards Red with black leather interior, black hood, 49,000 miles, service history, very good original condition.
£21,000–23,000 *DEV*

1987 Porsche 911 Turbo, 3.3 litres, left-hand drive, original Espresso Brown paintwork, excellent leather interior, factory sunroof, air conditioning, tool kit, 44,000km from new, very good condition.
£20,000–23,000 *BKS*

The 911 Turbo was the first European turbocharged production car, and it has been the longest lived. Its appeal was not the maximum power that theoretically was available, but the torque range. By 1977, the flat-six engine had grown to 3.3 litres and was producing 300bhp with awesome torque. This, combined with Porsche's legendary build quality and mechanical reliability, made the 911 Turbo arguably the world's most accomplished sports car.

l. **1987 Porsche 911 Turbo,** 3.3 litres, Grand Prix White with blue hood, leather interior, 41,000 miles, original condition.
£35,000–38,000 *DEV*

1988 Porsche 911 Carrera, 3.2 litres,
finished in Grand Prix White, air conditioning,
46,000 miles recorded, service history,
good original condition.
£24,000–26,000   *DEV*

r. **1988 Porsche 911 Turbo,** 3.3 litres, finished
in grey, leather interior, air conditioning, 51,000
miles, service history, excellent original condition.
£31,000–33,000   *DEV*

1988 Porsche 944 Turbo, 250bhp, air
conditioning, 72,000 miles, service history,
excellent original condition.
£14,000–16,500   *DEV*

1988 Porsche 959, 2849cc, 6 cylinders, 450bhp at 6,500rpm, top speed over 192mph,
excellent condition.
£165,000–180,000   *Pou*

Only 200 Porsche 959s were produced for customers, plus a number of works models.

1989 Porsche 911LE Turbo, 3.3 litres, 330bhp,
finished in Baltic Blue, 14,500 miles, excellent
original condition.
£43,000–47,000   *DEV*

r. **1989 Porsche 930 Turbo Cabriolet,** 3299cc,
6 cylinders, 300bhp at 5,500rpm, top speed 161mph.
£28,000–33,000   *Pou*

RELIANT

Established in 1935 by T. L. Williams, Reliant started out by making small three-wheeled commercial vehicles. The first three-wheelers designed for private use appeared in 1952, and in 1956 the company adopted fibreglass bodywork, which has clothed all subsequent Reliants. These days, although the small three- and four-wheelers paid the rent, the firm is much better known for its sports cars, the first being the Sabre of 1961 to 1963. That grew into the far more harmonious Sabre Six of 1962 to 1964, then in 1966 the ground-breaking, Ogle-designed Scimitar appeared. In GTE form, it created a new class of car, the sports estate. This cross-country carry-all with sports appeal lasted from 1968 to 1986, a total of 16,000 being produced.

1963 Reliant Sabre Six SE2S Two-Door Coupé, dry-stored 1982–90, completely restored, fewer than 1,000 miles since, modified with Kenlowe fan and Toyota Celica 5-speed gearbox, very good condition throughout.
£6,000–8,000 *BKS*

The Reliant Sabre Six SE2S was introduced in 1962 with fibreglass bodywork, and 109bhp available from its 2553cc, overhead-valve, Ford Zephyr six engine, the attractively styled GT was good for over 110mph. This particular car was one of only 77 built between 1963 and 1966.

RELIANT Model	ENGINE cc/cyl	DATES	CONDITION		
			1	**2**	**3**
Sabre 4 Coupé & Drophead	1703/4	1961-63	£4,500	£2,750	£1,000
Sabre 6 " "	2553/6	1962-64	£6,000	£3,500	£1,500
Scimitar GT Coupé SE4	2553/6, 2994 V6	1964-70	£4,500	£2,500	£1,000
Scimitar GTE Sports Estate SE5/5A	2994/V6	1968-75	£4,500	£2,000	£750
Scimitar GTE Sports Estate SE6/6A	2994/V6	1976-80	£6,000+	£3,500+	£1,250
Scimitar GTE Sports Estate SE6B	2792/V6	1980-86	£8,000	£5,000	£2,000
Scimitar GTC Convertible SE8B	2792/V6	1980-86	£9,000	£8,000	£5,500

1975 Reliant Scimitar GTE Series 5A, 2944cc, V6, 135bhp at 5,500rpm, 4-speed manual gearbox, resprayed, stored for past 10 years, 55,100 miles from new, sound original condition, requires attention.
£5,750–6,500 *C*

Best of the GTEs according to those in the know is the revised and updated SE5A produced from 1971 to 1975, particularly models from 1972 on with Ford Granada-spec 135bhp 3-litre V6. The SE6 from 1975 is a wider, heavier, softer, 'executive' Scimitar, created by splitting the SE5 moulds to add 4in extra length and 3in more width. It may be a better family formula, but it feels slightly softer in character too.

1975 Reliant Scimitar GTE, 2994cc, V6, rebuilt manual gearbox with overdrive, new rear axle 7,000 miles ago, front suspension rebushed, white with brown vinyl interior, good condition.
£900–1,200 *BRIT*

RENAULT

1909 Renault AX 9hp Two-Seater with Dickey,
coachwork by Gibbs & Co, restored
20 years ago, unused for some time, VCC dating
certificate, very good condition throughout.
£12,750–14,000 *S*

1911 Renault AX Two-Seater with Dickey,
white with red vinyl interior, new tan hood,
non-original Zenith carburettor, brass bulb horn,
Stewart speedometer, JM Amortisseurs to assist
damping, very good condition throughout.
£9,750–11,000 *S*

*The Renault AX was introduced in 1905 to a public
still wary of the complexities of the motor car and
equally aware of its frailties. That it remained in
production with only minor updates for nine years,
at a time of rapid developments in automotive
engineering, is testimony to the success of the initial
design. The twin-cylinder engine was simple and
robust, while the three-speed gearbox was simplicity
itself. The engine had an unparalleled flexibility
between 5 and 35mph in top gear, and would only
require top gear for all but the steepest of gradients.*

1912 Renault AX Two-Seater, restored, maroon
with cream wings, beige buttoned leather
upholstery, beige hood, Rotax brass headlamps,
P&H oil sidelamps, Lucas Sentry rear lamps,
double-twist bulb horn, Lucas mirrors, AT
speedometer, spare tyre, very good condition.
£12,750–14,000 *BKS*

Make the Most of Miller's
*Veteran Cars are those manufactured up
to 31 December 1918. Only vehicles built
before 31 December 1904 are eligible for
the London/Brighton Commemorative
Run. Vintage Cars are vehicles that were
manufactured between 1 January 1919
and 31 December 1930.*

c1916 Renault Type EU 12CV Open Drive Town Car, 2815cc monobloc engine, replica Town Car
coachwork, interior trimmed in red velvet, opera lamps on scuttle, electric starting, one headlamp bracket
needs repairing, otherwise very good condition.
£8,750–11,500 *BKS*

*The Renault works at Billancourt were placed on a war footing at the outbreak of WWI. Apart from staff
cars, the company made lorries, shells, light tanks, aero engines and complete aircraft. In September 1918,
for his great contribution in arming the French troops, Louis Renault was made an Officer of the Légion
d'Honneur. The Type EU, available between 1916 and 1920, was one of the mainstays of that contribution
to the Allied war effort.*

RENAULT Model	ENGINE cc/cyl	DATES	CONDITION 1	2	3
40hp	7540/6	1919-21	£30,000	£20,000	£10,000
SR	4537/4	1919-22	£10,000	£7,000	£5,000
EU-15.8HP	2815/4	1919-23	£8,000+	£5,000	£2,000
GS-IG	2121/4	1920-23	£5,000	£3,000	£2,000
JP	9123/6	1922-29	£25,000	£20,000	£15,000
KJ	951/4	1923-29	£6,000	£4,000	£2,000
Mona Six	1474/6	1928-31	£7,000	£5,000	£3,000
Reinastella	7128/8	1929-32	£25,000	£20,000	£15,000
Viva Six	3181/6	1929-34	£10,000	£7,000	£3,000
14/45	2120/4	1929-35	£7,000	£5,000	£2,000
Nervahuit	4240/8	1931	£12,000	£10,000	£7,000
UY	1300/4	1932-34	£7,000	£5,000	£2,000
ZC/ZD2	4825/8	1934-35	£12,000	£10,000	£7,000
YN2	1463/4	1934-39	£7,000	£5,000	£2,000
Airline Super and Big 6	3620/6	1935	£10,000	£8,000	£5,000
18	2383/4	1936-39	£9,000	£5,000	£3,000
26	4085/6	1936-39	£12,000	£8,000	£5,000

Veteran pre-war models like the 2 cylinder AX, AG and BB are very popular, with values ranging between £6,000 and £15,000. The larger 4 cylinder cars like the AM, AZ, XB and VB are very reliable and coachbuilt examples command £30,000+, with 6 cylinder coachbuilt cars commanding a premium.

1953 Renault 4CV Saloon, 4 cylinder rear-mounted engine, 3-speed gearbox, left-hand drive, resprayed in blue, interior reupholstered, good condition.
£1,750–2,000 *S*

This car was imported to the UK in the early 1980s for film work, then dry-stored.

1966 Renault Dauphine Gordini, full service history, excellent condition.
£3,000–3,500 *UMC*

With 38bhp squeezed from its 845cc engine, the hot Gordini version of the Dauphine could reach a frantic 75mph.

1968 Renault Caravelle Cabriolet, 1108cc, 4 cylinders, red with black interior, detachable hardtop, very good mechanical condition.
£3,500–4,000 *BRIT*

The Caravelle, a development of the earlier Floride, was restyled and improved in a number of ways. Its specification included disc brakes all-round, while the five-bearing, 1108cc engine of later models produced 51bhp. The Cabriolet was particularly stylish.

1972 Renault 4 F6 Van, 1108cc, 4-speed all-synchromesh gearbox, very good condition throughout.
£350–500 *S*

RENAULT Model	ENGINE cc/cyl	DATES	CONDITION 1	2	3
4CV	747/ 760/4	1947-61	£3,500	£2,000	£850
Fregate	1997/4	1952-60	£3,000	£2,000	£1,000
Dauphine	845/4	1956-66	£1,500	£1,000	£350
Dauphine Gordini	845/4	1961-66	£2,000	£1,000	£450
Floride	845/4	1959-62	£3,000	£2,000	£600
Caravelle	956/ 1108/4	1962-68	£4,500	£2,800	£750
R4	747/ 845/4	1961-86	£2,000	£1,500	£350
R8/R10	1108/4	1962-71	£1,800	£750	£200
R8 Gordini	1108/4	1965-66	£8,000	£5,000	£2,000
R8 Gordini	1255/4	1966-70	£8,000	£5,500	£2,500
R8S	1108/4	1968-71	£2,000	£1,200	£400

RENAULT-ALPINE

In the 1950s and early 1960s, almost every specialist maker in France wanted to form a relationship with Renault, and Renault encouraged a sort of unofficial competition between them. It was won by Jean Redélé, who competed with some success with modified Renaults and who, in 1955, founded Société Automobiles Alpine. This was taken over by Renault in 1971 and is still the company's specialist sports car division.

1972 Renault-Alpine 1600S, 1598cc, engine rebuilt, finished in purple, very good condition. **£18,000–21,000** *CLAR*

1974 Renault-Alpine A110 1600SC Berlinette, restored 1990–93 at a cost of over £45,000, fuel injection replaced by twin carburettors, modified to use unleaded fuel, excellent condition. **£17,500–20,000** *BKS*

The A110 of 1963 established the classic Alpine shape. Initially, its rear-mounted, 1108cc Renault R8 engine produced 87bhp, but by the time production ended in 1977, the engine was developing 180bhp. The A110 was particularly successful in rallying, and in 1973 won the first World Rally Championship. Examples went on to win no fewer than 17 major international rallies. Among the many successes, a 1-2-3 in the 1969 Alpine Rally stands out.

REO

1906 Reo 16hp, 3400cc, 2 cylinders, under-floor-mounted engine, dummy bonnet, 2-speed planetary-gear transmission with chain drive, well maintained, excellent condition. **£9,500–11,000** *COYS*

A difference of opinion about the design of future automobiles led Ransom E. Olds to part company with the Olds Motor Works, in January 1904, to make more expensive and more highly developed machines than Oldsmobile's modestly priced, single-cylinder Curved Dash Runabout, which had been introduced in 1901. Predictably, his former partners objected to the use of the Olds name, so the R. E. Olds Co was simply rechristened the Reo Motor Co. All of Reo's early production comprised single- and twin-cylinder buggies that, not surprisingly, bore some resemblance to the Curved Dash Runabout. By 1906, Reo held fourth place in the US sales charts.

RILEY

Like many of the early automobile firms around Coventry and Birmingham, Riley came to car making via bicycle manufacture, producing its first car in 1898. In the 1920s and 1930s the Coventry firm produced some very appealing and highly regarded small sporting cars before being taken over by Morris in 1938. The immediate post-war products, the RM series cars, were hallmark Riley sporting saloons, still much appreciated for their looks and assured handling. For many these RMs also rate as the last real Rileys before the company was reduced to producing dull badge-engineered look-alikes under the BMC banner. The Riley name eventually faded away for good in 1969.

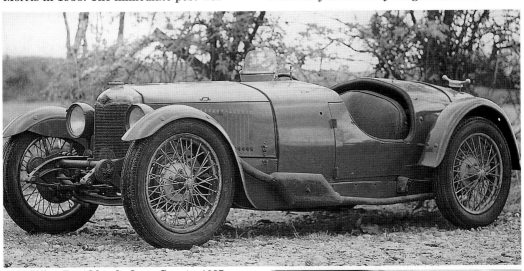

1928 Riley Brooklands Open Sports, 1087cc, 4 cylinders, stored for 40 years, front helmet wings in place of originals, excellent original condition. **£35,000–38,000** *COYS*

The Riley Nine was introduced in 1926, and its double-overhead camshaft engine was a landmark in the history of the small car. Such a fine engine attracted the motor racing fraternity, and the great J. Parry Thomas managed to extract 50bhp from the 1087cc unit. After his death, Reid Railton continued to develop the car, which finished up with a virtually new chassis, 10½in shorter than the original. This dropped below the front axle line and was underslung at the rear, producing a scuttle height of only 36in. In 1927, Railton won a race at Brooklands in the car, setting a fastest lap of 98.62mph. This feat, combined with the car's rakish good looks, led Riley to market the design as the Brooklands Speed Model. Standard production cars could top 80mph, but a handful of special racing machines wrote the model's name in the history books. This example is believed to be one of those cars and to have raced in such events as the JCC 1,000 miles in 1932.

l. **1933 Riley 9hp March Special Tourer,** double-overhead-camshaft engine, 4-speed gearbox, spiral-bevel rear axle, red with black interior, long-range biflex headlamps, twin rear-mounted spares, full weather equipment. **£8,000–9,000** *BKS*

Designed by the then Earl of March, later Duke of Richmond and Gordon, the March Special was produced for the 1932/33 season only. The Earl was a partner in the firm of Kevill-Davies & March, which previously had been responsible for March Specials on Hillman and AC chassis. The only sports car offered by Riley that year, the Special was built on both the 9hp and 6/12hp Special Series chassis, although all but a handful were 9hp models.

RILEY Model	ENGINE cc/cyl	DATES	CONDITION		
			1	2	3
9hp	1034/2	1906-07	£9,000	£6,000	£3,000
Speed 10	1390/2	1909-10	£10,000	£6,000	£3,000
11	1498/4	1922-27	£7,000	£4,000	£2,000
9	1075/4	1927-32	£10,000	£7,000	£4,000
9 Gamecock	1098/4	1932-33	£14,000	£10,000	£6,000
Lincock 12hp	1458/6	1933-36	£9,000	£7,000	£5,000
Imp 9hp	1089/4	1934-35	£35,000	£28,000	£20,000
Kestrel 12hp	1496/4	1936-38	£8,000	£5,000	£2,000
Sprite 12hp	1496/4	1936-38	£40,000	£35,000	£20,000

Many Riley 9hp 'Specials' available ideal for VSCC and club events.

1937 Riley Lynx Sprite Special Series 12hp Tourer, 4-speed pre-selector gearbox, stone guards to lamps and radiator, Jaeger rev counter and speedometer, Redex gauge, original green leather interior, 80mph top speed, original specification, requires recommissioning.
£11,500–13,000 *BKS*

In 1936, Riley was able to bask in the glory of competition success: a 1-2-3-4 class win in the French Grand Prix for sports cars; and Freddie Dixon repeating his 1935 TT victory at an average speed of 78.01mph, then winning the Brooklands 500 at 116.86mph. Against this background, the company was producing a range of four- and six-cylinder touring and sports cars that had all the hallmarks of race breeding. That year, the 1.5 litre Sprite engine became available in the Lynx tourer and Kestrel saloon. The Special Series cars, with tuned engines, were essentially sports cars in four-seater touring form.

1952 Riley RMA 1½ Litre Saloon, 1496cc, 4 cylinders, engine rebuilt, resprayed in ivory, new fabric roof and head lining, good condition.
£2,750–3,500 *BRIT*

Following the Nuffield Group's take-over of Riley late in 1938, a rationalised range was offered, comprising saloon and drophead versions of the 1½ and 2½ litre models. These, however, were short-lived due to the outbreak of war. Development of a new model began during 1944. Announced in August 1945, this car was a sleek sports saloon with a fabric-covered roof and styling that was clearly influenced by the Continental Touring Saloon of 1937/38. The RMA, as the model was known, bristled with innovations, including rack-and-pinion steering and Torsionic independent front suspension.

1947 Riley RMA Saloon, 1496cc, 4 cylinders, good condition.
£1,600–1,700 *DB*

> **Miller's is a price GUIDE not a price LIST**

r. **1963 Riley 1.5 Saloon,** 1489cc, BMC B-Series twin-carburettor engine, 68bhp, sound condition.
£600–700 *BKS*

l. **1969 Riley Elf MkIII Two-door Saloon,** automatic transmission, well maintained, fewer than 28,000 miles from new, original bill of sale, excellent original condition.
£3,900–4,300 *BKS*

A luxury Mini with more boot space and a wood-trimmed interior, the Riley Elf (with its Wolseley Hornet stable-mate) debuted in 1961. The 848cc original was superseded by the 1 litre MkII Elf in 1963. Subsequent improvements included hydrolastic suspension, a diaphragm clutch and, for the 1966 MkIII, wind-up windows and face-level ventilation!

| RILEY | ENGINE | DATES | CONDITION | | |
Model	cc/cyl		1	2	3
1½ litre RMA	1496/4	1945-52	£6,000	£3,500	£1,500
1½ litre RME	1496/4	1952-55	£6,000	£3,500	£1,500
2½ litre RMB/F	2443/4	1946-53	£9,000	£7,000	£3,000
2½ litre Roadster	2443/4	1948-50	£13,000	£11,000	£9,000
2½ litre Drophead	2443/4	1948-51	£20,000	£18,000	£10,000
Pathfinder	2443/4	1953-57	£3,500	£2,000	£750
2.6	2639/6	1957-59	£3,000	£1,800	£750
1.5	1489/4	1957-65	£3,000	£2,000	£850
4/68	1489/4	1959-61	£1,500	£700	£300
4/72	1622/4	1961-69	£1,600	£800	£300
Elf I/II/III	848/4	1961-66	£1,500	£850	£400
Kestrel I/II	1098/4	1965-67	£1,500	£850	£400

ROCHET-SCHNEIDER

The Rochet-Schneider company was one of the very earliest motor manufacturers, producing its first model before the turn of the last century. Edouard Rochet had worked with his father producing bicycles in the late 1880s before, in 1894, they joined forces with Théophile Schneider. The first motor car followed that same year, being basically a 6hp single-cylinder Benz clone, of which some 240 had been built by 1901. Also that year Société Lionnaise de Vélocipedes et Automobile Rochet Schneider, which had been formally established in 1896, opened a factory in Lyons, from which new two- and four-cylinder models were launched at the season's Paris Salon. Meanwhile, from the Rochet factory in the French capital, a smaller model had been introduced alongside the 6hp. Known as the Rochet Petit, it was powered by a 4½hp single-cylinder Aster engine mated, via a cone clutch, to a two-speed Bozier gearbox.

1902 Rochet-Schneider Rochet-Petit, Vis-à-Vis coachwork by Bergeon Cie, 4½hp, single-cylinder engine, cantilever folding hood, wheel-operated steering, full lighting equipment, good condition.
£13,500–15,000 *COYS*

ROLLS-ROYCE

Charles Rolls and Henry Royce came from widely differing backgrounds, Royce being the son of an impoverished mill worker, and Rolls having been born into a life of privileged comfort. Royce's first job was selling newspapers, then in 1877 he became an apprentice at the Great Northern Railway Locomotive Works. He never completed his apprenticeship, but took a variety of engineering posts before setting up his own business to produce electrical devices. After buying a secondhand Decauville motor car in 1903 and finding it disappointing, he built the first Royce car in 1904. It had a 1.8 litre, two-cylinder engine which, even then, was noted for its quiet running.

Meanwhile, Charles Rolls had obtained a mechanical engineering degree at Cambridge, where his Peugeot had been the first motor car of any kind on campus. Rolls was also an accomplished driver. He won a 1,000-mile reliability trial, and in 1903 set a world land-speed record of 93mph aboard a Mors. By then, he was already in business selling exclusive foreign motor cars. The two men met shortly afterwards, and when Rolls took the wheel of a Royce car, he was won over, later remarking that Royce 'was the man I had been looking for for years.'

At the 1904 Paris Salon, two Royces were displayed, and days later the pair agreed to name their cars Rolls-Royce, forming Rolls-Royce Ltd in 1906. From the beginning of their partnership, they established Rolls-Royce's credentials as an exclusive producer of very expensive and superb motor cars. The 40/50, which became known universally as the Silver Ghost, really could make a plausible claim to being the 'best car in the world', although in the 1930s, for example, such an extravagant statement was harder to justify in the face of rival luxury contenders at home and abroad.

The Silver Ghost was continually developed through the years until it was replaced in 1925 by the New Phantom, later referred to as the Phantom I. In 1931, Rolls-Royce bought Bentley – some suggest the primary motive was to stifle competition from the magnificent 8 Litre Bentley. In 1949, Rolls-Royce entered a new era with the Silver Dawn, the first Rolls-Royce offered complete by the factory, rather than as a chassis to be fitted with bespoke coachwork of the owner's choosing. However, Rolls-Royce continued to offer chassis to coachbuilders alongside its factory-bodied cars until the Silver Shadow was launched in 1965. This Rolls-Royce was the first to feature monocoque construction with an integral body and chassis which, at a stroke, removed the scope for coachbuilt bodies. However, the Phantom V Limousine still retained a separate chassis.

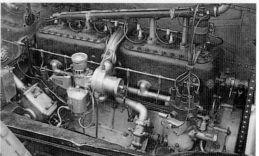

1920 Rolls-Royce 40/50 Silver Ghost Open Tourer, coachwork by Park Ward, chassis No. 69RE, engine No. M124, Stephen Grebel headlights, twin pillar-mounted spotlamps, rear Auster screen, front brakes added, many original features, good condition throughout.
£100,000–110,000 *S*

In 1910 the adventurous Charles Rolls was the first man to be killed in a flying accident. The impact on the company was far from disastrous as by then Rolls had largely lost interest in motorcars.

ROLLS-ROYCE Model	ENGINE cc/cyl	DATES	CONDITION		
			1	**2**	**3**
Silver Ghost 40/50	7035/6	pre-WWI	£350,000+	£120,000	£80,000
Silver Ghost 40/50	7428/6	post-WWI	£110,000+	£70,000	£40,000
20hp (3 speed)	3127/6	1922-25	£29,000+	£23,000	£15,000
20hp	3127/6	1925-29	£30,000+	£24,000	£15,000
Phantom I	7668/6	1925-29	£50,000+	£28,000	£22,000
20/25	3669/6	1925-26	£30,000+	£18,000	£13,000
Phantom II	7668/6	1929-35	£40,000+	£30,000	£20,000
Phantom II Continental	7668/6	1930-35	£60,000+	£40,000	£28,000
25/30	4257/6	1936-38	£24,000+	£18,000	£12,000
Phantom III	7340/12	1936-39	£38,000	£28,000	£14,000
Wraith	4257/6	1938-39	£38,000	£32,000	£25,000

Prices will vary considerably depending on heritage, originality, coachbuilder, completeness and body style. A poor reproduction body can often mean the value is dependent only upon a rolling chassis and engine.

1921 Rolls-Royce 40/50 Silver Ghost, coachwork by Nordberg, chassis No. 33NE, engine No. 469, engine rebuilt, carburettor, cooling system and electrical equipment overhauled, new kingpins and brake linings, restored mechanically, dry-stored since early 1980s.
£57,000–63,000 *S*

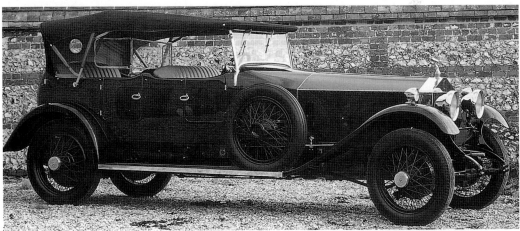

1923 Rolls-Royce Silver Ghost Open Tourer, coachwork by Barker, chassis No. 23EM, engine No. S22, 7428cc, 6 cylinders, front-wheel brakes, restored, well maintained, excellent condition.
£60,000–70,000 *COYS*

By 1908, the Silver Ghost – so named after the striking silver plating and paintwork of the 13th 40/50 produced – was Rolls-Royce's only model. For 1909, capacity was increased to 7428cc and the gearbox changed to a three-speed unit – it reverted to four speeds with direct top in 1914 – and two years later a torque drive was fitted, while power rose to 58hp. By 1919, power had increased to 70hp at 2,200rpm, and four-wheel brakes appeared in 1923. Production ceased in 1925 after 6,173 examples had been built.

1924 Rolls-Royce Silver Ghost,
7428cc, 6 cylinders.
£57,000–62,000 *BLE*

1926 Rolls-Royce Silver Ghost,
7428cc, 6 cylinders.
£120,000–130,000 *BLE*

1926 Rolls-Royce Silver Ghost Sedanca Deville, 7428cc, 6 cylinders.
£100,000–110,000 *BLE*

1925 Rolls-Royce 20hp Six Light Saloon,
coachwork by Hooper, chassis No. GPK38, engine
No. G1350, body-off restoration, new upholstery,
added rear lights, radiator brightwork in good
condition, paintwork excellent, near original condition.
£33,500–37,500 *S*

*This 20hp saloon with six-light coachwork is unique,
Rolls-Royce themselves having commissioned the
bodywork for exhibition at the Scottish Show.*

**1928 Rolls-Royce Phantom I Weymann
Limousine,** chassis No. 87AL, sliding division
between front and rear compartments, front
upholstered in brown leather, rear in tan cloth,
77,300 miles recorded, good overall condition.
£21,000–24,000 *BKS*

*Developed as a successor to the Silver Ghost, the
Phantom appeared in 1925. It had a six-cylinder
bi-block power unit, although both blocks shared a
common detachable cylinder head with pushrod-
operated overhead valves, which produced an
estimated 100bhp. At 7668cc, the Phantom engine had
a marginally greater capacity than its predecessor.*

1928 Rolls-Royce Phantom I, skiff coachwork in
the style of Barker, 7668cc, 6 cylinders, white with
black wings.
£40,000–50,000 *FHF*

1930 Rolls-Royce Phantom I, 7668cc, 6 cylinder engine.
£29,000–31,000 *BLE*

1933 Rolls-Royce 20/25 Thrupp & Maberly Sports Saloon, chassis No. GAW22, finished in black and maroon, P100 headlamps, louvred bonnet, red-badge radiator, good condition.
£18,000–19,000 *RCC*

Sir Henry Royce, made a baronet after success in the 1931 Schneider Trophy air race, died in 1933.

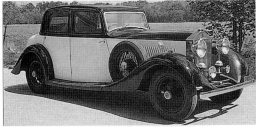

1931 Rolls-Royce 20/25, chassis No. GPS24, engine No. G4C, 3669cc, 6 cylinders, D-backed saloon coachwork, restored, black over yellow livery, reupholstered in light tan hide, new head lining, rear luggage carrier and fog lamp, regularly serviced, bodywork, interior and brightwork in very good condition.
£14,750–16,250 *BRIT*

1934 Rolls-Royce 20/25 Touring Saloon, coachwork by Hooper, chassis No. GRF22, engine No. V5B, long chassis, restored, new head lining, sunroof, opening windscreen, front and rear blinds, modern radio, undertrays and jacking device, dry-stored, good condition.
£17,500–20,000 *S*

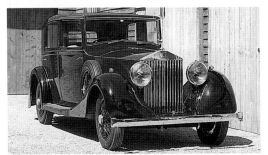

1935 Rolls-Royce 20/25 Sedanca Limousine, coachwork by Windovers, chassis No. GLJ38, engine No. G27T, 3699cc, 6 cylinder, overhead-valve in-line engine, 4-speed manual gearbox with synchromesh on upper 2 ratios, leather seats to front compartment, Bedford cord to rear, sound unrestored condition, requires recommissioning.
£17,500–20,000 *C*

ROLLS-ROYCE Model	ENGINE cc/cyl	DATES	CONDITION 1	2	3
Silver Wraith LWB	4566/4887/6	1951-59	£25,000	£17,000	£10,000
Silver Wraith SWB	4257/4566/6	1947-59	£20,000	£13,000	£10,000
Silver Wraith Drophead	4257/4566/6	1947-59	£50,000	£35,000	£25,000
Silver Dawn St'd Steel	4257/4566/6	1949-52	£25,000+	£15,000	£10,000
Silver Dawn St'd Steel	4257/4566/6	1952-55	£30,000+	£20,000	£15,000
Silver Dawn Coachbuilt	4257/4566/6	1949-55	£35,000+	£25,000	£18,000
Silver Dawn Drophead	4257/4566/6	1949-55	£60,000	£50,000	£30,000
Silver Cloud I	4887/6	1955-59	£18,000	£10,000	£8,000
SCI Coupé Coachbuilt	4887/6	1955-59	£30,000	£20,000	£15,000
SCI Conv (HJM)	4887/6	1955-59	£80,000+	£60,000+	£40,000
Silver Cloud II	6230/8	1959-62	£19,000	£10,000	£8,000
SCII Conv (HJM)	6230/8	1959-62	£80,000	£75,000	£40,000
SCII Conv (MPW)	6230/8	1959-62	£60,000	£40,000	£32,000
Silver Cloud III	6230/8	1962-65	£25,000	£12,000	£10,000
SCIII Conv (MPW)	6230/8	1962-65	£70,000	£45,000	£35,000
Silver Shadow	6230/6750/8	1965-76	£14,000	£9,000	£7,000
S Shadow I Coupé (MPW)	6230/6750/8	1965-70	£15,000	£10,000	£8,000
SSI Drophead (MPW)	6230/6750/8	1965-70	£33,000	£25,000	£18,000
Corniche fhc	6750/8	1971-77	£15,000	£11,000	£8,000
Corniche Convertible	6750/8	1971-77	£28,000	£22,000	£18,000
Camargue	6750/8	1975-85	£35,000	£25,000	£18,000

1930 Rolls-Royce Phantom II Tourer, chassis No. 10GY, engine No. TO55, rebodied in the style of a Thrupp & Maberly Tourer, finished in red over black, fawn leather interior, Auster screen, good general condition. **£31,000–35,000** *S*

1930 Rolls-Royce Phantom II Sedanca, coachwork by Windover, chassis No. 64GY, engine No. QS65, long wheelbase, full mechanical overhaul, polished aluminium bonnet, Ace wheel discs, original black leather interior. **£45,000–50,000** *COYS*

The Phantom II, introduced in 1929, was said to have been the last model that Henry Royce designed himself.

1931 Rolls-Royce Phantom II Tourer, chassis No. 186GY, engine No. VO85, 5648cc, 6 cylinders, £15,000 engine rebuild, new cylinder head, good condition throughout. **£31,000–35,000** *COYS*

Shortly after WWII, this car was rebodied with elegant open tourer coachwork by Chamberlain's of Hartley Wintney. It has been owned and used regularly by the same family for more than 30 years.

1931 Rolls-Royce Phantom II Continental Special Sports Saloon, 7668cc, 6 cylinders, excellent original condition throughout.
£85,000–90,000 *COHN*

1933 Rolls-Royce Phantom II, coachwork by Muller, 7668cc, 4-speed manual gearbox, finished in green with green upholstery, sunroof, full history, very good condition.
£37,000–40,000 *H&H*

1933 Rolls-Royce Phantom II Continental Touring Saloon, coachwork by Barker, chassis No. 15MW, engine No. YN45, engine, suspension, brakes and electrics overhauled, resprayed, chromework replated, original tan leather upholstery, interior woodwork repolished, 2 sets of wheel discs, tool kit, original leather-bound owner's manual, excellent condition throughout.
£37,500–42,500 *BKS*

Designed as a car for the enthusiastic owner/driver, the Continental version of the Phantom II was built on the 144in chassis. It was intended for high-speed touring while retaining the impeccable manners and innate dignity expected of a Rolls-Royce. Only 281 examples of this model were built.

1934 Rolls-Royce Phantom II Hooper Limousine, chassis No. 148PY, traditional D-back, 6 light coachwork, finished in black and maroon, black leather interior, rear-mounted trunk, correct lamps, good overall condition.
£24,000–26,000 *RCC*

1933 Rolls-Royce Phantom II Continental Saloon, coachwork by Park Ward, chassis No. 72MY, engine No. ZM95C, full mechanical overhaul in early 1970s, cosmetically restored, roof finished in grained black leather, original silver-black leather upholstery, full history, good overall condition.
£53,000–58,000 *S*

This car was ordered with the new type of air silencer, an improvement that became standard on later cars. It also had Lucas P100 headlamps, an untarnishable centre lamp and Andre Hartford Telecontrol shock absorbers. The dual Lucas horns are thought to be the first so fitted.

l. **1937 Rolls-Royce Phantom III Sports Saloon,** coachwork by Arthur Mulliner, 7340cc, extensively restored at a cost of over £30,000, new head lining and carpets, bare metal respray.
£27,000–30,000 *H&H*

1938 Rolls-Royce Phantom III Seven-Seater Limousine, coachwork by Barker, chassis No. 3CM121, 7340cc, division between front and rear compartments, unrestored condition.
£23,000–27,000 *BKS*

Although Rolls-Royce had many years' experience in building V12 aero engines, its first V12 car was the Phantom III of late 1935. This had overhead valves operated by a single camshaft between the cylinder banks. This particular car is from the last series to be built with hydraulic tappets and a heat exchanger to ensure quick warm-up of the oil.

1936 Rolls-Royce 25/30 Sports Saloon, coachwork by Park Ward, division between front and rear compartments, restored, finished in black with red leather interior, excellent condition.
£35,000–40,000 *VIC*

1936 Rolls-Royce 25/30 Touring Limousine, division between front and rear compartments, sunroof, picnic tables and cabinet, new chrome, front leather, carpets and head lining, excellent condition throughout.
£19,000–20,500 *Mot*

1938 Rolls-Royce 25/30 Limousine, coachwork by Hooper, chassis No. GMP15, engine No. V27L, occasional seats, blinds all-round, division between front and rear compartments, tool tray, driving light, twin Lucas short-trumpet horns, finished in black over Tartan Red with black wings and yellow coachline, original condition.
£15,500–17,500 *S*

l. **1938 Rolls-Royce 25/30 Limousine,** coachwork by James Young, 4-speed manual gearbox, restored at a cost of over £20,000, working intercom, radio, excellent condition throughout.
£17,500–20,000 *H&H*

This car is one of only two long-chassis examples known with seven seats.

1939 Rolls-Royce Wraith Park Ward Six Light Limousine, chassis No. WMB36, occasional seats, correct P100 headlamps, trumpet horns, Ace wheel discs, resprayed in white, good condition.
£15,000–17,000   *RCC*

r. **1954 Rolls-Royce Silver Wraith 'Empress Line' Touring Limousine,** coachwork by Hooper, 4566cc, excellent original condition.
£62,500–67,500   *COHN*

1948 Rolls-Royce Silver Wraith Sports Saloon, coachwork by Park Ward, 4257cc, 6 cylinders, 4-speed manual gearbox, restored, 98,999 miles recorded, very good condition throughout.
£10,500–12,000   *H&H*

1953 Rolls-Royce Silver Dawn Standard Steel Saloon, automatic transmission, left-hand drive, bench front seat, requires some minor restoration, good condition.
£18,500–20,000   *RCC*

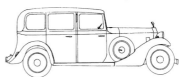

1956 Rolls-Royce Silver Cloud Saloon, left-hand drive, finished in black and silver, blue/grey leather interior, requires some restoration, good condition.
£14,000–15,500 *RCC*

The SI, II and III were Bentley's equivalents to the Rolls-Royce Silver Cloud I, II and III. Although virtually identical, apart from the distinctive radiator Bentley versions can often be cheaper than Rolls-Royce counterparts. This is not a factor of rarity as with the launch of the Silver Cloud II in 1959 Rolls-Royce versions outnumbered Bentley offerings for the first time.

1961 Rolls-Royce Silver Cloud II Saloon, new air conditioning system, finished in black with tan interior, good overall condition.
£15,000–16,500 *RCC*

1958 Rolls-Royce Silver Cloud I Standard Steel Saloon, 4887cc, 6 cylinders, automatic transmission, 106mph top speed, finished in black over sand, tan interior, tools, inspection lamp, log book, history.
£15,000–17,500 *BKS*

The Silver Cloud I was the last Rolls-Royce model to be powered by a six-cylinder engine, which it shared with the Silver Wraith.

1964 Rolls-Royce Silver Cloud III, 6230cc, V8, excellent condition.
£48,000–52,000 *BLE*

1963 Rolls-Royce Silver Cloud III, electric windows, reading lights, rear control for radio, rev counter, new wings and sill panels in 1975, resprayed, new stainless steel exhaust, cooling system hoses, choke, hot air pipes and leather spring covers, brake system overhauled, shock absorbers reconditioned, well maintained, excellent condition.
£20,000–23,000 *S*

1964 Rolls-Royce Silver Cloud III SCT100,
coachwork by James Young, chassis No. CCL35,
engine No. CL17C, 6230cc, V8, 4-speed automatic
transmission, power steering and brakes rebuilt,
new rear springs, Midnight Blue livery with
contrasting coachlining, chromework renewed,
wood cappings and fascia restored, new switches
and front window motor, excellent condition.
£30,000–34,000 *S*

*James Young built a number of special bodies on
the Cloud chassis, arguably the most sought-after
being the elegant SCT100 touring limousine
coachwork in aluminium. A total of 42 – from 47
produced – long-wheelbase Silver Cloud III chassis
were bodied by the Bromley firm. The bespoke
design, defined by a lower roof line, sloping bonnet,
spacious interior and distinctive paired headlights,
is unmistakably of its time.*

1964 Rolls-Royce Silver Cloud III, 6230cc,
V8, restored, finished in silver-grey over deep
red, Sand leather interior, very good
condition throughout.
£18,000–20,000 *BRIT*

*The Silver Cloud III and its Bentley equivalent,
the SIII, were introduced in October 1962. The
former was the ultimate development of the
Cloud range and was distinguishable from its
predecessors by the four-headlamp configuration.
It was built for three years before being replaced
by the Silver Shadow late in 1965.*

Miller's is a price GUIDE
not a price LIST

l. **1967 Rolls-Royce
Silver Shadow
Mulliner Park Ward
Coupé,** 6230cc, V8,
excellent condition.
£13,000–14,500 *EPP*

*The T1 and T2 were
Bentley's equivalents to
the Rolls-Royce Silver
Shadow I and II.
Although virtually
identical, apart from
the distinctive radiator
Bentley versions can often
be cheaper than Rolls-
Royce counterparts despite
the fact that Bentley
versions are far rarer.*

1969 Rolls-Royce Silver Shadow Convertible, chassis No. 4145, completely overhauled at a cost of
£23,000, engine rebuilt, new powered hood, upholstery refurbished, 3,000 miles since restoration,
excellent condition.
£15,000–18,000 *COYS*

*The arrival of the Silver Shadow, in late 1965, marked a major change in Rolls-Royce motor cars.
Previously, they had employed separate chassis, but the newcomer featured unitary construction. At its
heart was Rolls-Royce's familiar 6230cc alloy V8 engine with a power output of around 220bhp. Most
notably, the car was equipped with disc brakes and all-round independent suspension that incorporated
an engine-driven self-levelling system. The year after the Silver Shadow's launch, a two-door coupé, with
coachwork by Mulliner Park Ward, joined the line-up. This was followed in 1968 by a similarly-styled
drophead coupé.*

1971 Rolls-Royce Corniche Two-Door Saloon, coachwork by Mulliner Park Ward, restored 1994 at a cost of £10,000, Caribbean Blue with dark blue Everflex roof and upholstery, very good condition. **£12,000–14,000** *BKS*

Introduced in March 1971, the Corniche was a revised version of the Mulliner Park Ward-bodied two-door Silver Shadow coupé. The engine was Rolls-Royce's aluminium V8, with a capacity of 6750cc and producing around 10 per cent more power than standard. This propelled the car to a top speed of 120+mph with impressive acceleration to match. The Corniche received advanced split-level air conditioning and a redesigned fascia in 1976. In 1977, it benefited from the many improvements – most notably rack-and-pinion steering – introduced on the Shadow II range. The model proved a major success, remaining in production well into the 1990s; the last (convertible) examples were delivered in 1995.

1973 Rolls-Royce Corniche Two-Door Saloon, coachwork by Mulliner Park Ward, partially restored, some history, excellent condition throughout. **£13,000–15,000** *BKS*

1974 Rolls-Royce Silver Shadow Four-Door Saloon, minor paint blemishes, original light tan leather upholstery, 41,000 miles from new. **£9,500–11,000** *BKS*

In 1970, the Silver Shadow's engine capacity was increased to 6750cc, improving performance.

1975 Rolls-Royce Silver Shadow Saloon, 95,000 miles from new, good original condition. **£7,000–8,000** *RCC*

1974 Rolls-Royce Silver Shadow, 6750cc, long wheelbase, electric division between front and rear compartments, small rear window, 85,000 miles recorded, full service history, good condition. **£10,000–12,000** *VIC*

1975 Rolls-Royce Camargue Two-Door Coupé, coachwork styled by Pininfarina, Richmond Blue with Surf Blue hide interior, dark blue sheepskin over-rugs, front head restraints, well maintained, full service history, 28,250 miles recorded, excellent mechanical condition. **£33,500–37,500** *S*

1976 Rolls-Royce Corniche Coupé, 6750cc, V8, finished in Rosewood with beige hide interior, very well maintained, some service history, valuable registration number, excellent condition.
£17,600–18,000 *BRIT*

The Mulliner Park Ward styled Corniche was produced between 1971 and 1977, 504 being convertibles and 780 coupés.

1976 Rolls-Royce Corniche Coupé, carburettor rebuilt, new fuel pump and exhaust system, brakes, suspension and steering overhauled, 3,000 miles since, very good condition throughout.
£16,000–18,000 *PA*

1977 Rolls-Royce Silver Shadow II, 6750cc, V8, resprayed in Mason's Black, interior woodwork refurbished, service history, excellent condition.
£10,000–12,000 *BRIT*

The Silver Shadow II was built between 1977 and 1980. Its discreet facelift included revised bumper styling and a front air dam, while the interior received a modified fascia. Very late examples had a headlamp wash/wipe system.

1978 Rolls-Royce Silver Shadow II, 6750cc, V8, very good condition.
£10,000–12,000 *PA*

l. **1978 Rolls-Royce Silver Wraith II,** 6750cc, V8, finished in Chestnut with dark brown vinyl roof, interior trimmed in tan Parker-Tex, well maintained, 44,000 miles recorded, excellent condition throughout.
£10,500–12,500 *BRIT*

Produced between 1977 and 1980, with a run of 2,144, the Silver Wraith II was a carry-over of the long-wheelbase Silver Shadow I. Some examples were fitted with the limousine division, and the model was visually identifiable by a vinyl roof and smaller rear window.

1979 Rolls-Royce Silver Shadow II, 6750cc, headlamp wash/wipe, lambswool over-rugs, complete tool kit, full service history, very good condition.
£8,000–9,000 *H&H*

1979 Rolls-Royce Silver Shadow II, 6750cc, finished in Peacock Blue with Magnolia leather interior, full service history, 88,000 miles recorded.
£11,000–12,000 *VIC*

1981 Rolls-Royce Corniche Coupé, dark blue with dark blue leather interior, service history, 57,000 miles recorded, excellent condition throughout.
£20,000–23,000 *PA*

1980 Rolls-Royce Silver Spirit, 6750cc, finished in Cardinal Red, full service history, alarm, very good condition.
£9,750–11,250 *H&H*

The Rolls-Royce Silver Spirit was introduced in October 1980 to replace the ageing Silver Shadow.

r. **1981 Rolls-Royce Silver Spirit,** finished in Ice Green with light beige interior, full service history, 62,000 miles recorded, very good condition.
£11,000–12,000 *VIC*

1983 Rolls-Royce Camargue Coupé, full mechanical and electrical overhaul, bare metal respray in Claret, beige Everflex roof, interior refurbished, CD player, alarm, 12,000 miles in past 6 years, very good condition.
£25,500–28,000 *S*

ROVER

The first Rover wasn't a car at all, but a bicycle made in 1884, when J. K. Starley and W. Sutton adopted the Rover name for their advanced 'safety bicycle' which, in many ways, was the forerunner of the modern cycle. The Coventry company made its first motorcycle in 1902, followed in 1904 by the first Rover car, an 8hp, single-cylinder model costing £200. Its early reputation was enhanced in 1905, when Rover cars finished fifth and 12th in the Tourist Trophy race. In 1924, Rover abandoned motorcycle production and, in 1929, after a boardroom clear-out, S. B. Wilks was appointed managing director, establishing a quality-first philosophy that served the company well through the years with its solidly middle-class customers.

The much-loved and so-called 'Auntie' Rover, the P4, was launched in 1950 and helped establish Rover's post-war reputation for dependable and robust quality cars. The big P5 saloon, launched in 1959, became a newsreel fixture outside 10 Downing Street as a fleet of these cars loyally served ministers and prime ministers from Harold Wilson to Margaret Thatcher. The stylish P6, especially in V8 form, has also become a favourite, admired and enjoyed in enthusiastic every-day use.

In 1967, as pressure increased on independent makers, Rover merged into the Leyland Motor Corporation, and in 1970 produced the Range Rover, which is still going strong. Rover weathered the BL years and emerged on top when the organisation was named Rover Group in 1986. Today, as part of BMW, the company offers a wider range than ever.

1921 Rover 12 Five-Seater Tourer, 2279cc, 4 cylinders, 12hp, finished in burgundy with black wings, trimmed in dark blue hide, Auster screen, serviceable weather equipment, original tools, concours winner, very good condition.
£11,000–15,000 *BRIT*

During WWI, Rover produced munitions, motor-cycles and staff cars, but after the war only two models were built – the popular twin-cylinder, air-cooled 8hp and the sturdy 12/14, the design of which dated back to 1912. The latter was an excellent car, which gained a reputation for ruggedness and reliability, remaining in production until 1925. This particular example has appeared in a number of TV series, including The House of Elliot.

1933 Rover 10/25 Saloon, 1185cc, 4 cylinders, green leather interior, sunroof, restored, excellent condition throughout.
£5,750–6,500 *BRIT*

Introduced in 1929, the 10/25 proved a great success for Rover in the burgeoning market for small quality cars. Production continued until 1933, by which time 15,000 had been built.

1953 Rover P4 75 Saloon, 2103cc, 4-speed gearbox, original paperwork, excellent original condition throughout.
£2,750–3,500 *H&H*

A 1939 Rover 14/16/20 instruction manual and a 1961 Rover 80/100 manual.
£4–6 each *LF*

ROVER Model	ENGINE cc/cyl	DATES	CONDITION 1	2	3
10hp	998/2	1920-25	£5,000	£3,000	£1,500
9/20	1074/4	1925-27	£6,000	£4,000	£2,000
10/25	1185/4	1928-33	£7,000	£4,000	£2,500
14hp	1577/6	1933-39	£6,000	£4,250	£2,000
12	1496/4	1934-37	£7,000	£4,000	£1,500
20 Sports	2512/6	1937-39	£7,000	£4,500	£2,500

l. **1956 Rover P4 75 Saloon,** 2300cc, 6 cylinders, 4-speed manual gearbox, freewheel facility, good unrestored condition throughout. **£1,400–1,800** *H&H*

1961 Rover P4 100, 2625cc, 6 cylinders, good condition. **£2,450–3,000** *PA*

1961 Rover P4 80 Saloon, 2286cc, 4 cylinders, dry-stored for 20 years, brakes require attention, body needs tidying, 49,286 miles from new, good condition. **£1,300–1,600** *H&H*

r. **1962 Rover P4 100 Saloon,** 2625cc, 6 cylinders, original tyres, tool kit, touch-up paints and manuals, 27,500 miles from new, excellent condition throughout. **£6,000–7,000** *H&H*

ROVER Model	ENGINE cc/cyl	DATES	CONDITION 1	2	3
P2 10	1389/4	1946-47	£3,200	£2,500	£1,000
P2 12	1496/4	1946-47	£3,500	£2,800	£1,200
P2 12 Tour	1496/4	1947	£7,500	£3,500	£1,500
P2 14/16	1901/6	1946-47	£4,200	£3,000	£1,000
P2 14/16 Sal	1901/6	1946-47	£3,700	£2,500	£700
P3 60	1595/4	1948-49	£5,000	£2,500	£1,000
P3 75	2103/6	1948-49	£4,000	£3,000	£800
P4 75	2103/6	1950-51	£4,000	£2,000	£1,200
P4 75	2103/6	1952-64	£3,500	£1,800	£1,200
P4 60	1997/4	1954-59	£3,200	£1,200	£1,200
P4 90	2638/6	1954-59	£4,000	£1,800	£1,200
P4 75	2230/6	1955-59	£3,800	£1,200	£1,000
P4 105R	2638/6	1957-58	£4,000	£2,000	£1,000
P4 105S	2638/6	1957-59	£4,000	£2,000	£1,000
P4 80	2286/4	1960-62	£3,000	£1,200	£800
P4 95	2625/6	1963-64	£3,000	£1,600	£500
P4 100	2625/6	1960-62	£3,800	£2,000	£1,000
P4 110	2625/6	1963-64	£3,800	£2,000	£1,000
P5 3 litre	2995/6	1959-67	£4,000	£2,500	£1,000
P5 3 litre Coupé	2995/6	1959-67	£5,500	£3,800	£1,000
P5B (V8)	3528/8	1967-74	£6,250	£4,500	£1,500
P5B (V8) Coupé	3528/8	1967-73	£6,250	£4,500	£1,500
P6 2000 SC Series 1	1980/4	1963-65	£2,200	£800	-
P6 2000 SC Series 1	1980/4	1966-70	£2,000	£800	-
P6 2000 SC Auto Series 1	1980/4	1966-70	£1,500	£600	-
P6 2000 TC Series 1	1980/4	1966-70	£2,000	£900	-
P6 2000 SC Series 2	1980/4	1970-73	£2,000	£900	-
P6 2000 SC Auto Series 2	1980/4	1970-73	£1,500	£800	-
P6 2000 TC Series 2	1980/4	1970-73	£2,000	£900	-
P6 3500 Series 1	3500/8	1968-70	£2,500	£1,400	-
P6 2200 SC	2200/4	1974-77	£1,750	£850	-
P6 2200 SC Auto	2200/4	1974-77	£2,500	£1,000	-
P6 2200 TC	2200/4	1974-77	£2,000	£1,000	-
P6 3500 Series 2	3500/8	1971-77	£3,000	£1,700	-
P6 3500 S Series 2	3500/8	1971-77	£2,000	£1,500	-

1963 Rover P4 110 Saloon, 2625cc, 63,000 miles recorded, good condition. **£950–1,100** *H&H*

r. **1964 Rover P4 95 Saloon,** 2625cc, 6 cylinders, 4-speed manual gearbox, restored, excellent condition throughout. **£950–1,100** *H&H*

1965 Rover P5 MkII, 3 litres, original tool kit, manuals and documents, stored since late 1970s, 34,650 recorded miles, very original car.
£4,500–5,500 *CGC*

1966 Rover P5 MkIII, 3 litres, 6 cylinders, automatic transmission.
£1,250–1,500 *CGC*

1972 Rover 3.5 Litre Saloon, 3528cc, V8, Arden Green with Buckskin leather interior, new brake servo and water pump, well maintained, very good condition.
£4,800–5,600 *BRIT*

1970 Rover P5B Coupé, 3528cc, V8, automatic transmission, good condition.
£3,400–4,000 *PA*

1966 Rover P6 2000 TC, 1978cc, 4 cylinders, original specification, period wing mirrors, fog lamps and badge bar, 4,350 miles from new, excellent condition.
£6,000–7,000 *BRIT*

Introduced in 1963, the Rover 2000 proved a worthy successor to the legendary P4 Series. By 1966, it was available in the more sporting TC guise, which boasted 124bhp and excellent handling. It was available only with a manual gearbox. The 2000 TC became one of the most popular sports saloons of its time.

1972 Rover P6 2000 SC Saloon, 1978cc, 4 cylinders, 4-speed manual gearbox, 70,800 miles recorded, good condition.
£800–1,200 *H&H*

1973 Rover P6 2000, leather interior, unrestored, excellent condition.
£3,700–4,400 *THOR*

1975 Rover P6 2200 SC, 2200cc, excellent original condition.
£1,800–2,000 *FCV*

r. **1975 Rover P6 2200 TC,** manual gearbox, leather interior, full history, 84,000 miles recorded, good condition.
£1,000–1,400 *Mot*

l. **1972 Rover P6 3500S,** manual gearbox, restored, concours winner, excellent condition throughout.
£5,500–6,500 *Mot*

1973 Rover P6 3500 Saloon, 3528cc, V8, automatic transmission, white with black vinyl trim.
£2,450–3,000 *MEA*

1975 Rover P6 3500 Saloon, 3528cc, V8.
£3,300–3,700 *H&H*

Prices

The price ranges given reflect the average price a purchaser should pay for a similar vehicle. Condition, rarity of model, pedigree, restoration and many other factors must be taken into account when assessing values.

l. **1976 Rover P6 3500S Saloon,** 3528cc, manual gearbox, leather interior, resprayed, good condition throughout.
£1,500–2,000 *H&H*

This particular car was one of the last to be produced.

1975 Rover P6 3500 Saloon, automatic transmission, engine rebuilt, full history, good condition.
£1,600–2,000 *UMC*

SAAB

1980 Saab 99 Turbo, 1985cc, 4 cylinders, 145bhp, excellent original condition.
£1,100–1,350 *H&H*
This particular car was one of only 500 homologation models made.

SAAB Model	ENGINE cc/cyl	DATES	CONDITION 1	2	3
92	764/2	1950-53	£3,000	£1,500	£1,000
92B	764/2	1953-55	£3,500	£1,500	£1,000
93-93B	748/3	1956-60	£3,000	£1,500	£1,000
95	841/3	1960-68	£3,000	£1,500	£1,000
96	841/3	1960-68	£4,000	£1,800	£1,000
96 Sport	841/3	1962-66	£3,500	£1,500	£1,000
Sonnett II	1698/4	1967-74	£3,500	£1,500	£1,000
95/96	1498/4	1966-80	£3,000	£1,000	£800
99	1709/4	1968-71	£2,000	£1,200	-
99	1854/4	1970-74	£2,000	£1,000	-
99	1985/4	1972-83	£2,000	£1,000	£500
99 Turbo	1985/4	1978-83	£3,000	£1,000	£500

SALMSON

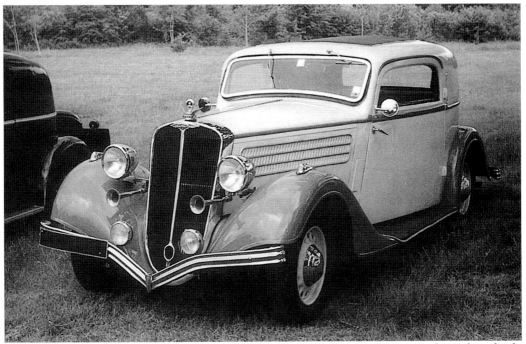

1938 Salmson S4 DA Coupé, 1720cc, 4-cylinder in-line engine, 45bhp at 3,500rpm, mechanical overhaul in 1993, engine rebuilt, resprayed, chrome trim replated, good condition.
£4,500–5,000 *Pou*

SCAT

1922 SCAT 3 Litre Tourer, 5 seater, dual-cowl, fabric-covered body, Harper Patent detachable wire wheels, nickel fittings, Auster screen, hood and tonneau cover, good overall condition.
£14,000–16,000   *BKS*

The SCAT, built by Societa Ceirano Automobili Torino and financed by Newton & Bennett of Manchester, was a conventional car in all respects, built to exacting standards. Its pedigree included victory in the Targa Florio races of 1911, 1912 and 1914.

SIATA

1956 Siata, 1100cc, good condition.
£7,000–8,000   *DB*

SINGER

George Singer built his first motor car in 1905, and his Coventry-based company went on to produce some delightful small cars, becoming a significant force towards the end of the 1920s, when the firm was ranked third in the UK sales league behind Austin and Morris. Outstanding models were the peppy little Singer Nine of the 1930s and the 1½ litre Le Mans. After the war, Singer struggled to compete with the big players, and in 1955 was acquired by the Rootes empire. There, the marque lingered as a deluxe Hillman and Sunbeam variant until it faded away for good in 1970.

1914 Singer 10hp, 4 cylinders, restored, VCC dated, good condition.
£12,000–14,000   *SVV*

SINGER Model	ENGINE cc/cyl	DATES	CONDITION		
			1	2	3
10	1097/4	1918-24	£5,000	£2,000	£1,000
15	1991/6	1922-25	£6,000	£3,000	£1,500
14/34	1776/6	1926-27	£7,000	£4,000	£2,000
Junior	848/4	1927-32	£6,000	£3,000	£1,500
Senior	1571/4	1928-29	£7,000	£4,000	£2,000
Super 6	1776/6	1928-31	£7,000	£4,000	£2,000
9 Le Mans	972/4	1932-37	£13,000	£8,000	£5,000
Twelve	1476/6	1932-34	£10,000	£7,000	£6,000
1.5 litre	1493/6	1934-36	£3,000	£2,000	£1,000
2 litre	1991/6	1934-37	£4,000	£2,750	£1,000
11	1459/4	1935-36	£3,000	£2,000	£1,000
12	1525/4	1937-39	£3,000	£2,000	£1,000

1929 Singer Junior 8hp Four-Door Saloon, 848cc, finished in red and black with brown interior, original specification, good condition.
£1,700-2,000 *BKS*

The Singer Junior was introduced in 1927 and compared favourably in price with contemporary Austin and Morris products, but was more spacious and better appointed. It was the first genuinely cheap British car to be powered by an overhead-camshaft engine, and proved a great success, over 25,000 examples being built by 1930.

1928 Singer Junior, 848cc, 4 cylinders, completely overhauled 28 years ago, approximately 3,000 miles since, good condition throughout.
£6,000-7,000 *CGC*

1934 Singer Nine Le Mans, 1029cc, 4 cylinders, restored at a cost of £17,000, British Racing Green with red hide upholstery, very good condition.
£14,750-16,500 *COYS*

In 1932, the successful Singer Junior was replaced by the Nine, and when sports versions became available in 1933, Singer discovered a new market for the car. Capacity was 972cc, the overhead-camshaft, four-cylinder engine producing 26.5bhp and being mated to a four-speed manual gearbox. It was the marque's first attempt at endurance racing, however – when a standard two-seater sports model, driven by Barnes and Langley, finished 13th overall at Le Mans in 1933 – that led Singer to introduce the more powerful Nine Le Mans. Equipped with twin SU carburettors, its engine pushed out 35bhp at 4,500rpm, enough to provide a 75mph top speed and 0–50mph in 17 seconds. The Nine Le Mans was subsequently raced with success in numerous events. Production of all Nines ended in 1940.

l. **1951 Singer Nine 4AB Roadster,** 1498cc, 4 cylinders, 4-speed manual gearbox, requires restoration. **£2,300–2,500** *H&H*

1953 Singer SM 1500 Four-Seater Tourer, excellent condition. **£5,500–6,500** *WILM*

STANDARD

After serving an engineering apprenticeship and working for a firm of civil engineers, R. W. Maudsley set up the Standard company in Coventry in 1903. As the firm developed in the 1920s, it began to specialise in medium-range cars, but in 1928 introduced a small car, the Nine, in an attempt to overcome financial difficulties. In 1929, John Black joined Standard and spurred the company's resurgence in the 1930s. In 1945, with Black in control, Standard acquired the Triumph name which, ironically, would eclipse and outlast the parent marque. Standard merged with British Leyland in 1961, and by the end of 1963 was no more.

l. **1924 Standard 11/9 Four-Seater Tourer,** excellent condition. **£7,000–8,500** *DB*

STANDARD Model	ENGINE cc/cyl	DATES	CONDITION 1	2	3
SLS	1328/4	1919-20	£5,000	£4,000	£1,000
VI	1307/4	1922	£5,000	£4,000	£1,000
SLO/V4	1944/4	1922-28	£5,000	£4,000	£1,000
6V	2230/6	1928	£10,000	£8,000	£5,000
V3	1307/4	1923-26	£4,000	£3,000	£1,000
Little 9	1006/4	1932-33	£4,000	£2,000	£1,000
9	1155/4	1928-29	£5,500	£3,000	£1,000
Big 9	1287/4	1932-33	£4,500	£3,250	£2,000
15	1930/6	1929-30	£6,000	£4,000	£2,000
12	1337/6	1933-34	£4,000	£3,000	£1,500
10hp	1343/4	1933-37	£4,000	£2,500	£1,000
9	1052/4	1934-36	£4,200	£2,500	£1,000
Flying 9	1131/4	1937-39	£3,200	£1,800	£750
Flying 10	1267/4	1937-39	£3,500	£2,200	£1,000
Flying 14	1176/4	1937-48	£4,500	£2,200	£1,000
Flying 8	1021/4	1939-48	£4,500	£2,400	£1,000

1926 Standard Warwick Tourer, 1390cc, 14hp, 4-speed gearbox, history and log sheets for 70 years, very good condition.
£6,500–7,500 *H&H*

This particular car is one of only four known surviving examples worldwide.

1935 Standard Little Nine, 1052cc, 4 cylinders, finished in beige with black wings, brown leather trim, good condition.
£2,750–3,250 *BRIT*

The Standard Motor Company built a vast range of motor cars, probably being best known for the pre-war Flying range, from 8hp to a 20hp V8. Prior to the introduction of this series in 1936, the most popular Standards were in the 9 and 10hp range, the 9hp being available in two forms: the Big Nine with an engine capacity of 1287cc, and the Little Nine, introduced in 1931 and excellent value at £155.

1946 Standard 8 Tourer, non-original colour, good restored condition.
£4,000–5,000 *Mot*

r. **1947 Standard Flying Eight Tourer,** 1009cc, 4 cylinders, original blue leather interior, good condition throughout.
£3,750–4,500 *BRIT*

STANDARD Model	ENGINE cc/cyl	DATES	CONDITION 1	2	3
12	1609/4	1945-48	£2,000	£950	£250
12 DHC	1509/4	1945-48	£3,200	£2,000	£500
14	1776/4	1945-48	£3,000	£950	£250
Vanguard I/II	2088/4	1948-55	£2,200	£1,000	£250
Vanguard III	2088/4	1955-61	£1,800	£900	£200
Vanguard III Est	2088/4	1955-61	£2,000	£1,000	£250
Vanguard III Sportsman	2088/4	1955-58	£2,500	£1,200	£400
Vanguard Six	1998/6	1961-63	£2,000	£1,000	£500
Eight	803/4	1952-59	£1,250	£500	-
Ten	948/4	1955-59	£1,400	£800	-
Ensign I/II	1670/4	1957-63	£1,000	£800	-
Ensign I/II Est	1670/4	1962-63	£1,000	£850	-
Pennant Companion	948/4	1955-61	£1,800	£850	£300
Pennant	948/4	1955-59	£1,650	£825	£250

STAR

1904 Star, twin-cylinder, 7hp, chain drive, 3/4 seater tonneau, completely restored, VCC dated, excellent condition.
£32,000–36,000 *Mot*

STONELEIGH

1924 Stoneleigh Chummy Four-Seater, completely restored, excellent condition.
£7,000–8,000 *S*

This particular car is one of only two known surviving examples.

STUDEBAKER

c1927 Studebaker President, finished in black over mushroom, rear-mounted trunk, twin spares, scuttle sidelamps, opening windscreen, well-furnished interior with blinds, laminated wood steering wheel and occasional seats, Bedford cord upholstery, 57,000km recorded, good condition.
£9,000–10,000 *S*

In the 1920s, Studebaker established a line of really large six-cylinder cars – the Light, the Special and the Big Six – which became known for their reliability and economy. The introduction in 1927 of the model ES Big Six President was marked by extensive styling changes. A custom-designed Studebaker was offered, with lowered coachwork with two-tone paintwork, disc wheels, a French-style visor and luxury interior trim. A seven-passenger saloon was sold at first, while later models included a seven-passenger touring car and a limousine. The President Six was carried over as a first-series Studebaker until late 1928.

l. **1960 Studebaker Hawk,** 4200cc, good condition throughout.
£3,000–3,500 *LF*

STUTZ

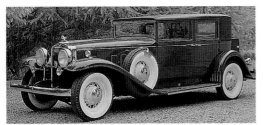

1932 Stutz DV32 Long Wheelbase Four-Door Sedan, chassis No. DV-60-1490, engine No. DV 33198, 322.06cu in, 8 cylinder in-line engine, double overhead camshafts, 156hp at 3,900rpm, 3-speed gearbox, finished in red and burgundy with black leather top, cream wheels, light grey broadcloth interior, restored, excellent condition. **£34,000–38,000** *C*

Stutz's final engineering tour de force was the magnificent DV32 powerplant of late 1931. Developed from the SV16 Vertical-Eight, it boasted four valves per cylinder, double overhead camshafts and dual ignition. A lone DV32 driven by the highly experienced French racer and Stutz exponent, Edouard Brisson, represented Stutz's final fling at Le Mans. Sixteen laps into the 1932 race, and after a steady march from a mid-field start to ninth place, the Stutz crashed violently at White House Corner while avoiding Minoia's spinning Alfa Romeo. Brisson was thrown clear of the wreck, but this mishap closed the chapter on Stutz's attempt to carry the Stars and Stripes in international racing.

1975 Stutz Blackhawk, 7456cc, V8, finished in black, black hide upholstery, 10,500 miles recorded, excellent condition. **£10,000–13,000** *BRIT*

Following a break of almost 35 years, the illustrious Stutz name reappeared in 1969 on the striking Blackhawk Coupé. Initially, this machine was powered by a 6½ litre Pontiac V8, but by 1972 a 7½ litre Pontiac engine was specified, giving a power output of 431bhp. The price for such exclusivity, however, was high, more than three times the cost of a Cadillac Eldorado. The coachwork was designed by Virgil Exner and built by Carrozzeria Padana of Modena, where final assembly was carried out. Fewer than 60 Blackhawks are believed to have been produced, and customers included Elvis Presley, who was alleged to have owned two.

SUNBEAM

The firm that became Sunbeam was started in 1859 by 23-year-old John Marston, and initially made tinplate and japanned goods in Wolverhampton. In 1887, Marston changed the name to Sunbeam Cycles, and the company gained a reputation for turning out fine bicycles. A Sunbeam car appeared in 1901, but it was the arrival of French designer Louis Coatalen – who had previously worked at Humber and Hillman – that propelled the company towards its glory years in the 1920s with a string of successful GP cars, record breakers and fine sports and touring machines.

In the early 1930s, the best Sunbeams rivalled Bentley and Alvis, although they were not quite a match in outright performance. By then, the company was in trouble as part of the unwieldy and inefficient Sunbeam-Talbot-Darracq combine, and Rootes bought the marque in 1935. After the war, Sunbeam initially continued its sporting tradition: a Sunbeam MkIII won the 1955 Monte Carlo Rally, and the Sunbeam Rapiers of the early 1960s proved useful in rallying and touring car racing. Eventually, though, most Sunbeams became nothing more than slightly peppier and posher Hillmans. Chrysler acquired Rootes in 1964, and the Sunbeam marque faded into the sunset in 1976.

1921 Sunbeam 4½ Litre 24hp Tourer, restored at a cost of £70,000, maroon and black livery with black upholstery and interior trim, black canvas hood and hood bag, nickel and brass fittings, Rotax lighting equipment, rear luggage carrier, twin side-mounted spares, Wilmot Breedon calormeter, excellent condition. **£31,000–34,000** *BKS*

With the expertise gained from wartime aero engineering work, and its manufacturing experience prior to WWI, Sunbeam was well placed to develop a range of refined touring cars in the post-war years. The 24hp model of 1921 was powered by a smooth 4½ litre, six-cylinder sidevalve engine, had a four-speed gearbox and featured underslung rear suspension. A luxury touring car in all respects, it commanded a new price of £1,510. Only 11 examples of this car are known to survive.

r. **1946 Sunbeam-Talbot Ten,** 1185cc, 4 cylinders, body-off rebuild, finished in black, very good condition throughout. **£4,500–5,000** *BRIT*

SUNBEAM Model	ENGINE cc/cyl	DATES	CONDITION		
			1	2	3
12/16	2412/4	1910-14	£25,000	£16,000	£12,000
16/20	4070/4	1910-15	£32,000	£22,000	£15,000
24	4524/6	1919-22	£30,000	£19,000	£11,000
3 litre	2916/6	1925-30	£48,000	£30,000	£20,000
14/40	2200/4	1925-30	£18,000	£10,000	£8,000
16	2040/6	1927-30	£16,000	£12,500	£10,000
20	2916/6	1927-30	£22,000	£15,000	£10,500
Speed 20	2916/6	1932-35	£15,000	£10,000	£8,000
Dawn	1627/4	1934-35	£8,000	£5,000	£3,500
25	3317/6	1934	£10,000	£8,000	£4,000

Prices can vary depending on replica bodies, provenance, coachbuilder, drophead, twin cam etc.

1961 Sunbeam Alpine, completely overhauled, finished in Old English White, interior trimmed in blue, hard and soft tops, excellent condition.
£3,500–4,000 *S*

In 1953, the Sunbeam name was revived by the Rootes Group for the Alpine, a sporting two-seater version of the 90. Later, Rootes set about producing a two-seater to compete in the lucrative US sports car market with Triumph, MG and Austin-Healey. Introduced in 1959 and built on the Hillman Husky II floorpan, this new Sunbeam Alpine employed Rapier running gear and the 1½ litre, overhead-valve, four-cylinder engine that powered many of Rootes' other products. In Alpine form, it boasted an aluminium cylinder head and twin carburettors, and produced 78bhp – sufficient to propel the sleekly-styled two-seater to within a whisker of 100mph.

1963 Sunbeam Alpine, 1592cc, automatic transmission, new brake pipes and exhaust, requires some restoration, good all-round condition.
£1,800–2,000 *H&H*

l. **1968 Sunbeam Alpine V,** red with black interior, white hood and red hard top, good condition throughout. **£4,600–5,300** *BKS*

The Alpine was progressively improved through the Series up to the introduction of the 1725cc Alpine V in 1965. Production of Alpines ceased in 1968.

1966 Sunbeam Tiger, 4260cc, V8, very good condition. **£11,000–13,000** *EPP*

SUNBEAM-TALBOT/ SUNBEAM Model	ENGINE cc/cyl	DATES	CONDITION 1	2	3
Talbot 80	1185/4	1948-50	£3,500	£2,250	£1,000
Talbot 80 DHC	1185/4	1948-50	£6,000	£4,500	£2,000
Talbot 90 Mk I	1944/4	1949-50	£4,000	£2,100	£750
Talbot 90 Mk I DHC	1944/4	1949-50	£7,000	£4,750	£2,000
Talbot 90 II/IIa/III	2267/4	1950-56	£5,000	£3,000	£1,500
Talbot 90 II/IIa/III DHC	2267/4	1950-56	£7,000	£5,000	£2,250
Talbot Alpine I/III	2267/4	1953-55	£11,000	£7,500	£3,750
Talbot Ten	1197/4	1946-48	£3,500	£2,000	£750
Talbot Ten Tourer	1197/4	1946-48	£7,000	£4,000	£2,000
Talbot Ten DHC	1197/4	1946-48	£6,500	£4,000	£2,000
Talbot 2 litre	1997/4	1946-48	£4,000	£2,500	£1,000
Talbot 2 litre Tourer	1997/4	1946-48	£7,500	£4,000	£2,250
Rapier I	1392/4	1955-57	£1,200	£700	£300
Rapier II	1494/4	1957-59	£1,800	£900	£300
Rapier II Conv	1494/4	1957-59	£3,000	£1,500	£450
Rapier III	1494/4	1959-61	£2,000	£1,200	£400
Rapier III Conv	1494/4	1959-61	£3,500	£1,600	£600
Rapier IIIA	1592/4	1961-63	£2,000	£1,200	£400
Rapier IIIA Conv	1592/4	1961-63	£3,600	£1,700	£650
Rapier IV/V	1592/ 1725/4	1963-67	£2,000	£700	£250
Alpine I-II	1494/4	1959-62	£6,000	£3,500	£1,800
Alpine III	1592/4	1963	£6,500	£4,000	£1,250
Alpine IV	1592/4	1964	£6,500	£4,000	£1,250
Alpine V	1725/4	1965-68	£7,000	£4,000	£1,250
Harrington Alpine	1592/4	1961	£8,000	£4,750	£1,250
Harrington Le Mans	1592/4	1962-63	£10,000	£6,500	£3,000
Tiger Mk 1	4261/8	1964-67	£15,000	£10,000	£6,000
Tiger Mk 2	4700/8	1967	£13,000	£8,000	£6,000
Rapier Fastback	1725/4	1967-76	£1,100	£700	£250
Rapier H120	1725/4	1968-76	£1,500	£800	£300

SUZUKI

l. **1982 Suzuki SC 100 GX Sports Coupé,** 970cc, rear-mounted 4 cylinder engine, 47bhp, 4-speed manual gearbox, 4 seater, original specification, rear chrome luggage carrier, chrome nudge bars, 64,000 miles from new, good condition throughout.
£1,400–1,700 *BKS*

SWALLOW

1955 Swallow Doretti, 1991cc, 4 cylinders, original, unrestored, good overall condition.
£3,500–4,000 *BKS*

1955 Swallow Doretti, 1991cc, 4 cylinders, overdrive, non-original doors, requires some work, sound condition.
£2,800–3,500 *BKS*

SWIFT

1915 Swift, 4 cylinders, 10hp, restored, VCC dated, good condition.
£11,000–13,500 *SVV*

r. **1923 Swift Open Tourer,** 4 cylinders, 12hp, 4-speed manual gearbox, black and yellow with maroon interior, detailed history, excellent condition throughout.
£10,000–12,000 *H&H*

TALBOT

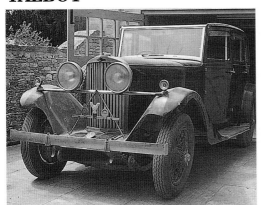

1936 Talbot 10 Sports Tourer, 1185cc,
4 cylinders, cream with blue leather interior,
comprehensive restoration, weather equipment
includes hood, sidescreens and full tonneau cover
in blue mohair, excellent condition throughout.
£8,000–10,000 *BRIT*

1933 Talbot 95 Four-Door Saloon, coachwork
by Darracq, Wilson pre-selector gearbox, side-
mounted spares, black with blue fabric interior,
completely restored 1954, stored since 1958,
original unmodified condition.
£9,750–11,000 *S*

*Talbot scored many successes in the touring and
sporting fields, and under chief engineer George
Roesch built superbly engineered and understated
cars of great distinction. The Type 65 was the first
of an illustrious line of Roesch Talbots, which
included the 3 litre 95.*

*The Sunbeam-Talbot story began in 1935 following
the Rootes Group's acquisition of the British
Sunbeam and Talbot marques after the collapse of
the Sunbeam-Talbot-Darracq combine. The famous
Roesch-designed Talbot's were replaced by a new
10hp Talbot, which used the mechanical
components of the contemporary Hillman Minx,
and a 3 litre model based on the Humber Super
Snipe. From 1938, they were marketed as
Sunbeam-Talbots to capitalise on the previous
achievements of those great firms.*

1937 Talbot BD 105 Four-Seater Open Tourer, relica coachwork in the style of Vanden Plas built
c1986, Wilson pre-selector gearbox, comprehensive mechanical rebuild 1993, radiator and fuel tank
overhauled, new replica exhaust system, rewired, some replating, excellent condition throughout.
£24,000–27,000 *BKS*

*Launched in 1931, the Talbot 105 was fitted with a six-cylinder engine of 2960cc, which developed 105bhp
at 4,500rpm. In touring form, it had a compression ratio of 6.6:1, but for racing this was increased to
10.2:1, and the output rose to 140bhp.*

TALBOT Model	ENGINE cc/cyl	DATES	CONDITION		
			1	2	3
25hp and 25/50	4155/4	1907-16	£35,000	£25,000	£15,000
12hp	2409/4	1909-15	£22,000	£15,000	£9,000
8/18	960/4	1922-25	£8,000	£5,000	£2,000
14/45	1666/6	1926-35	£16,000	£10,000	£5,000
75	2276/6	1930-37	£22,000	£12,000	£7,000
105	2969/6	1935-37	£30,000	£20,000+	£15,000

Higher value for tourers and coachbuilt cars.

TALBOT-LAGO

1949 Talbot-Lago Grand Sport T26 GS Coupé, coachwork believed to be by Saoutchik, 4.5 litres, 6 cylinders, 3 Zenith-Stromberg carburettors, 190bhp, Wilson pre-selector gearbox, short wheelbase chassis, Rudge centre-lock wire wheels, Marchal headlamps, original leather interior, 125mph top speed, unused for 30 years, 46,000km, excellent condition.
£116,000–120,000 *S*

The Venetian born Major Anthony Lago took control of the French Talbot and Darracq marques in 1935, following the collapse of the Sunbeam-Talbot-Darracq combine. He inspired Ing. Becchia to design an inclined-valve cylinder head for the existing Talbot engine block, which went on to become one of the few power units to see Grand Prix success both before and after WWII. It also powered the successful series of Lago Specials, later Talbot-Lagos. The Talbot-Lago Grand Sport was equipped with the T26 record engine, a mighty 4.5 litre six. Between 1947 and 1953, 36 Grand Sport chassis were made, of which only a handful had the short 2.65m wheelbase.

TOYOTA

1974 Toyota Corona MkII, 1968cc, original tool kit and radio, unmodified, 35,000 miles recorded, good condition.
£1,800–2,000 *H&H*

This particular car is believed to be one of only three examples in the UK.

TOYOTA Model	ENGINE cc/cyl	DATES	CONDITION 1	2	3
Celica TA22 & TA23 Coupé	1588/4	1971-78	£1,400	£1,000	£350
RA28 Liftback	1968/4	1971-78	£1,400	£600	£350
Crown MS65, MS63, MS75, Saloon, Estate, Coupé	2563/6	1972-75	£1,500	£1,000	£500

Plus a premium of £200–400 for the Coupé and £200–500 for a Twin-Cam GT.

TRIUMPH

Triumph's long history is full of ironies. It was the most seemingly British of makes, yet it was founded by two ex-patriot Germans. In later years, when the defunct Triumph company was taken over by Standard, it went on to eclipse and outlast its parent.

Starting out as a bicycle maker, founded by Siegfried Bettman and Mauritz Schulte, the company turned to motorcycles in 1902, and in 1923 the first Triumph motor car appeared. The car and motorcycle sides of the business separated in 1936, and in June 1939 the receivers were called in to close down the car business. That might have been the end of the Triumph story, but in 1944 Sir John

Black acquired the remains of Triumph for his Standard Motor Company. What he got was a name, a bit of residual goodwill, and precious little else. Yet somehow, over the next two decades, Triumph achieved a sporting reputation to rival MG and Austin-Healey and, on the saloon side, eclipsed Standard's own offerings.

In the glory years of the 1950s and 1960s, Triumph's TR roadsters stood out as worthy best-of-breed contenders in the no-nonsense sports car stakes. From the bluff-fronted TR2 to the chisel-chinned TR6, they were as true-Brit as a sports car could be. The Triumph name eventually passed on in 1980.

1953 Triumph Mayflower, 1247cc, 4-cylinder in-line engine, resprayed, original interior, dry-stored for last 3 years, 60,000 miles recorded.
£1,150–1,400 *Pou*

1955 Triumph TR2, 1991cc, engine uprated with 1¾in SU carburettors, 4 branch stainless steel exhaust, 150bhp, original right-hand drive.
£5,250–6,250 *H&H*

1948 Triumph Roadster, brakes, shock absorbers and springs overhauled, original paintwork and leather upholstery, very original condition.
£11,500–13,500 *COYS*

A few months before WWII, Triumph went into receivership, and when hostilities ended, the Standard Motor Company picked up the pieces. One aim of the newly formed Triumph Motor Co was to produce a quality saloon to rival the Jaguar. The first cars used the 1799cc, four-cylinder Standard engine with a four-speed, column-change gearbox, and had either razor-edge saloon or two- or four-seater roadster coachwork. The curvaceous lines of the 1800 Roadster incorporated a dickey seat beneath a hinged glass lid that served as a windscreen for passengers. Producing 65bhp, the car was good for 70mph.

Triumph TR2 (1953–55)

Engine: 1991cc, overhead-valve in-line four, twin SU carburettors.
Power output: 90bhp at 4,800rpm.
Top speed: 105mph.
0–60mph: 12 seconds.
Production: 8,628.
If ever there was a sports car that epitomised the British bull-dog spirit, it must be the Triumph TR2. Spend a minute in that cosy cockpit and your dress sense will change. You'll start smoking

a pipe, wearing corduroys, cravat and flat cap, and sprouting a wing-commander's handle-bar moustache. It's as true-Brit as a car can be, born in the golden age of British sports cars, but aimed at the lucrative US market, where the Jaguar XK120 had already scored a hit. The TR2 is no conventional beauty certainly, but with its bluff-fronted, honest demeanour, it was a worthy best-of-breed contender in the budget sports car arena and the cornerstone of a stout sporting tradition.

TRIUMPH Model	ENGINE cc/cyl	DATES	CONDITION 1	2	3
TLC	1393/4	1923-25	£6,000	£4,000	£1,500
TPC	2169/4	1926-30	£6,000	£4,000	£2,000
K	832/4	1928-34	£4,000	£2,000	£1,000
S	1203/6	1931-33	£5,000	£3,000	£1,500
G12 Gloria	1232/4	1935-37	£6,000	£4,000	£2,000
G16 Gloria 6	1991/6	1935-39	£7,000	£4,500	£2,000
Vitesse/Dolomite	1767/4	1937-39	£14,000	£10,000	£6,000
Dolomite	1496/4	1938-39	£7,000	£4,000	£2,000

Did You Know?

A pre-production TR2, with careful tuning and rudimentary streamlining, was officially timed at just under 125mph on the Jabbeke autoroute in Belgium. The Triumph sporting tradition was firmly established when TR2s came first and second in the 1954 RAC Rally.

1960 Triumph TR3A, 2 litres, bodywork and electrics fair, left-hand drive, mostly good condition.
£4,000–5,000 *BKS*

Little different from the TR2 it replaced, the TR3 was introduced in October 1955. Changes to the Standard Vanguard-derived 2-litre engine boosted power from 90 to 95bhp, but the most obvious difference was the 'egg box' radiator grille. A redesigned cylinder head resulted in 100bhp by mid-1956, then in August the TR3 appeared with front disc brakes and stronger Phase III Vanguard rear axle. Revised in looks, but mechanically indistinguishable from its predecessor, the TR3A appeared during 1957. New front-end styling featured a full-width grille, and for the first time there were locking door and boot lid handles, as well as an improved interior. A 2138cc engine option was listed from 1959.

1958 Triumph TR3A, 2138cc, 4 cylinders, 4-speed gearbox with reconditioned overdrive, galvanised chassis, new Koni shock absorbers, converted to right-hand drive, excellent condition.
£9,000–11,000 *H&H*

1961 Triumph TR3A, 2137cc, 4 cylinders, 4-speed manual gearbox, right-hand drive, chrome refurbished, new hood, very good condition throughout.
£7,000–8,000 *H&H*

1960 Triumph TR3A, 1991cc, overdrive gearbox, restored, chromework and grille in excellent condition, wire wheels, halogen headlamps, service history, excellent condition.
£13,000–14,500 *H&H*

r. **c1960 Triumph TR3A,** overdrive, wire wheels, totally restored, excellent condition throughout.
£12,000–14,000 *UMC*

Triumph Herald (1959–71)

Body styles: Saloon, Coupé, Convertible, Estate and Van.
Construction: Separate backbone chassis with bolt-on steel body panels.
Engine: 948–1296cc in-line four.
Power output: 38–61bhp.
Top speed: 70–85mph.
0–60mph: 18–28 seconds.
Price today: Saloon, £500–2,000; Convertible, £1,000-3,000.
Production: 486,000

1959 Triumph Herald Saloon, finished in green, red upholstery, well-maintained, excellent original condition.
£600–700 *S*

The Herald saloon was introduced in mid-1959. Styled by Michelotti, it utilised a development of the 948cc, four-cylinder Standard 10 engine in a separate chassis. All-independent suspension (a first for a small British saloon) was a feature, while a collapsible steering wheel was also fitted. The Herald was remarkably economical and went on to become one of the most successful of small British cars, remaining in production until 1971.

1964 Triumph Herald Convertible, 1147cc, 4 cylinders, restored 6 years ago, new outriggers, brake pads, discs, starter and hood very good condition.
£1,350–1,600 *H&H*

Miller's Starter Marque

Starter Triumphs: *Herald and Vitesse saloons and convertibles; Spitfire; Dolomite, Toledo and variants.*

- Although the sporting TRs captivate most, there are several entry-level saloons and open cars that provide an enjoyable introduction to the Triumph sporting tradition.

- The Herald looks quintessentially British, with its unfussy and modest straight-edged styling, yet this pretty little saloon was actually styled in Italy by 'haute-carturier' Michelotti. Underneath the stylish body, though, the Herald was a pragmatic mix of stone-age and modern. It was one of the last mainstream cars to be built on a separate chassis, and the first mass-produced British car with all-round independent suspension. It endured as a frugal family favourite, selling nearly half a million in its lifetime.

- The Herald's certainly not fleet of foot, so unless it's first-of-breed purity you're after, avoid early cars with the puny 948cc engine. Instead, go for the 1147cc version or, preferably, one of the last 1296cc cars. The Herald has many virtues, not least offering frugal fun at 40+mpg. The one-piece bonnet also gives unrivalled engine access for DIY tinkerers, while bolt-on body panels make for easy repair. However, handling was certainly not the best. In the wet and in sudden throttle-off conditions, the car's high-pivot, swing-axle rear suspension would pitch it suddenly into unpredictable oversteer. However, unless you drive like a hooligan, the Herald's handling deficiencies will be of little concern. Herald's can also rust quite ferociously.

- Finally, because of its separate chassis, the Herald saloon can be safely turned into a convertible. The roof unbolts, and there are several rag-top conversion kits available.

1963 Triumph TR4, good condition.
£7,250–8,000 *H&H*

l. **1965 Triumph Herald 12/50 Saloon,** 1147cc, 4 cylinders, stored for some years, 12,000 miles recorded, good condition.
£2,250–2,750 *BRIT*

The Herald's original 948cc engine was enlarged to 1147cc during 1962. In 1964, Triumph announced a slightly more upmarket model, known as the 12/50 Sunshine Saloon, which was fitted with a sliding roof as standard.

1971 Triumph Vitesse 2-Litre MkII Convertible,
1998cc, 6 cylinders, overdrive, extensively restored
at a cost of over £10,000, Minilite-type wheels,
very good condition.
£5,000–6,000 *BRIT*

*The Triumph Vitesse was introduced in 1962 and
combined a 1596cc, six-cylinder engine with the
Triumph Herald body. With a weight of only 17cwt,
this provided quite formidable performance, the
Vitesse being capable of out-accelerating a number of
contemporary sports cars. In 1966, the engine was
enlarged to 2 litres, which further boosted
performance, and in the following year the rear
suspension was revised, giving the model a long-
overdue improvement in handling. This particular car
is from the last year of production.*

1964 Triumph TR4, overdrive, completely
restored 1990/98, engine and gearbox overhauled,
modified to use unleaded fuel, new panels and
parts where necessary, finished in green with tan
interior, Surrey top, seat belts, Category Two
immobiliser, very good condition.
£13,000–14,500 *BKS*

*Introduced in 1961, the TR4 featured a Michelotti-
styled bodyshell, while beneath the skin there were
several changes. Rack-and-pinion steering, a wider
track and an all-synchromesh gearbox contributed
to improved drivability, while wind-up windows
were a big advance on the TR3's sidescreens. The
standard engine was the 2138cc unit and, when
equipped with the optional overdrive, the TR4
was good for almost 110mph.*

1964 Triumph TR4, 2138cc, 4-speed gearbox
without overdrive, wire wheels, completely rebuilt,
converted from left-hand drive, excellent condition.
£7,500–8,500 *H&H*

1970 Triumph TR6, 2498cc, 6 cylinders,
right-hand drive, engine rebuilt with fast road
camshaft and gas-flowed cylinder head,
differential overhauled, Spax shock absorbers,
bare metal respray.
£7,250–8,000 *BRIT*

1970 Triumph TR6, 2498cc, 6 cylinders,
extensively restored, engine overhauled,
new stainless steel exhaust, new wings,
door skins, rear deck panel, bonnet and sills,
interior reupholstered, new carpets, new
black mohair soft top and tonneau cover,
very good condition.
£7,800–8,600 *BRIT*

l. **1971 Triumph TR6,** good condition.
£6,300–7,000 *PA*

1971 Triumph TR6, 150bhp, original right-hand drive, restored, full history, very good condition.
£7,500–8,500 *Mot*

TRIUMPH Model	ENGINE cc/cyl	DATES	CONDITION 1	2	3
1800/2000 Roadster	1776/2088/4	1946-49	£14,000	£8,000	£5,000
1800	1776/4	1946-49	£4,000	£2,000	£1,000
2000 Renown	2088/4	1949-54	£4,000	£2,000	£1,000
Mayflower	1247/4	1949-53	£2,000	£1,000	£500
TR2 long door	1247/4	1953	£10,000	£8,000	£5,000
TR2	1247/4	1953-55	£9,000	£6,000	£5,000
TR3	1991/4	1955-57	£9,000	£8,500	£3,500
TR3A	1991/4	1958-62	£9,500	£8,500	£3,500
TR4	2138/4	1961-65	£9,000	£6,000	£3,000
TR4A	2138/4	1965-67	£9,000	£6,500	£3,000
TR5	2498/6	1967-68	£9,000	£7,500	£4,000
TR6 (PI)	2498/6	1969-74	£8,000	£7,500	£3,500
Herald	948/4	1959-61	£1,000	£400	£150
Herald FHC	948/4	1959-61	£1,500	£550	£300
Herald DHC	948/4	1960-61	£2,500	£1,000	£350
Herald 'S'	948/4	1961-64	£800	£400	£150
Herald 1200	1147/4	1961-70	£1,100	£500	£200
Herald 1200 FHC	1147/4	1961-64	£1,400	£800	£300
Herald 1200 DHC	1147/4	1961-67	£2,500	£1,000	£350
Herald 1200 Est	1147/4	1961-67	£1,300	£700	£300
Herald 12/50	1147/4	1963-67	£1,200	£600	£250
Herald 13/60	1296/4	1967-71	£1,300	£600	£200
Herald 13/60 DHC	1296/4	1967-71	£2,500	£1,500	£500
Herald 13/60 Est	1296/4	1967-71	£1,500	£650	£300
Vitesse 1600	1596/6	1962-66	£2,000	£1,250	£550
Vitesse 1600 Conv	1596/6	1962-66	£2,800	£1,350	£600
Vitesse 2 litre Mk I	1998/6	1966-68	£1,800	£800	£300
Vitesse 2 litre Mk I Conv	1998/6	1966-68	£4,500	£2,200	£1,000
Vitesse 2 litre Mk II	1998/6	1968-71	£2,000	£1,500	£300
Vitesse 2 litre Mk II Conv	1998/6	1968-71	£5,000	£2,500	£600
Spitfire Mk I	1147/4	1962-64	£2,000	£1,750	£300
Spitfire Mk II	1147/4	1965-67	£2,500	£2,000	£350
Spitfire Mk III	1296/4	1967-70	£3,500	£2,500	£450
Spitfire Mk IV	1296/4	1970-74	£5,000	£2,500	£350
Spitfire 1500	1493/4	1975-78	£3,500	£2,500	£750
Spitfire 1500	1493/4	1979-81	£5,000	£3,500	£1,200
GT6 Mk I	1998/6	1966-68	£5,000	£4,000	£1,200
GT6 Mk II	1998/6	1968-70	£6,000	£4,500	£1,400
GT6 Mk III	1998/6	1970-73	£7,000	£5,000	£1,500
2000 Mk I	1998/6	1963-69	£2,000	£1,200	£400
2000 Mk III	1998/6	1969-77	£2,000	£1,200	£500
2.5 PI	2498/6	1968-75	£2,000	£1,500	£900
2500 TC/S	2498/6	1974-77	£1,750	£700	£150
2500S	2498/6	1975-77	£2,500	£1,000	£150
1300 (FWD)	1296/4	1965-70	£800	£400	£150
1300TC (FWD)	1296/4	1967-70	£900	£450	£150
1500 (FWD)	1493/4	1970-73	£700	£450	£125
1500TC (RWD)	1296/4	1973-76	£850	£500	£100
Toledo	1296/4	1970-76	£850	£450	£100
Dolomite 1500	1493/4	1976-80	£1,350	£750	£125
Dolomite 1850	1854/4	1972-80	£1,450	£850	£150
Dolomite Sprint	1998/4	1976-81	£5,000	£4,000	£1,000
Stag	2997/8	1970-77	£9,000	£5,000	£2,000
TR7	1998/4	1975-82	£4,000	£1,200	£500
TR7 DHC	1998/4	1980-82	£5,000	£3,500	£1,500

1971 Triumph TR6, 2498cc,
excellent condition throughout.
£7,500–8,500 *EPP*

1971 Triumph TR6, 150bhp, right-hand drive,
new silencer and front brake callipers, Spax
adjustable dampers, Mota Lita steering wheel,
overdrive inoperative, paint requires attention.
£3,900–4,500 *BKS*

*Triumph's first six-cylinder TR, the short-lived
TR5, was restyled for 1969 by Karmann. The
resulting TR6 had a full-width nose and Kamm
tail, but under the skin the chassis remained
basically the same as the all-independently-
suspended TR4A, while the 2.5 litre, fuel-injected
power unit was unchanged. Handling was
improved over that of the TR5 courtesy of wider
wheels and a front anti-roll bar. Good for 120mph
with acceleration to match, the six-cylinder TRs are
arguably the most exciting Triumphs ever made.*

Triumph TR6 (1969–76)

From the original TR2 of 1953, beloved of the
cravat and corduroy crew, Triumph's sporting
roadwear kept broadly abreast of the times,
and in the late 1960s combined polo-neck
smartness with a touch of chest-wig brawn in
the clean-cut and butch TR6. Some think the
TR6 granite-jawed handsome, others find it
almost thuggish. Whatever, it's just about as
hairy-chested as the classic TRs got, with its
2.5 litre six-cylinder engine which, in fuel-
injected form, heaved you along with 150
galloping horses.

The TR6 may look true-Brit, but the crisp
lines came courtesy of Germany's Karmann,
who squared off the friendly curves of the TR4,
created in 1964 by Italian Michelotti.

The TR6 was by far the most prolific of the
TR2–6 series. More than 94,619
TR6s were exported to the USA, where
legislators emasculated the bull-dog Brit.
Many US TR6s have found their way back to
the UK, but US-spec cars had carburettors
instead of fuel injection, together with other
performance wilting mods. Know what you're
buying and pay less for a US-spec car.

Pick of the bunch: Beefiest and best are
pre-1973 British-spec TR6s, which pumped
out 152bhp. After that, revised fuel injection
reduced power output to 125bhp.

l. **1973 Triumph TR6,** 2498cc, 150bhp,
4-speed manual gearbox with overdrive,
original right-hand drive, substantially
rebuilt, bare metal respray, seats
retrimmed, half tonneau, 72,000 miles
recorded, very good condition.
£7,000–8,000 *H&H*

r. **1973 Triumph TR6,** 2498cc, restored,
uprated to 150bhp, finished in Signal Red
with black leather interior, very good
condition throughout.
£10,500–11,500 *BC*

1966 Chevrolet Bel Air Four-Door Sedan, with flashing lights and siren, requires attention.
£600–1,000 *S*

1924 Morris-Guy Motor Fire Engine, coachwork by John Morris, 4 cylinders, 4-speed crash gearbox, good condition.
£15,500–18,000 *S*

1951 Austin Sheerline DA1 Ambulance, Startin body, 6 cylinders, 4 litres, overhead-valve single-carburettor engine, average 8–10mpg, low-ratio gears, built-in electric/hydraulic jacking system on all wheels, twin bells, red flashing emergency lamp on roof, restored and preserved.
£5,000–5,500 *BAm*

1938 Austin Big 6 Ambulance, Thomas Startin body, mainly wood with canvas roof, restored to original condition.
£5,500–6,500 *BAm*

1942 Austin K2/Y Ambulance, 6 cylinders, 63bhp overhead-valve engine, 3462cc, 4 forward gears, one reverse driving rear wheels only, rebuilt engine, good condition.
£3,000–4,000 *PC*

This ambulance arrived in Guernsey a few weeks after the liberation in 1945. It was given to the States of Guernsey in November 1945, who used it at the airport for 24 years. It was then used by the Police as a mobile command post for a further six years, before being sold and left to deteriorate. It was then taken to Jersey and restored to its present condition.

1967 Austin Princess DA3 Ambulance, Vanden Plas Lomas body, triple carburettors, electric emergency horns, blue light on radiator grille, original equipment, restored, excellent condition.
£5,500–6,500 *BAm*

r. **1972 Bedford J1 Ambulance,** Herbert Lomas body, 6 cylinders, 4 litres, diesel engine, original equipment, very good condition.
£2,250–2,500 *BAm*

1917 Ford Model T Pick-Up,
2890cc, 4 cylinders, epicyclic gearbox,
mechanically sound.
£5,750–6,500 *BRIT*

*Henry Ford's universal car commenced
production in 1908 and transformed the
American way of life almost overnight. Over
15 million were built, many of which still exist.*

1930 Morris Commercial T2 Box Van,
1622cc, good condition.
£8,250–9,000 *LF*

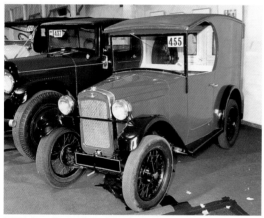

1937 Austin 7 Light Van, restored,
very good condition.
£4,750–5,500 *CGC*

**1933 Foden R-Type Flat-Bed
Lorry,** Gardner 6LW engine,
vacuum-assisted 4-wheel brakes,
2-range 4-speed gearbox, hubometer,
very good condition.
£9,000–11,000 *BKS*

1936 Morris 8 Series I 5cwt Van, 918cc, 4
cylinders, 5,000 miles since full restoration,
good condition throughout.
£4,500–5,500 *BRIT*

*The Series I Morris 8 van was produced
from September 1934 until the outbreak of
WWII in 1939. The van differed from the
Saloon and Tourer by having small-centre
wire wheels as opposed to the Magna type
used on the car variants.*

1942 Austin K2 Short Wheelbase Lorry,
dropside body, 6 cylinders, 3460cc, restored.
£2,500–3,000 *CGC*

1938 Harrods Electric Delivery Van,
maximum speed 18.6mph, enclosed cab,
rear-door loading, nickel-iron battery
missing, excellent condition.
£3,750–4,500 *S*

1968 Morris Minor Van, 1300cc engine, bare metal
respray, 80,000 recorded miles, good condition.
£3,500–4,000 *ESM*

1970 Bedford J-Type 30cwt Lorry,
dropside body, good condition.
£4,750–5,500 *LF*

**1990 Fleur de Lys Vintage-Style
Box Van,** 1995cc, 24,500 recorded
miles, excellent condition.
£6,000–6,500 *DDM*

l. **1934 Austin 12/4 Taxicab
Landaulette,** coachwork by
Strachan's successors,
horometrical taximeter, restored,
excellent condition.
£18,500–22,500 *BKS*

*The horometrical taximeter was
a complex device that charged by
the mile when the speed exceeded
5.3mph, and by the minute when
the cab was going slower or was
hired and waiting.*

1966 Beardmore Taxi, 4 cylinders, Ford
Consul MkII 1703cc engine, provision for
4 passengers, slight restoration required.
£2,500–3,000 *S*

*This cab covered over half a million miles
during service in London as a hire vehicle.*

1925 Austin 20 Hearse, coachwork by Thomas Start,
Birmingham, very good condition.
£14,000–15,000 *CLH*

1918 Daimler Hearse, 1950 DC27 chasssis, 4086cc,
very good condition.
£8,000–10,000 *CLH*

1958 Ford Thames AA Van,
excellent condition.
£4,500–5,500 *EDVV*

1942 GMC CCKW 353 Lorry, 6 cylinders, long wheelbase, 7mpg, good condition.
£2,250–2,500 *IMPS*

1943 Dodge WC 41 2x4 Maintenance and Repair Truck, fully restored.
£8,000–10,000 *NMV*

1941 Commer Q2 Truck, 6 cylinders, 80bhp, 4-speed gearbox, good condition.
£4,500–5,000 *IMPS*

1942 Chevrolet BK Half-Ton Truck, 216cu in petrol engine, 3 forward gears and reverse, rear-wheel drive, restored.
£5,500–6,000 *NMV*

1942 Bedford 15cwt Truck, fully restored.
£3,250–3,750 *NTMV*

1941 GMC CCKW 352 Truck, short wheelbase, excellent condition.
£2,250–2,500 *IMPS*

l. **1943 White M3A1 Scout Car,** original Hercules JXD 320 5500cc petrol engine, 6 cylinders, 87bhp, 8mpg, fully restored, good condition.
£8,000–9,000 *PC*

This vehicle was one of 21,000 supplied to the Allies during WWII. After the war it saw service with the Greek army before being imported to the UK and restored.

1942 Hillman Utility MkIIB Van, 4 cylinders, 30bhp, 1185cc, 4 forward gears and reverse, good condition.
£4,500–5,000 *PC*

1944 Standard Utility Estate, 4 cylinders, 36bhp, 1260cc, 4 forward gears and reverse, good condition.
£4,500–5,000 *PC*

1943 Bedford QLS General-Purpose Truck, fully restored.
£3,500–4,000 *NTMV*

1947 Willys Jeep CJ 2A, 4 cylinders, 134.2cu in, 71bhp, 3 forward gears and reverse, good condition.
£5,500–7,500 *PC*

1956 Austin Champ GS, Rolls-Royce overhead-valve engine, 4 cylinders, 2838cc, 69bhp, 5 forward gears and reverse, fully restored.
£2,500–3,000 *PC*

c1950 Daimler Ferret MkI Scout Car, Rolls-Royce overhead-valve engine, 6 cylinders, 4258cc, 95bhp, 5 forward gears and reverse.
£4,000–4,500 *PC*

l. **1982 Mercedes 230E G-Wagon,** 2.3 litres, 4 cylinders, 4 forward gears and reverse, good condition.
£3,000–5,000 *PC*

This vehicle was supplied to the Argentine army in 1982 and used in the Falklands War. It was captured by the Gurkhas and shipped with them to Hong Kong. Later, it was imported to the UK.

A Coach, by Askham & Son, Cambridge, electric lighting, reupholstered, wheels restored, good condition.
£11,750–13,500 *TSh*
This hybrid example, smaller than a full-size coach, is similar in style to a Town Coach.

A Governess Cart, by Purvis of Newcastle, to suit 14.2–15.2hh pony, with Warner 16-spoke wheels, back rest and cushion for whip, good condition.
£600–800 *TSh*

A Continental Miniature Victoria, to suit up to 13hh, full elliptic springs, occasional seat, black vinyl hood, shafts, handbrake, very good condition.
£1,100–1,300 *TSh*

A Bow-Top Gypsy Wagon, believed to have been built for Appleby Fair, to suit a cob, fully fitted, good condition.
£3,000–3,5000 *TSh*

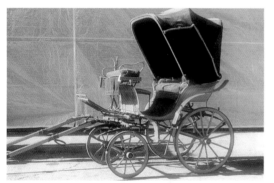

A Continental Miniature Chaise, to suit up to 13hh, varnished natural wood, red vinyl and navy wool upholstery, occasional seat, handbrake, three-position hood in old black leather.
£1,150–1,350 *TSh*

A Spanish Opera Bus, to suit a pair of horses 15hh and upwards, seating for 4, reupholstered, completely restored.
£2,900–3,400 *TSh*

c1900 Reading Wagon, by Samuel Dunton & Sons, interior mostly complete, mahogany drawer with gold leaf designs, traditional corner cupboard, cast iron stove, very original condition.
£9,250–10,250 *BKS*

A Postillion Landau, by Steuart & Co, Calcutta, India, rubbered English pattern wheels, black leather and velvet interior, rear section with high rumble seat, restored, excellent condition.
£16,000–18,000 *TSh*
Steuart & Co were Calcutta's leading coachbuilders, and this example was probably built for a Maharajah.

l. **1953 Mochet Velocar CM-125 Commerciale,** Zurcher single-cylinder, two-stroke engine, 125cc, 3-speed manual gearbox with reverse, 4-wheel cable brakes, heavy-duty wheels and tyres, left-hand drive, original unrestored condition.
£2,000–2,500 *C*

In 1951 Charles Mochet's production plant in Puteaux brought out a new model, the CM-125. It was a great improvement on the crude Type-K that had been built since 1948. In 1953, after production of the Luxe and the Grande Luxe, the market for small utility vehicles in rural France was growing, and Mochet produced a few examples of the Commerciale. This may be the only one in existence.

1959 BMW Isetta 300, single cylinder engine, 297cc, 4-speed manual gearbox and reverse with synchromesh, left-hand drive, partly restored, good running order.
£1,200–1,700 *C*
The design for the BMW Isetta was taken from an idea that originated with the Iso company in Milan, Italy. It was probably the most popular and recognisable of all bubble cars.

1963 Messerschmitt KR200 Roadster, single-cylinder 191cc Fichtell 7 Sachs engine, tandem seating, direct handlebar steering with twist-grip throttle, 4-speed gearbox, conventional foot-pedal brakes, chromed motorcycle-type exhaust system, very good condition throughout.
£6,500–7,500 *S*

c1970 Formula 1 Racing Car, by Triang Toys Ltd, one-piece moulded plastic, with plastic aerofoil, engine and wheels, 48in (122cm) long.
£75–100 *CARS*

ERA-type Child's Motorised Car, monoposto body, tubular chasis, Briggs & Stratton 5hp petrol engine, adjustable pedals, good condition.
£2,100–2,500 *C*

c1950 Giordani Pedal Car, heavy-gauge steel monocoque, wire wheels with spinners, seat missing, minor damage.
£650–750 *CARS*

This car was inspired by the Ferrari driven by Fangio and Moss.

1948 Austin Path Finder Pedal Car,
60in (152.5cm) long.
£1,200–1,800 *JUN*

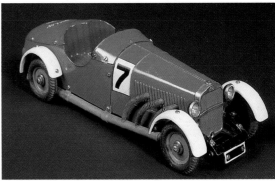

c1928 Mercedes Two-Seater Sports Car, by Märklin, tinplate, clockwork, excellent condition, 15in (38cm) long.
£2,900–3,400 *C*

Mercedes-Benz 300SL Sports Roadster Pedal Car, moulded plastic, metal chassis frame, 6-volt battery with charging unit.
£200–250 *CARS*

Veteran Two-Seater Car, ¼-scale display model, brass screen, button-back upholstery, solid tyres, spoked wheels.
£115–130 *C*

Morgan V-Twin Trike Model Car, display model, alloy body, bucket seats, copper radiator, outside exhausts, spare wheel to tail, dummy headlamps.
£160–200 *C*

Austin J40 Pedal Car, steering modified to rack-and-pinion, originally converted to electric drive, original pedal assembly and engine panel supplied, radiator, instrument panel, hubcaps rechromed, new seats.
£250–400 *PA*

c1950 Austin J40 Pedal Car, requires full restoration, parts and upholstery.
£150–200 *CARS*

1939 Atco Trainer Car, motorised, 1hp, requires restoration.
£900–1,000 *TAY*
This car was used to teach road safety and elementary engineering to children.

1937 Jaguar SS100, ⅓-scale model, powered by 12-volt battery, forward and reverse gears, working headlamps, horn.
£950–1,100 *PA*
This one-off model is capable of carrying an adult.

c1970 Austin A40 Pedal Car, by Triang Toys Ltd, moulded plastic one-piece monocoque, metal windscreen, wheels and fittings, 34in (86.5cm) long, with original box.
£150–200 *CARS*

l. A Schuco tinplate clockwork
Grand Prix racing car, model
No. 7, stamped 'No. 1070' on base,
7in (18cm) long.
£140–160 *CGC*

r. A coachbuilder's wooden model
of a Rolls-Royce Phantom III,
including mascot, 17in (43cm) long,
with original wooden box.
£400–425 *DRJ*

A car transporter, by Triang Toys Ltd, 26in (66cm) long.
£50–55 *DRJ*

A wooden model of a Triumph 1800
Roadster, by David Cooper, with
detailed dashboard, brightwork,
cream leather interior,
on a presentation display base,
in a glazed cabinet.
£1,725–1,825 *C*

A Dooling Tether Racer,
.61cu in engine, custom
4-branch exhaust, 16¾in
(42.5cm) long, together
with a copy of *Vintage
Miniature Racing Cars*,
No. 15, signed by
the author.
£1,000–1,300 *C*

A presentation model of a WWI armoured car, solid polished steel,
detailed suspension and steering, detachable wheels with rubber
tyres, double revolving gun turrets with 3 cannons, opening doors,
vents and louvred bonnet, brass fittings and hub nuts, c1916,
together with sales brochure and 2 postcard photos.
£2,300–2,700 *C*

Ernest Wregge, Ferrari, depicting the rear light of a Ferrari Daytona, commissioned by Noel Blanc, signed, 1987, 47 x 40in (119.5 x 101.5cm).
£2,800–3,300 *C*

Geo Ham, Rally Monte Carlo à la Hotchkiss Victorieuse Suède 1932, lithograph on card, signed, 22 x 29in (55 x 74cm).
£800–1,000 *S*

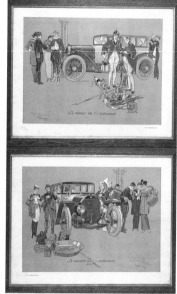

René Vincent, Le Départ and Le Retour de l'Ambusque, colour lithographs, signed in pencil and dated '1915', 23 x 30in (59 x 76cm).
£460–500 *C*

Terence Cuneo, RAC Veteran Car Run, 1967, depicting cars on The Mall after the start in Hyde Park, oil on canvas, signed and dated 'February 1968', 32 x 39in (81.5 x 99cm).
£3,250–3,750 *C*

Commissioned by Dunlop to promote sales of tyres for vintage and veteran cars, this work bears the Dunlop logo to the caption at the base of the picture. It also features a mouse within the picture, Cuneo's well-known trademark signature.

l. Ernest Wregge, Jaguar XK120, commissioned by Noel Blanc, signed, 1989, framed and glazed, 42 x 54in (106.5 x 137cm).
£3,750–4,250 *C*

E. Montaut, Chauffeuse and Vertige, lithographs with hand colouring and facsimile signatures, 24 x 30in (61 x 76cm).
£925– 975 *C*

Alfredo de la Maria, Rolls-Royce, depicting a 1912 Rolls-Royce Silver Ghost London to Edinburgh Tourer, oil on canvas, signed, 52 x 60in (132 x 152.5cm).
£5,500–6,000 *C*

l. Bugatti T57, depicting 3 variations: T57SC Atalantique, T57S Roadster by Corsica and T57C Stelvio tourer by Gangloff, watercolour and gouache highlighted with white, Bugatti badge motif, unsigned, believed original artwork for book illustration, 20 x 18in (51 x 45.5cm).
£250–275 *C*

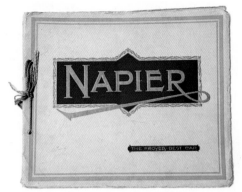

A Michelin poster, depicting Mr Bibendum riding a bicycle, c1910, framed and glazed, 30 x 47in (76 x 119.5cm).
£485–525 *BKS*

Deen, Le Démon Rouge dans le Cycle de la Mort, printed by S. A. Frameries, Liège, No. 454, slight damage, 48 x 32in (122 x 81.5cm), framed and glazed.
£255–285 *BKS*

Napier De Luxe brochure, with colour and monochrome plates, c1913, 10 x 12in (25.5 x 30.5cm).
£550–650 *PC*

l. Seven Ferrari parts books, for the Berlinetta Boxer, 365GT/2+2, 1968 Dino 246GT, 1969 Dino 246GT, 1970 Dino 246GT, 365GT 2+2 and 330GT, fully illustrated.
£325–350 *S*

The Motor report on the 1958 Earl's Court Motor Show, 11½ x 8¼in (29 x 21cm).
£8–10 *LF*

A brochure for the Jaguar XK100 and XK120, c1950, 10 x 14½in (25.5 x 37cm).
£60–65 *PC*

An Austin St Ives brochure for the Ruby Pearl, 1935, 7½in (19cm) square.
£80–85 *PC*

A brochure for the Morris 10 De Luxe, 1938, 11¼ x 8¾in (28.5 x 22cm).
£30–35 *PC*

A German combination mechanical clock and perpetual calendar, in the form of a petrol pump and cigarette lighter, brass-plated steel, c1950.
£250–350 *BKS*

A silver-plated deskpiece, with a Jaeger 8-day clock in the form of a Bugatti radiator, owners' club badge to reverse, 8in (20.5cm) high.
£475–575 *C*

A motoring aneroid barometer, c1930.
£130–150 *BC*

A brass clock in the form of a wheel, by Jaeger LeCoultre, c1930, 7½in (19cm) diam.
£700–1,000 *LE*

A Boyce Motometer Junior for a Lagonda, 6in (15cm) wide.
£125–145 *DRJ*

A pair of electric coach lamps for a Pierce-Arrow, each with a hexagonal fluted nickel-plated case, spade-type mounting bracket and domed finial, 3 bevelled glass lenses and faceted Ruby sight glass mounted in the door panel, one cracked, stamped, c1910, 14¼in (36cm) high overall.
£1,700–1,900 *S*

A French brass eight-horn Testephone, c1912, 28in (71cm) long.
£2,200–2,500 *PC*

The Testephone was named after its designer, Etienne Teste.

l. A pair of Powell & Hanmer brass oil sidelamps, c1910, 10in (25.5cm) high.
£220–240 *CGC*

An illuminated Esso sign, late 1930s.
£450–500 *MSMP*

An AA single-sided enamel sign,
pre-WWI, 8in (20.5cm) diam.
£130–150 MSMP

A Mobiloil 'A' sign, 1930,
19½in (49.5cm) high.
£240–280 *TPS*

An AA Hotel double-sided enamel
sign, 1930s, 25in (63.5cm) high.
£150–175 *JUN*

A Bowser petrol pump, 1920s,
81in (205.5cm) high.
£450–500 *CRC*

A Wayne 1880 petrol pump
with electric clock-face, c1950,
fitted with a Fina Diesel
globe, c1960, repainted,
84in (213.5cm) high.
£550–600 *TPS*

A Beckmeter petrol pump,
1960s, 70in (177cm) high.
£300–400 *CRC*

A Shell Aviation Spirit two-gallon can,
repainted, 1930s, 13in (33cm) high.
£30–40 *TPS*

A hand-cranked gear-oil
pump, repainted, new hose,
1940s, 26in (66cm) high.
£22–25 *TPS*

An MG Castrol record-breaker mascot,
depicting the EX 135 world speed record car,
1939, 4½in (11.5cm) long.
£250–275 *PC*

A Supermarine S.6B Schneider
Trophy seaplane mascot,
on a Rolls-Royce Phantom
radiator cap, 6in (15cm) high.
£1,400–1,500 *S*

A Charlie Chaplin
brass mascot,
cane replaced,
4¾in (12cm) high.
£1,150–1,300 *S*

r. A Lalique Chrysis
glass mascot, acid-
etched, 1931–39,
5⅝in (14.5cm) high.
£3,300–3,600 *S*

l. A Lalique Archer
glass mascot,
wheelcut and
engraved, 1926–39,
6in (15cm) high.
£1,475–1,575 *S*

r. A Cadillac goddess
mascot, designed
by William Schnell,
made by Ternstedt,
die-cast zinc and
chrome plated, c1930,
9in (23cm) long.
£500–600 *S*

A silver dashboard St Christopher, Birmingham 1926,
1½in (4cm) wide.
£180–200 *BC*

A Lalique Coq Nain glass mascot,
moulded marks, c1928, perfect condition.
£700–750 *BKS*

*Most of these mascots had their claws
removed to fit the metal mounts.*

A brass greyhound, stamped
'Desmo', 1930s, 6in (15cm) long.
£90–95 *PC*

An American cast aluminium rotary
blade mascot, 7in (18cm) wingspan.
£120–135 *DRJ*

A silver-plated bronze mascot,
with ivory face, signed 'Sertorio',
c1925, 8½in (21.5cm) high.
£600–650 *PC*

A Lalique Naiade glass mascot,
marked, 1920–39, 5in (13cm) high.
£4,650–5,000 *S*

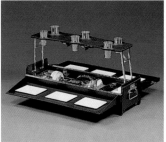

An Edwardian Sirram wicker picnic hamper, 11in (28cm) wide.
£225–250 *PPH*

A Drew & Sons four-person picnic set, the black leathercloth-covered case with brass handles, catches and edging, fitted interior, c1905, 13¾in (35cm) wide.
£6,500–8,000 *S*

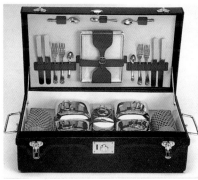

A James Dixon two-person picnic tea set, with leather case, fitted interior, c1905.
£250–300 *BKS*

A Sirram six-person picnic set, with hopsack covering, shaped to fit under a boot lid, 1950s, 26¾in (68cm) wide.
£2,000–2,300 *C*

A Coracle six-person table picnic set, the black leathercloth-covered case with brass catches and handles, 2 pairs of folding brass legs, with fitted interior, c1909, 24¾in (63cm) long.
£13,000–15,000 *S*

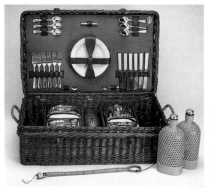

l. A Coracle wicker six-person picnic set, with fitted interior, original can locking bar with brass lock and key, c1925.
£500–700 *BKS*

A Coracle four-person picnic set, the black leathercloth case with nickel catches, lock and handles, c1920.
£800–1,000 *BKS*

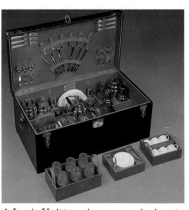

A Brexton picnic set, with fitted interior, 1950s, 14in (35.5cm) wide.
£50–60 *PPH*

A Louis Vuitton six-person picnic set, the leather-lined interior with French fittings, c1910, 35½in (90cm) wide.
£6,500–8,000 *S*

A Coracle six-person wicker picnic set, with fitted interior, c1920.
£2,900–3,400 *BKS*

A Power Petroleum two-gallon
fuel can, 1930s.
£50–60 *MSMP*

An Esso Extra Motor Oil stand,
with 8 quart-size bottles, 1950s.
£80–100 *MSMP*

A French Mathis plate, late
1920s, 8½in (21.5cm) diam.
£125–150 *PC*

A Ruddspeed
decanter, in the form
of a Bugatti radiator.
£375–425 *BKS*

A Sadler teapot, slight damage,
mid-1930s, 9in (23cm) long.
£80–85 *DRJ*

A copper foot warmer,
c1910, 10in (25.5cm) long.
£20–25 *LF*

Two French plates, used to publicise
Mathis cars, c1925, 8in (20.5cm) diam.
£100–110 each *PC*

A French plate, souvenir of the Fiat factory
convention, 1957, 16in (40.5cm) wide.
£125–145 *PC*

A French plate, featuring
a Renault racing car, 1920s,
10in (25.5cm) diam.
£125–145 *PC*

A silver cigarette case, in the
form of an Opel radiator,
c1912, 3½in (9cm) high.
£400–435 *PC*

A glass posy holder, for the
interior of a limousine,
c1925, 7in (18cm) high.
£80–85 *DRJ*

1977 Triumph Spitfire, 1500cc, restored, mechanical components replaced or rebuilt as required, new body panels, resprayed in Inca Yellow, very good condition.
£2,650–3,250 *H&H*

1979 Triumph Spitfire, 1500cc, 56,000 miles recorded, good condition.
£4,000–5,000 *WILM*

1981 Triumph Spitfire, 1500cc, 30,000 miles recorded, original condition.
£5,000–6,500 *SJR*

1972 Triumph GT6, 1998cc, 6 cylinders, 4-speed manual gearbox with overdrive, 51,317 miles, full history, good condition.
£3,600–4,300 *H&H*

1969 Triumph 2.5 PI MkI, 2498cc, 6 cylinders, automatic transmission, new big-end and main bearings, uprated rear springs, brakes overhauled, new stainless steel exhaust, very good condition.
£1,900–2,400 *BRIT*

A more powerful variant of the very successful Triumph 2000, which had made its debut in 1963, the 2.5 with Lucas fuel injection appeared in 1968. Acclaimed by the press for its excellent performance, the car quickly found its niche in the executive saloon market. The styling of both the 2000 and the 2.5 PI was revamped later the following year, and today early examples are rarely encountered.

1971 Triumph 2000 Saloon, 1998cc, 6 cylinders, automatic transmission, finished in brown, original radio, 29,700 miles recorded, excellent condition.
£1,450–1,800 *H&H*

r. **1978 Triumph Dolomite 1500 HL,** 16,446 miles recorded, history, excellent condition throughout.
£1,650–2,000 *H&H*

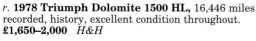

Triumph Stag (1970–77)

Engine: 2997cc, V8, cast-iron block, alloy cylinder heads, double overhead camshafts, twin carburettors.
Power output: 146bhp.
Transmission: Four-speed manual (optional overdrive); three-speed automatic.
Brakes: Front discs, rear drums.
Top speed: 115+mph.
0–60mph: 10.5 seconds.
Production: 25,877.

With crisp, convertible four-seater styling and a burbling V8, British Leyland's blue-print for the Triumph Stag must surely have come straight from Dearborn, Michigan, where Ford's Mustang had created the 'pony car' idiom and galloped off with record-breaking sales. Where the Mustang had a wild stallion on its grille, British Leyland substituted a leaping stag and a litany of blunders. Instead of using the redoubtable 3.5 litre Rover V8, available in-house and off the shelf, Triumph insisted on developing its own 3 litre V8 which, as soon as it hit the road, earned a rotten reputation from which the Stag never recovered. Over the next seven years, fewer than 26,000 Stags were made, and with all the money swallowed up by producing an engine for a single low-selling model, there was nothing left to develop the Stag into the car it should have become.

Fortunately, specialists and enthusiasts have long since found the solutions to the Stag's main problems of overheating, warped cylinder heads and blown head gaskets, yet there are still some rogue cars out there. Evidence of regular and careful maintenance to engine and radiator is essential; be very wary of a car that overheats on a test run – the damage has probably already been done. Many owners have done what Triumph should have done originally by installing Rover's robust V8. This is an acceptable – even desirable – practice.

1972 **Triumph Stag,** 2997cc, V8, automatic transmission, fully restored.
£7,250–8,000 *BRIT*

1972 **Triumph Stag,** overdrive, extensively restored, excellent condition.
£4,350–5,000 *CGC*

l. 1972 **Triumph Stag,** 2997cc, V8, manual overdrive gearbox, completely restored at a cost of £17,000, excellent condition.
£8,000–9,000 *Mot*

r. 1973 **Triumph Stag,** 2997cc, V8, restored at a cost of £16,000, new engine 1995, big-bore exhaust system, 2 new wings, MkII factory alloy wheels, finished in French Blue with matching hardtop, mohair hood, black vinyl interior, very good condition.
£5,500–6,250 *BRIT*

1974 Triumph Stag, 2997cc,
V8, good condition throughout.
£6,000–6,500 *EPP*

1977 Triumph Stag, 2997cc, V8, manual
overdrive gearbox, finished in maroon with
beige leather interior, original canvas hood,
very good condition.
£5,300–6,000 *BRIT*

1977 Triumph Stag MkII, 2997cc, V8, automatic
transmission, very good condition throughout.
£6,500–7,000 *EPP*

1980 Triumph TR7 V8 Conversion, 3528cc,
automatic transmission, good condition throughout.
£2,650–3,350 *BRIT*

1977 Triumph TR7 Fixed-Head Coupé, 1998cc,
4 cylinders, automatic transmission, good condition.
£800–900 *LF*

1980 Triumph TR7 V8 Convertible, good condition.
£2,000–2,200 *H&H*

TROJAN

l. **c1926 Trojan Three-Door Tourer,** 1488cc, 4-cylinder 2-stroke engine, chain drive with 2 forward gears and reverse, good condition.
£5,000–6,000 *TRJ*

TVR

l. **1955 TVR Jomar Notchback Coupé,** 1098cc, FWA Coventry Climax overhead-camshaft engine, 72bhp at 6,200rpm, MG TD 4-speed manual gearbox, fibreglass body, 20,000 recorded miles, extensively rebuilt, requires finishing.
£5,800–6,500 *H&H*

The Jomar was the forerunner of the Grantura and derived its name from the names of the importers of the cars into the USA – John and Margaret Saidel. It was timed at Silverstone in 1960 at 130mph.

1992 TVR Griffith, 4 litres, finished in Mica Blue with Magnolia hide interior, 34,000 miles recorded, full history, very good condition.
£18,000–22,000 *VIC*

TVR Model	ENGINE cc/cyl	DATES	CONDITION 1	2	3
Grantura I	1172/4	1957-62	£4,000	£3,000	£2,000
Grantura II	1558/4	1957-62	£4,500	£3,000	£2,000
Grantura III/1800S	1798/4	1963-67	£5,000	£3,000	£2,200
Tuscan V8	4727/8	1967-70	£12,000	£7,000	£6,000
Vixen S2/3	1599/4	1968-72	£5,000	£3,000	£1,500
3000M	2994/6	1972-79	£7,000	£4,000	£3,000
Taimar	2994/6	1977-79	£7,500	£5,000	£3,500

VALE

r. **1932 Vale Special Two-Door Roadster,**
Triumph engine, restored, little use since,
finished in green with brown leather interior,
excellent condition throughout.
£7,500–9,000 *BKS*

*The Vale Special took its name from the Maida Vale
district of north London, where the company was
based. Introduced in 1932, the first Vale Special
used an 832cc Triumph sidevalve engine producing
28bhp; later models were Coventry-Climax powered.
The marque lasted from 1932 to 1936. Estimates of
total production range from 32 to 103 cars.*

VAUXHALL

Modern Vauxhalls, like the fun Tigra, Vectra
and four-wheel-drive Frontera, are the latest
chapter of an automotive adventure that began
in south London in 1903. That was the year
the first tiller-steered Vauxhall motor car
chugged out on to the cobbles in the Thames-
side district that gave the company its name.
But the intriguing history of the company that
uses the griffin crest as its emblem goes back
even further – to the 12th century and a
Plantagenet mercenary named Fulk Le
Breant, a hired sword for the unpopular King
John. He adopted the half-eagle/half-lion
griffin as his crest and acquired a house on the
south side of the River Thames; over centuries,
the name Fulk's Hall evolved into Fawkes
Hall, Foxhall and, ultimately, Vauxhall.

By an odd coincidence, Fulk Le Breant was
also granted the manor of Luton, where the
car company would make its home from 1905.
At around this time, distinguished engineer
and designer Laurence Pomeroy joined the
company, setting Vauxhall on a path to the
forefront of automotive design and sporting
achievement, first with the Prince Henry
models, then with the immortal 30/98.

In 1925, the firm's poor finances led to
General Motors taking control and successfully
shifting the emphasis of the marque towards
the mass market. In the 1950s, the
transatlantic influence really became
prominent with the gaudy Crestas and F-Type
Victors. General Motors had also held a
majority shareholding in the German car
maker Opel since the late 1920s. For many
years, Vauxhall and Opel remained completely
separate operations, but from the mid-1970s
the model lines converged, with most design
input coming from Germany. The Opel-
inspired products gave new impetus to
Vauxhall, and in 1984 the Cavalier even beat
Ford models to the top of the sales chart.

1935 Vauxhall Big Six Newmarket Limousine, 7 seater, black over ivory coachwork, original green
leather upholstery and interior wood cappings, twin side-mounted spares, excellent condition throughout.
£9,800–11,000 *S*

*The Vauxhall Ironworks, a marine engineering company based in London, built their first motor car in
1903, before moving to Luton. The faster-than-average Prince Henry model, devised by Laurence H.
Pomeroy, appeared in 1910, while the later Velox, also known as the 30/98, proved one of the greatest fast
touring cars of the Vintage period. General Motors, thwarted in their attempt to buy Austin and wanting to
gain a foothold in Britain, assumed control of Vauxhall in 1925, investing heavily in the company. The Big
Six B-Series was announced for 1936 and comprised the BY, BX and longer-wheelbase (130in) BXL. A
26.3hp, 3.2 litre, overhead-valve engine was used, together with a four-speed gearbox with synchromesh on
the top two ratios.*

Vauxhall PA Cresta/Velox (1957–62)

Top speed: 89–95mph.
0–60mph: 16–18 seconds.
Price in 1957: £1,073.17s.
Production: 173,764.

l. **1956 Vauxhall Cresta,** 2262cc, 3-speed gearbox, restored, 40,600 miles recorded. **£3,500–4,000** *WILM*

Miller's Starter Marque

Starter Vauxhalls: *PA Cresta / Velox (1957–62); F-type Victor (1957–61).*

- There certainly are cheaper Vauxhalls than the PA Cresta and F-Type Victor – the Viva is one example – but these glamorous American-influenced cars really stand out on any street.

- Vauxhall's rivals at BMC, Rootes and Standard-Triumph must have been all shook up when the ice-cream-coloured PA Velox and Cresta were unveiled in 1957, dripping with chrome and gaudier than a Las Vegas neon sign. All of which means they offer the best of both worlds to today's retro crowd, who'd far rather have been teenagers in 1950s America. The Velox is merely wildly overstated, but the Cresta, with even more tinsel and extra luxury trimmings is the favourite.

- Some purists – if that's the right word – prefer the pre-1960 PA with its three-piece rear window, although later models have a slightly more eager 2.6 litre straight-six in place of the earlier 2.2.

- The automatic version of the PA was advertised with the unforgettable script: 'Just a "Go" pedal and a "Whoa" pedal'.

- The 1957 F-Type Victor looked for all the world like a scaled-down '56 Chevrolet, festooned with chrome and colour schemes inspired by Lyon's Maid lollies. It was all a bit too gaudy for suburban sensibilities, and in 1959 Vauxhall toned down the Victor, removing some of the tinsel.

- What to watch: Both the PA Cresta/Velox and F-Type Victor have the advantage of being based on generally commonplace and readily available British mechanicals and running gear. That's the good news; on the down side, both can rust rampantly – and with the PA's large expanses of metal, curing this can become an exercise akin to painting the Forth Bridge. Some trim items are hard to find.

1960 Vauxhall Victor De Luxe, 1508cc, 4 cylinders, customised, electrically-operated boot lid, chrome wheels, whitewall tyres, sidewinder exhaust, Blaupunkt stereo/radio, excellent condition throughout. **£2,350–2,850** *H&H*

Vauxhall F-Type Victor (1957–61)

Engine: 1508cc, in-line four.
Power output: 48–55bhp at 4,500rpm.
Top speed: 75+mph.
0–60mph: 24 seconds.
Price in 1957: £758.17s.
Production: 390,747.

1962 Vauxhall Victor Saloon, 1507cc, 4-speed gearbox with floor-change, original manuals and handbooks, 34,300 miles recorded, excellent condition throughout. **£1,850–2,250** *H&H*

l. **1980 Vauxhall Silver Aero,** 2279cc, 4 cylinders, turbocharged, electrically-controlled Recaro front seats, Voxson audio system, fewer than 17,000 miles recorded, excellent condition throughout. **£4,250–4,750** *BRIT*

The Silver Aero was a factory-designed concept car, based on the Cavalier sports hatch. It was first exhibited at the 1980 Motor Show and, although public response was encouraging, this car remains the only example built.

VAUXHALL Model	ENGINE cc/cyl	DATES	CONDITION		
			1	2	3
D/OD	3969/4	1914-26	£35,000	£24,000	£18,000
E/OE	4224/4	1919-28	£90,000	£60,000	£35,000
Eighty	3317/6	1931-33	£10,000	£8,000	£5,000
Cadet	2048/6	1931-33	£7,000	£5,000	£3,000
Lt Six	1531/6	1934-38	£5,000	£4,000	£1,500
14	1781/6	1934-39	£4,000	£3,000	£1,500
25	3215/6	1937-39	£5,000	£4,000	£1,500
10	1203/4	1938-39	£4,000	£3,000	£1,500
Wyvern LIX	1500/4	1948-51	£2,000	£1,000	£500
Velox LIP	2200/6	1948-51	£2,000	£1,000	£500
Wyvern EIX	1500/4	1951-57	£2,000	£1,320	£400
Velox EIPV	2200/6	1951-57	£3,000	£1,650	£400
Cresta EIPC	2200/6	1954-57	£3,000	£1,650	£400
Velox/Cresta PAS/PAD	2262/6	1957-59	£2,850	£1,300	£300
Velox/Cresta PASY/PADY	2262/6	1959-60	£2,700	£1,500	£300
Velox/Cresta PASX/PADX	2651/6	1960-62	£2,700	£1,300	£300
Velox/Cresta PASX/PADX Est	2651/6	1960-62	£2,700	£1,300	£300
Velox/Cresta PB	2651/6	1962-65	£1,600	£800	£100
Velox/Cresta PB Est	2651/6	1962-65	£1,600	£800	£100
Cresta/Deluxe PC	3294/6	1964-72	£1,500	£800	£100
Cresta PC Est	3294/6	1964-72	£1,500	£800	£100
Viscount	3294/6	1964-72	£1,700	£900	£100
Victor I/II	1507/4	1957-61	£2,000	£1,000	£250
Victor I/II Est	1507/4	1957-61	£2,100	£1,100	£300
Victor FB	1507/4	1961-64	£1,500	£900	£200
Victor FB Est	1507/4	1961-64	£1,600	£1,000	£300
VX4/90	1507/4	1961-64	£2,000	£900	£150
Victor FC101	1594/4	1964-67	£1,600	£900	£150
Victor FC101 Est	1594/4	1964-67	£1,800	£1,000	£200
101 VX4/90	1594/4	1964-67	£2,000	£1,500	£250
VX4/90	1975/4	1969-71	£1,000	£600	£100
Ventora I/II	3294/6	1968-71	£1,000	£375	£100
Viva HA	1057/4	1963-66	£1,000	£350	£100
Viva SL90	1159/4	1966-70	£1,000	£350	£100
Viva Brabham	1159/4	1967-70	£2,000	£1,000	£800
Viva	1600/4	1968-70	£500	£350	£100
Viva Est	1159/4	1967-70	£500	£400	£100

VOISIN

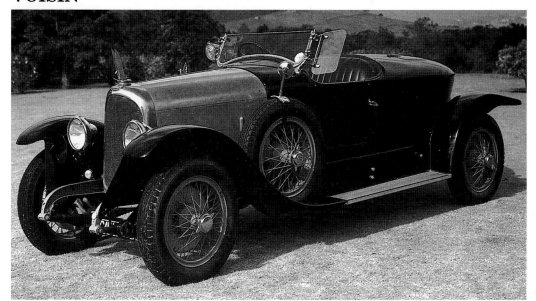

1920 Voisin Type C1 Boat-Tailed Sports Two-Seater, coachwork by Feval, finished in black with aluminium bonnet and red leather interior, front-wheel brakes, 8,000km since restoration, excellent condition.
£75,000–80,000 *BKS*

In 1907, Gabriel Voisin built the first practical aeroplane capable of leaving the ground under its own power, and his Avions Voisin company became the first mass producer of aircraft in the world. However, after WWI he turned away from aviation and began experimenting with motorised bicycles. A light two-seater economy car followed, but then he decided to produce a car that was unrivalled for prestige, comfort and speed. The resulting 4 litre Voisin M1 appeared in 1919. In 1920, it was redesignated C1 in honour of Gabriel Voisin's dead brother, Charles, although the mechanical specification remained the same. This particular car is said to have been used in competition and is a rare survivor of the marque.

VOLKSWAGEN

The Volkswagen Beetle may be the best-selling car in the world – a true people's car – but it had a long and painful birth. In the early 1930s, Adolf Hitler's vision for mass master-race motoring began to take shape when he entrusted Dr Ferdinand Porsche with the project. Some 630 or so Beetles were made before hostilities disrupted production. Back then, they were propaganda wagons, too, named KdF-Wagen, after the slogan of the Hitler Youth, *'Kraft durch Freude'*, which means 'strength through joy'.

When production resumed in 1945, the Beetle, as the more friendly Volkswagen, gathered an irresistible momentum, notching up 10,000 sales in 1946, 100,000 in 1950, and a million by 1955. In 1972, it overtook the Model T Ford's production record of 15 million. Today, the amazing story of the world's most popular car still hasn't come to an end, as every car that rolls off the remaining South American production lines adds to a 21-million-plus record that's unlikely ever to be beaten.

The Volkswagen story isn't all about the Beetle, though. The Beetle-based Karmann Ghia adds a bit of sporting style to the basic parent car, remaining practical and affordable. And, of course, the Golf GTi has become a latter-day icon.

1954 Volkswagen Beetle De Luxe, new engine 1971, well maintained, dry-stored, 64,000 miles recorded, excellent condition.
£4,200–4,700 *S*

1967 Volkswagen Beetle, 1300cc, very good condition throughout.
£900–1,100 *LF*

1978 Volkswagen 1200L Beetle, stored in delivery wax, rustproofed, 60 miles recorded, excellent condition.
£13,250–14,500 *S*

No car has had a longer life than the Volkswagen Beetle, which has been produced continuously since 1945. Over 1,000 cars a day continue to roll off the South American production line, making the car a 21 million plus bestseller. Plans for a 'People's Car' were announced by Adolf Hitler in 1934, and Dr Ferdinand Porsche designed the Volksauto along the lines of his famous 16-cylinder, rear-engined Grand Prix Auto Union, using an air-cooled, flat-four engine and a distinctive aerodynamic body. The dictator opened the Wolfsburg factory in 1938, but no vehicles reached the public until after the war, when the British motor industry, which had discounted the car as a commercial proposition, handed back the plant to the Germans. By 1972, the Beetle had overtaken the Model T Ford as the world's top-selling motor car. This particular 1978 last-edition Beetle 1200L was purchased new as an investment and remains unregistered.

l. **1973 Volkswagen Beetle Karmann Ghia Cabriolet,** 1600cc, 4 cylinders, 4-speed manual gearbox, left-hand drive, wide steel wheels, immobiliser, 75,000 miles recorded, very good condition.
£3,200–3,800 *H&H*

r. **1976 Volkswagen Karmann Cabriolet**, 1598cc, 4 cylinders, semi-automatic transmission, right-hand drive, brakes overhauled, Porsche wheels, hood serviceable, good condition.
£4,250–4,750 *BRIT*

Miller's Starter Marque

Starter Volkswagens: *Beetle.*

- One of several compelling reasons for owning a Beetle is that it's a classic that's still in production, which means readily available, cheap spares, especially for later models, although some items for early cars are hard to come by. Beetles are also very easy to work on: the world record for an engine swap – drive-up to drive-away – is just over three minutes. That buzzing air-cooled, four-cylinder engine is well nigh unburstable, too. Add the Beetle's lovable character into the mix, and it adds up to the anatomy of a starter classic.

- Best Beetles: Purists will plump for either the 1945–53 split-screen, 1131cc cars or the 1953–57 oval-window, 1200cc models. A good mid-way choice is the 1500cc version produced from 1966 to 1970: old enough to be classic, fast enough to keep up, and still pure in design. Finally, of course, you can still buy a brand-new one.

1972 Volkswagen Karmann Ghia Coupé, right-hand drive, stored, requires cosmetic attention and recommissioning.
£3,000–3,500 *BKS*

Hand-built by Karmann at its Osnabruck works, the Karmann Ghia coupé married a modified export Beetle floorpan, running gear, engine and gearbox to stylish Ghia coachwork.

1972 Volkswagen Variant 1600E, 1584cc, tool kit, original driver's instruction sleeve on sun visor, handbook, 25,000 miles recorded, concours winner, excellent condition.
£4,650–5,220 *H&H*

VOLKSWAGEN Model	ENGINE cc/cyl	DATES	CONDITION		
			1	2	3
Beetle (split rear screen)	1131/4	1945-53	£5,000	£3,500	£2,000
Beetle (oval rear screen)	1192/4	1953-57	£4,000	£2,000	£1,000
Beetle (slope headlamps)	1192/4	1957-68	£2,500	£1,000	£600
Beetle DHC	1192/4	1954-60	£6,000	£4,500	£2,000
Beetle 1500	1493/4	1966-70	£3,000	£2,000	£1,000
Beetle 1302 LS	1600/4	1970-72	£2,500	£1,850	£850
Beetle 1303 S	1600/4	1972-79	£3,000	£2,000	£1,500
1500 Variant/1600	1493/ 1584/4	1961-73	£2,000	£1,500	£650
1500/1600	1493/ 1584/4	1961-73	£3,000	£2,000	£800
Karmann Ghia/I	1192/4	1955-59	£5,000	£3,000	£1,000
Karmann Ghia/I DHC	1192/4	1957-59	£8,000	£5,000	£2,500
Karmann Ghia/I	1192/4	1960-74	£5,500	£3,000	£1,800
Karmann Ghia/I DHC	1192/4	1960-74	£7,000	£4,500	£2,000
Karmann Ghia/3	1493/4	1962-69	£4,000	£2,500	£1,250

VOLVO

Although the first production Volvo, the OV4, rolled off Swedish production lines in 1927, it took a while for the marque to make any impact in Britain. The early post-war PV444 and PV544, which lasted until 1965, were much admired for their roadholding and rally-winning capabilities. However, the first Volvo seen in any quantity on British roads was the Amazon saloon, which began life in 1956. These Amazon models (121/122/131/132/123GT) were certainly aptly named, because they're tough old road warriors, armoured like tanks. Built to withstand Swedish winters – and stray reindeer – this capable family four-seater helped create the reputation for strength and safety that Volvo has traded on ever since – the Amazon

had a padded dash top at birth, standard front seat belts from 1958, and dual-circuit brakes the following year.

Nearly half of the Amazons sold in Sweden are still on the road, and in Britain they're still more commonly encountered than many of our self-dismantling domestic products from the same period. A little more unusual is the P1800 sports car, a one-time flight of fancy by the sober Swedes. It's certainly stylish, and robust, too. In estate form, it's an uncommonly practical sports car.

If you're thinking of buying a classic Volvo, it's as well to remember that 'volvo' is the Latin word for 'I roll', and a good old Volvo will roll on and on for ever.

1964 Volvo 122S Amazon Four-Door Saloon, 1778cc, very good condition. **£2,400–2,800** *UMC*

1967 Volvo P1800S, 1778cc, 4 cylinders, resprayed, rechromed, reupholstered, very good condition throughout. **£3,200–3,800** *BRIT*

1971 Volvo P1800E, new exhaust, resprayed, service history, 60,000 miles recorded, fair condition. **£2,700–3,400** *S*

Did You Know?

In 1961, the producers of the television series *The Saint* approached Jaguar, offering the new E-Type a starring role. Jaguar wasn't interested, so the producers turned to Volvo, who leapt at the chance. Roger Moore drove a white P1800 in over 100 episodes. It's believed that five cars were used in the series, and one of them sold at auction in 1989 for an interstellar £42,000.

r. **1972 Volvo P1800ES Sports Estate** 1985cc, 4 cylinder in-line engine, 124bhp at 6,000rpm, completely restored, excellent condition. **£6,250–7,000** *Pou*

VOLVO Model	ENGINE cc/cyl	DATES	CONDITION 1	2	3
PV444	1800/4	1958-67	£4,000	£1,750	£800
PV544	1800/4	1962-64	£4,000	£1,750	£800
120 (B16)	1583/4	1956-59	£3,000	£1,000	£300
121	1708/4	1960-67	£3,500	£1,500	£350
122S	1780/4	1960-67	£4,500	£1,500	£250
131	1780/4	1962-69	£4,000	£1,500	£350
221/222	1780/4	1962-69	£2,500	£1,500	£300
123Gt	1986/4	1967-69	£3,000	£2,500	£750
P1800	1986/4	1960-70	£3,500	£2,000	£1,000
P1800E	1986/4	1970-71	£4,000	£2,500	£1,000
P1800ES	1986/4	1971-73	£5,000	£3,000	£1,000

c1972 Volvo P1800ES Sports Estate, manual gearbox, engine, suspension, brakes and steering restored, finished in dark green with original tan interior, good condition throughout.
£4,000–4,750 *BKS*

Introduced in 1960, the pretty P1800 sports coupé was initially built for Volvo by Jensen Motors, production being transferred to Sweden in 1963. It employed Volvo's rugged 4-cylinder overhead-valve engine in 1778cc form. Breathing through twin carburettors, this unit produced 100bhp, sufficient to propel the solidly-built coupé to a top speed of around 105mph. A capacity increase to 1985cc for the P1800E was followed by the adoption of fuel injection in 1969, maximum power increasing to 130bhp. Four-wheel disc brakes were standardised at the same time. By the end of the 1960s, the model was beginning to look dated, but the introduction of the P1800ES sports estate extended its lease of life. Production ceased in 1973 after 8,078 had been built.

1974 Volvo 1800ES Sports Estate, 1985cc, 4 cylinders, automatic transmission, Webasto-type sunroof, corrosion proofed, very good condition.
£2,750–3,250 *BRIT*

WANDERER

1937 Wanderer W25 Cabriolet, coachwork by Karosserie Glaser, 1950cc, 6 cylinders, single Solex carburettor, Bosch coil ignition, left-hand drive, completely restored, excellent condition.
£47,000–50,000 *S*

Wanderer produced bicycles and motorcycles before beginning car manufacture in 1911. A range of six-cylinder models, based on a Porsche design, was built by the Siegmar company during the 1930s, and gained a reputation for quality, finish and performance. In 1932, Wanderer formed part of the quartet, alongside Audi, DKW and Horch, known as Auto Union.

WILLYS

r. **1950 Willys Jeepster,** 2425cc, 4 cylinders, finished in red and white with whitewall tyres, red vinyl interior, gear linkage requires attention, excellent condition.
£5,350–6,000 *BRIT*

Produced between 1948 and 1951, the Jeepster was a civilian version of the WWII army Jeep. Initial versions were powered by the 134cu in L-head engine borrowed from the Whippet, which was enlarged to 148cu in (2425cc) in 1949.

WOLSELEY

1932 Wolseley Hornet Special Tourer, original black paintwork and dark green upholstery, stored, requires restoration.
£4,400–4,800 *S*

1969 Wolseley 16/60 Saloon, 1600cc, good condition.
£1,400–1,600 *LF*

WOLSELEY Model	ENGINE cc/cyl	DATES	CONDITION 1	2	3
10	987/2	1909-16	£16,000	£12,500	£9,000
CZ (30hp)	2887/4	1909	£18,000	£13,000	£9,000
15hp and A9	2614/4	1920-27	£12,000	£10,000	£8,000
20 and C8	3921/ 3862/6	1920-27	£11,000	£8,000	£6,000
E4 (10.5hp)	1267/ 1542/4	1925-30	£6,000	£4,000	£3,000
E6 and Viper and 16hp	2025/6	1927-34	£15,000	£12,000	£8,000
E8M	2700/8	1928-31	£18,000	£15,000	£12,000
Hornet	1271/6	1931-35	£10,000	£8,000	£4,500
Hornet Special	1271/ 1604/6	1933-36	£12,000	£8,000	£5,000
Wasp	1069/4	1936	£7,000	£5,000	£3,500
Hornet	1378/6	1936	£8,000	£6,000	£4,000
21/60 and 21hp	2677/ 2916/6	1932-39	£11,000	£6,000	£4,000
25	3485/6	1936-39	£8,500	£5,500	£4,000
12/48	1547/4	1937-39	£5,000	£3,000	£2,000
14/56	1818/6	1937-39	£6,000	£4,000	£2,000
18/80	2322/6	1938-39	£7,500	£5,500	£4,000

Early Wolseley cars are well made and very British and those with coachbuilt bodies command a premium of at least +25 per cent.

WOLSELEY Model	ENGINE cc/cyl	DATES	CONDITION 1	2	3
8	918/4	1939-48	£3,000	£2,000	£1,000
10	1140/4	1939-48	£3,500	£2,000	£1,000
12/48	1548/4	1939-48	£4,000	£2,000	£1,250
14/60	1818/6	1946-48	£4,500	£2,500	£1,500
18/85	2321/6	1946-48	£6,000	£3,000	£2,000
25	3485/6	1946-48	£7,000	£4,000	£2,500
4/50	1476/4	1948-53	£2,500	£1,000	£450
6/80	2215/6	1948-54	£3,000	£1,500	£750
4/44	1250/4	1952-56	£2,500	£1,250	£750
15/50	1489/4	1956-58	£1,850	£850	£500
1500	1489/4	1958-65	£2,500	£1,000	£500
15/60	1489/4	1958-61	£2,000	£700	£400
16/60	1622/4	1961-71	£1,800	£800	£400
6/90	2639/6	1954-57	£2,500	£1,000	£500
6/99	2912/6	1959-61	£3,000	£1,500	£750
6/110 MK I/II	2912/6	1961-68	£2,000	£1,000	£500
Hornet (Mini)	848/4	1961-70	£1,500	£750	£400
1300	1275/4	1967-74	£1,250	£750	£400
18/85	1798/4	1967-72	£950	£500	£250

COMMERCIAL VEHICLES

1929 Dennis 3 Ton Flat-Bed Truck, 4.7 litre, 4 cylinder petrol engine, completely restored, good condition.
£8,000–10,000 *BKS*

Brothers John and Raymond Dennis were pioneers in the infant motor industry as early as 1899, building their Speed King bicycles, motorcycles and tricycles initially, then beginning commercial vehicle production in 1904 at the Onslow Works, Guildford. The demand for commercial vehicles and fire engines at the outbreak of WWI was such that all production was focused on commercial vehicles from 1915 onwards.

1935 Austin 7 Van, good condition.
£3,250–3,750 *DB*

1949 Morris J Van, Oxford sidevalve engine, completely restored, RAC livery.
£8,500–9,000 *RAC*

Between 1948 and 1954, the RAC operated several Morris J vans, for use as signs vehicles and for road patrols.

1930 Austin 7 Chummy, restored, RAC livery, excellent condition.
£9,000–10,000 *RAC*

1939 Foden Model OG Flat-Bed Lorry, 3.8 litre, Gardner 4LK engine, lightweight 38cwt chassis employing electron castings and alloy steels, 4-wheel self-energising brakes, original specification, restored 1973, displayed at Leyland Commercial Vehicle Museum, Lancashire.
£6,500–8,000 *BKS*

Thanks to the success of their maximum-weight, Gardner-powered lorries, Foden gradually recovered from losses of £75,000 per year and a workforce cut to only 200. However, they were not so fortunate with small internal-combustion-engined trucks, the smallest of which was an Austin-powered 30hp 2 tonner. In the mid-1930s, the small models were replaced by the OG Series, using lightweight Gardner 3LW and, later, 4LK diesels. By then, these and the larger OGs had revived Foden's fortunes, and the workforce had been increased to 1,000 men.

> **Miller's is a price GUIDE not a price LIST**

Two copies of *Commercial Motor* magazine, 1954.
£3–5 each *PMB*

1971 Morris Minor Van, 1098cc, new engine 1988, new gearbox 1995, very good condition throughout. **£1,100–1,500** *LF*

The Minor Van was known as the O-Type, and this particular example was one of the final models, the Series V, with the 1098cc, 48bhp engine. Production ceased in 1971.

1969 Austin Morris Van, RAC livery, good condition. **£6,000–7,000** *RAC*

1981 Austin Taxi FX4 Cabriolet, 2570cc diesel engine, 3-speed automatic transmission, see-through removable top, sound system, electric points, finished in white over black, engine overhauled, very good condition. **£3,000–4,000** *H&H*

Only five of these cabs were commissioned to promote tourism in Great Britain, and this example was used in publicity shots.

r. 1980 Leyland Mini Pick-Up, 1300cc, 4-speed gearbox, completely rebuilt, new front wings, front panels, door skins, front floor well and sills, bed lined in checker-plate aluminium, bare metal respray in metallic British Racing Green, dashboard veneered, excellent condition. **£4,000–5,000** *H&H*

1973 Austin FX4/FL2 London Taxi, 2.2 litre, overhead-valve petrol engine, 4-speed manual gearbox, good condition. **£1,200–1,600** *S*

In a successful attempt to join the emerging hire market, Austin made a special version of the Heavy Twelve chassis available to a number of coachbuilders in 1930. By 1939, Austin was established as the leading manufacturer of taxis, with sales far in excess of their rivals, Morris-Commercial and Beardmore. Prototypes for a new cab were developed post-war, and the FX3/FL1 series was launched in 1949. A completely new design, the FX4, was introduced in diesel form in 1958. The basic styling was to become the oldest Austin design in production, beating the Mini by a few months. This particular FX4/FL2 dates from the final year of manufacture and is believed to be the last petrol-driven taxi built. It was acquired by the Sixth Marquess of Bath in 1981 and was formerly on show at Longleat.

1950 Daimler DC-27 Ambulance, coachwork by Barker, 4 litre, 6 cylinder petrol engine, pre-selector fluid-flywheel gearbox, partially restored.
£4,000–5,000 *BAm*

The Daimler DC-27 was the first chassis specifically designed for an ambulance. However, even when new, the braking system was questionable, resulting in several spectacular accidents. The DC-27 was mainly used by the London Ambulance Service from 1947 to 1962.

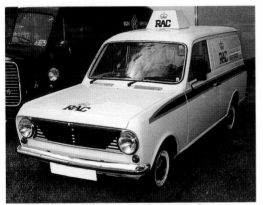

1980 Bedford HA Van, totally restored, RAC livery.
£3,000–4,000 *RAC*

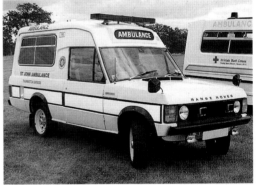

1976 Range Rover Ambulance, coachwork by Herbert Lomas, restored, still in service with St John Ambulance.
£2,000–2,500 *BAm*

Late 1950s Morris Commercial LSC Ambulance, coachwork by Wadham Bros, 'ballon' tyres, good condition.
£2,750–3,250 *BAm*

A powerful and comfortable ambulance, the Morris LSC was offered in both petrol and diesel versions.

CHILDREN'S CARS

l. **1930s Formula Racing Pedal Car,** pedal-powered, painted in red, handbrake on right, dummy exhaust on left.
£800–1,000 *SLM*

Jaguar XK120 Roadster Replica Pedal Car, moulded fibreglass on steel chassis, opening boot lid and bonnet with dummy engine, alloy and Perspex split windscreen, chromed metal parts, upholstered vinyl seat, battery for lights and horn.
£850–950 *CARS*

l. **1970s Cooper Bristol Eagle SE1 Car,** by Star Design, steel tube chassis, fibreglass body, 5.5bhp Honda engine, 18mph top speed, pneumatic tyres, hydraulic brakes, 4-point safety harness.
£2,200–2,500 *BKS*

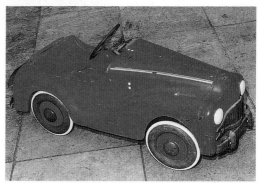

c1950 Triang Pedal Car, painted red with blue radiator grille, wheels and steering wheel.
£100–150 *JUN*

c1937 Triumph Dolomite Pedal Car, by Lines Bros, finished in white with red interior, wings and wheels.
£500–700 *JUN*

Use the Index!
Because certain items might fit easily into any of a number of categories, the quickest and surest method of locating any entry is by reference to the index at the back of this book.

l. **1937 Daimler Pedal Car,** by Lines Bros, finished in red with yellow coachlining.
£500–700 *JUN*

r. **1988 Jaguar XK120 Roadster Child's Car,** fibreglass body, 3hp Briggs & Stretton engine, rear-wheel brakes, finished in British Racing Green with black interior, virtually unused.
£750–900 *BKS*

c1960 Ford Zephyr/Zodiac Police Pedal Car, by Triang, pressed-steel body, battery for siren and bells, finished in dark blue with white decals.
£250–350 *CARS*

Mercedes-Benz 230 SLK Sports Roadster Replica Child's Car, moulded plastic body, finished in yellow, padded roll-over bar, 6 volt battery and charging unit.
£200–250 *CARS*

REPLICA, KIT & REPRODUCTION CARS

1958 'Merry Olds' Curved Dash Runabout Replica, 4hp, 4-stroke, air-cooled, single-cylinder Clinton engine, electric starting, centrifugal clutch, 2-speed transmission with reverse, chain drive, top speed 25mph, restored 1989, good condition.
£4,000–5,000 *BKS*

At the turn of the century, Ramsom E. Olds developed his first practical vehicle, the Oldsmobile Curved Dash Runabout. There was even a song at the time titled In My Merry Oldsmobile.

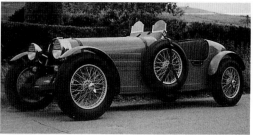

1979/1995 Teal Bugatti Type 35 Replica, 1695cc, 4 cylinder, overhead-camshaft, Austin Rover O-Series engine, box section steel chassis, hand-formed aluminium coachwork, finished in Bugatti Blue, black cloth tonneau and hood, 700 miles recorded, excellent condition.
£9,000–11,000 *BRIT*

During the 1920s and 1930s, the products of Ettore Bugatti were among the finest in the world and a force to be reckoned with in competition. These finely engineered motor cars have always had a loyal following and, as values have escalated during the past two decades, a number of replicas have been developed.

1995 Bugatti 2.3 Litre Type 55 'Jean Bugatti Roadster', replica chassis by Ray Jones, many genuine original items including front axle stamped 186, radiator, Scintilla magneto, starter, generator and dashboard starter/light switch, new crankcase, roller-bearing crankshaft and connecting rod assembly, original Bugatti cylinder blocks, correct-pattern gearbox, excellent condition.
£88,000–96,000 *BKS*

This is a replica in the true meaning of the word – a matching reproduction of the original model. It is extremely accurate and, wherever possible, employs the correct materials, dimensions and Bugatti-type nuts and bolts.

l. **1970 Gentry TF,** 1300cc, 4 cylinders, 4-speed manual gearbox with overdrive, Triumph Herald chassis, 10,885 miles from new, excellent condition throughout, concours winner.
£6,500–8,000 *H&H*

The Gentry TF is a classic 1950s replica, being available either as the traditional two-seater or as a more practical 2+2. It is designed to utilise the mechanical components from the Ford Escort MkII, or the Cortina MkIII, IV or V. Alternatively, the Triumph Herald, Vitesse and Spitfire are still popular as donor vehicles.

1981/1997 Gentry TF, excellent condition.
£10,000–11,000 *TPM*

1985 Hutson TF 1700,
1.7 litres, Austin Rover
O-Series engine, 4-speed
gearbox, steel chassis,
excellent condition.
£11,000–14,000 *NCC*

l. **1991 Hutson TF 1700,**
excellent condition.
£12,000–16,0000 *NCC*

*The Hutson Company
were successors to Naylor
Cars PLC. They made
and sold 61 cars from
1986. A prototype fitted
with a K-Series engine
has been made.*

1985 Naylor TF 1700, excellent condition.
£12,000–14,000 *NCC*

1990 Jaguar C-Type Replica, built by Heritage,
3.4 litre, 6 cylinder engine, fibreglass body, finished
in Ecurie Ecosse Blue, chrome wire wheels.
£17,500–19,000 *BC*

Don't Forget!
*If in doubt please refer to the 'How to
Use' section at the beginning of this book.*

1996 Jaguar D-Type Replica, built from Le
Mans Sports Cars kit, 4.2 litre Series I Jaguar
XJ6 engine and suspension, E-Type cam covers,
manual choke conversion, 5-speed Getrag gearbox,
limited-slip differential, ventilated disc brakes,
excellent condition.
£11,500–13,000 *COYS*

*The Jaguar D-Type was one of the most
charismatic sports racing cars ever made, not to
mention one of the most successful. Appearing in
1954, it featured aerodynamic bodywork, complete
with tailfin for high-speed stability, penned by ex-
aircraft designer Malcolm Sayer. Power came from
the now legendary twin-cam, dry-sump, 3442cc
six (later 3781cc), which produced 250bhp at
5,570rpm. Top speed was in excess of 170mph.
Not surprisingly, the D-Type dominated the
international endurance racing scene from the
outset until its demise, by which time just over
70 examples had been built.*

1996 Jaguar C-Type Replica, 3.4 litres,
6 cylinders, 4-speed manual gearbox with
overdrive, 1953 Le Mans winner specification,
aluminium body, finished in British Racing Green
with green leather interior, 16in wire wheels.
£35,000–40,000 *PORT*

1992 Jaguar D-Type Replica,
very good condition throughout.
£18,000–20,000 *EPP*

c1960 Maserati Tipo 61 'Birdcage' Sports Racing Replica, tubular-steel spaceframe chassis, inclined Lotus 2 litre, 4 cylinder engine, Lotus transmission.
£7,000–8,000 *BKS*

This Maserati 'Birdcage' look-alike caused tremendous excitement in recent years when it was advertised in the specialist press, apparently as a missing example of the last word in the development of the traditional front-engined sports racing car. It is, in fact, an affordable replica of that epoch-making Maserati Tipo 60/61 design.

1995 Lister-Jaguar Replica, 3781cc, 6 cylinders, dry-sump lubrication, Weber carburettors, hand-formed aluminium bodywork, Dunlop alloy wheels, built at a cost of over £150,000, dry-stored, unused, excellent condition.
£50,000–60,000 *COYS*

One of the most famous partnerships in motor racing was between Archie Scott-Brown and Lister. In 1957, Brian Lister built a Jaguar-engined sports racing car for Archie, and apart from suffering one or two teething problems, he used it to win 11 of the 14 races entered that year. Other makes of engine have been fitted to Lister chassis, but it is the 'Knobbly', so called because of its body shape, fitted with the 3.8-litre, twin-cam, Jaguar straight-six that has become the classic. In 1995, Lister Cars was commissioned to build this car, which is a painstaking re-creation of the original Scott-Brown car and is painted in the same green and yellow colour scheme.

Ferrari P4 Replica, by Noble Motorsports, Targa roof, only 12 built.
£30,000–35,000 *EPP*

1993 GTD 40 Replica, 5 litres, V8, finished in metallic blue and silver, grey hide interior, 7,750 miles recorded.
£25,000–28,000 *PORT*

1989 Brightwheel Viper Cobra Replica, 3528cc, Rover V8 engine and transmission, Ford Granada rear axle, brakes and suspension, walnut dashboard, woodrim steering wheel, good condition.
£9,500–11,000 *BRIT*

1972 BRA Cobra 427 Replica, 5 litre, Chevrolet V8 engine, 350bhp, 5-speed racing gearbox, Powr-Lok limited-slip differential, 0–60mph in 5 seconds, rust-proofed and wax-filled chassis, Jaguar suspension and brakes, replica Halibrand alloy wheels, finished in red with black leather interior, 6,000 miles recorded.
£16,000–19,000 *BKS*

This particular car is one of 30 examples produced by BRA before production moved to Germany.

1996 Dax Cobra Replica, 6.5 litre, Pontiac V8 engine, semi-automatic transmission, Halibrand-style wheels, Le Mans Blue with grey leather upholstery, full weather equipment.
£18,500–20,000 *BC*

1993 Heritage Mercedes-Benz 500K Replica, 5.7 litre, Chevrolet V8 engine, automatic transmission, right-hand drive, excellent condition.
£11,500–14,000 *BKS*

This car was constructed and sold in ready-built form by Heritage Motor Cars of the USA.

Late 1970s Kougar Jaguar, 3.8 litre Jaguar engine, 4.2 Jaguar running gear, very good condition.
£11,000–12,000 *EPP*

r. **1994 Westfield Lotus 7 Replica,** 1800cc, Zetec engine, all new parts, excellent condition throughout.
£10,000–12,000 *VIC*

1975 Porsche 935 Replica, 3294cc, 6 cylinders, twin turbochargers, twin injectors, dual ignition, good condition.
£30,000–35,000 *COYS*

By 1974, Porsche's 911 Turbo, designated 930, had arrived, and for the 1976 racing season, it had the right specification to contest the new Group 4 and 5 Championships. The Group 4 car was called the 934, and the Group 5 car, the 935. The latter was destined to become the most outstanding production-based car in the World Championship for Makes. This 935 replica is based on a 911 that was converted for racing with a proper 935 body kit, having first been fitted with an integral roll cage for extra rigidity. Its twin turbocharged, 3294cc engine, from USA Porsche specialist Motor Sport Designs, recorded an awesome 808bhp at 7,400rpm although, using 1.5 bar boost pressure, its race output was limited to 750bhp.

RESTORATION PROJECTS

1914 Briton Four-Seater Tourer, reupholstered in button-back brown leather, otherwise requires full restoration, one of four known to exist.
£4,750–5,250 *S*

1928 Rolls-Royce 20hp Tourer, panelled, open 4 seater tourer body frame, original wings, dashboard with correct instrumentation, Watford clock, pair of fork-mounted Lucas headlamps, new set of hoodsticks, restorable.
£8,000–10,000 *S*

1924 Rolls-Royce 20hp Rolling Chassis, mechanically complete, original engine and 3-speed gearbox, remains of original coachwork, as found condition.
£4,000–5,000 *S*

1933 Austin 7 Two-Door Saloon, barn discovery, unused for several years.
£1,200–1,500 *BKS*

Ruggedly built, economical and easily maintained by the home mechanic, the Austin 7 brought motoring within financial reach of the man in the street. A huge success from the moment deliveries commenced in January 1923, the 7 remained in production until 1939.

1933 Riley March Special, open sports coachwork by John Charles, 1089cc, 4 cylinders, partly restored, engine installed and running, believed complete.
£3,300–3,800 *COYS*

r. **1935 Rolls-Royce 20/25 Two-Door Fixed-Head Coupé,** coachwork by Freestone & Webb, original leather upholstery, engine partly dismantled, head missing, original specification.
£5,200–5,800 *BKS*

This particular car was the only 20/25 to be fitted with this design of Freestone & Webb coupé coachwork.

1937 MG TA Midget, barn discovery, engine running, but cracked block.
£3,800–4,300 *BKS*

Launched in 1936 as the successor to the PB Midget, the TA was a larger and roomier car. Its simple chassis design followed established Midget practice with semi-elliptic springing all-round, although hydraulic front dampers and Lockheed hydraulic brakes were new departures. Although traditionally styled, the two-seater TA broke with tradition by employing an overhead-valve engine instead of the previous overhead-camshaft type. Derived from the Morris 10's powerplant, the 1292cc engine produced around 50bhp at 4,500rpm, which was good enough to propel the lightweight TA to within a whisker of 80mph.

1948 AC 2 Litre Two-Door Saloon, triple SU carburettors, 76bhp, 4-speed Moss gearbox, body stripped to bare metal, engine incomplete.
£150–400 *BKS*

Introduced in 1947, the AC 2 Litre was a spacious and well-equipped touring car, endowed with 80mph performance. A variety of body styles, some coachbuilt, was available, including a four-door model from late 1952. This particular car was driven in the 1950 Monte Carlo Rally. It is believed that it was equipped with a non-standard, higher-reading speedometer and tuned engine especially for the event. Sadly, the car failed to finish, suffering the same fate the following year.

1952 Aston Martin DB2 Sports Saloon, major engine rebuild in 1961 at 97,000 miles, rear axle overhauled in 1964, little use since, coachwork partly stripped, much major work completed.
£11,000–12,000 *BKS*

The DB2 prototype, with the W. O. Bentley-designed, 2.6 litre, twin-camshaft engine and light alloy coachwork, ran at Le Mans in 1949, being offered to the public in the spring of 1950.

c1959 Austin A-Series Van, 4 cylinders, sound chassis and bodywork, Gold Seal engine fitted before long-term storage, requires interior trim and headlights.
£650–800 *S*

1957 Paramount, 1703cc, dry-stored for 25 years, one wheel missing.
£150–400 *BKS*

Production of Paramounts ceased in 1956, but this example was one of three chassis taken on by Barton Townley in Lancaster, who fitted it with a Rochdale MkVI fibreglass body.

1966 Morris Minor Saloon, 1000cc, running order.
£450–550 *ESM*

MICROCARS

1958 BMW Isetta, fully restored, excellent condition.
£2,750–3,250   *SWO*

1959 BMW Isetta, RAC livery, 865 miles
recorded, good condition.
£10,000–12,000   *RAC*

1962 BMW Isetta, 300cc, good condition.
£2,250–2,750   *H&H*

1962 BMW Isetta, 300cc, completely restored,
very good condition.
£5,750–6,250   *THOR*

1959 Messerschmitt KR200 Kabinenroller,
finished in yellow, wooden floor, very good
condition throughout.
£9,250–10,500   *S*

1959 Messerschmitt KR200, 191cc, 4-speed
gearbox, completely restored, many new parts,
very good condition throughout.
£3,900–4,400   *H&H*

r. **1960 Messerschmitt KR200,** 198cc, single-cylinder,
2-stroke engine, 4-speed gearbox, electric reverse, cable
brakes, original handbooks, service history, 14,928
miles recorded, good condition throughout.
£3,500–4,000   *C*

*The KR200 featured improvements over the earlier
KR175, such as revised steering, lighting, controls and
panoramic windscreen, and a 200cc engine capable of
62mph. Other refinements included an electric starter,
electrically-operated reverse gear, double-dip twin
headlamps and flashing indicators.*

RACING & RALLYING

1932 Alfa Romeo Monza, 2300cc, excellent condition.
£2,000,000+ *PC*

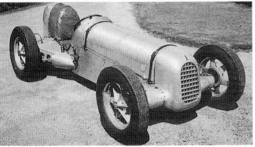

1938 Lightweight Single-Seater Special,
Austin overhead-camshaft engine, supercharged,
excellent condition.
£45,000–50,000 *BKS*

*This wonderful and, in its time, revolutionary sprint
and hill-climb car provides enduring early evidence
of the genius of Sir Alec Issigonis, creator of the
Morris Minor and the BMC Mini. He began planning
the machine as early as 1932, and from the outset
its design concept recognised the importance
of power-to-weight ratio, as opposed merely to high
power or sheer cubic capacity. Its advanced
specification included monocoque construction and
independent suspension with rubber springing.*

1949 Emeryson-JAP 500cc, chassis No. 500/7,
front-wheel drive, excellent condition throughout.
£9,500–11,000 *BKS*

*The 500cc Emeryson was constructed on a simple
ladder frame and featured all-independent suspension,
usually sprung by rubber bands, although coil springs
were also tried. It employed front-wheel drive, using the
transmission from a pre-war BSA three-wheeler. Since
this had no differential, a single transmission brake
was used. In 1951, Paul Emery's own car employed a
homemade disc brake, which is the earliest known use
of disc braking on any European car of any description.
The Emeryson's body style was a direct copy of the
Mercedes-Benz W154/39. This particular JAP-engined
example is one of only six known survivors.*

1953 Cooper MkVII, 500cc, Manx Norton engine,
restored, good condition.
£11,500–12,500 *Car*

*This is a very original example of the first
spaceframe Cooper.*

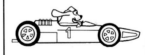

1958 Volpini Formula Junior Single-Seater, 1100cc, front-mounted Fiat engine, 4-speed gearbox, restored, very good condition.
£20,000–23,000 *BKS*

Italian constructor Volpini first took to the race tracks in the early 1950s, as a builder of single-seater racing cars for the then Formula 3.

1959 Elva 100 Formula Junior, 998cc, BMC engine, ready-to-race, very good condition throughout.
£19,000–21,000 *Car*

This car competed successfully in VSCC events during 1997.

1966 MG-Based ERA Replica, 1798cc, MGB engine and running gear, alloy body, black single seat, wire wheels, disc brakes.
£4,800–5,500 *H&H*

1969 Merlyn MkIIA Formula Ford, 1600cc, completely restored, excellent race-ready condition.
£14,000–16,000 *Car*

1961 Gemini Mk3A Formula Junior Single-Seater, 1100cc, Ford engine, rebuilt 1990, new frame, new bodywork, rewired, supplied with original chassis.
£11,000–13,000 *BKS*

This was originally one of the rear-engined Geminis built in 1961 by Geoff Rumble for Graham Warner's famous Chequered Flag team. Its FIA paperwork records its history as the 1961 'Works No. 2 car prepared for Mike Parkes'.

1968 Vixen Imp Formula 4, 875cc, full-race Carter Imp engine, ready to race.
£7,000–8,000 *Car*

1971 Elden MkVIII Formula Ford, 1600cc, race-ready condition.
£14,000–16,000 *Car*

Tony Brise began his racing career with this car, using it to win 23 races in 1971. He went on to race in Formula 1, but was killed in an aircraft crash in 1975.

1972 Surtees TS8 Formula 5000, 5 litre, fuel-injected Chevrolet V8 engine, unused since rebuild.
£17,000–20,000 *BKS*

Under the guidance of 1964 Formula 1 World Champion John Surtees, Team Surtees produced some of the best quality and most enduring major-Formula single-seater racing cars of the 1970s. The TS8 made its debut in 1972, when multiple motor-cycle World Champion Mike Hailwood led the works team. Widely regarded as the fastest and most spectacular driver in contemporary Formula 5000, Hailwood won the opening round of that year's British and European Championship at Mallory Park.

1918/30 Rolls-Royce/Liberty 27 Litre Special 'Satis', 1930 Rolls-Royce Phantom II chassis, shortened to 11ft wheelbase, 1918 Packard V12 Liberty aero engine, 420hp, leather-trimmed bucket seats, passenger seat with belt and grab handle, 'diddy' box between tank and seats, twin rear-mounted spare wheels.
£49,000–56,000 *BKS*

For many years, the racing motorist has been fascinated by the concept of fitting the largest possible engine into a comparatively modest chassis in the quest for speed. Count Louis Zborowski and Richard Noble are surely kindred spirits with their massive aero-engined creations, Chitty-Chitty-Bang-Bang I, II and III, and Thrust I and II respectively. Although radically different machines, generations apart, they provided that excitement of speed and power at the limit.

1955 Kieft Sports Racing Two-Seater, BMC B-Series engine to MGA spec, finished in blue, good original condition.
£14,500–16,000 *BKS*

This is the last of the seven conventional two-seater sports cars made by Kieft.

1963 Marina, 6700cc, Rolls-Royce Shadow engine, Cooper Formula 1 suspension, excellent condition.
£65,000–75,000 *Car*

This unique car was built by the Mann brothers and raced by Jimmy Bulmer in sports car events.

1962 Marcos Luton Gullwing GT, 1300cc, finished in yellow, good condition.
£12,000–14,000 *Car*

This car ran in the 1963 Autosport *Championship, and has been a racing car all its life.*

1965 Alfa Romeo Giulia TZ1, styled by Zagato, 1.6 litres, tubular spaceframe chassis, aluminium body, 0–60mph in 4½ seconds, 131mph top speed, finished in red with black interior, new Plexiglass in rear window, original unrestored condition.
£67,500–75,000 *S*

In competition, the TZ1 scored class wins at Le Mans and in the FISA Cup at Monza, the Sebring 12-Hours, the Tour de France, the Targa Florio and the 1,000km at Nürburgring. It is believed that only 124 examples of this coupé were built.

1968 Chevron B8 GT, 2000cc, BMW engine, not raced since 1989, requires some restoration.
£33,000–37,000 *Car*

1951/53 Aston Martin DB2 Two-Seater GT Coupé, 2.6 litres, completely restored by R. S. Williams, concours condition.
£140,000–160,000 *BKS*

This DB2 was built as a lightweight works racer. Its race record includes appearances at Le Mans in 1951 (seventh overall, third in class) and in the 1952 Mille Miglia (13th overall, second in class). Of the latter event, Reg Parnell commented: '. . . I can honestly say that I'd rather compete in the Mille Miglia in an Aston Martin than in any car . . .'

1968 McLaren M6 GT, 5735cc, Chevrolet LT1 V8 engine, 370hp at 6,000rpm, excellent condition.
£50,000–55,000 *Pou*

1959 Ferrari 250 GT Berlinetta 'Tour de France', 2953cc, V12, 36 DCL3 Weber carburettors, 260bhp at 7,000rpm, matching engine/chassis numbers, 4-speed manual gearbox, 16in wheels with Dunlop racing tyres, Houdaille shock absorbers replaced by Koni units, otherwise original, sound condition.
£290,000+ *C*

Ferrari made a distinction between Coupés and Berlinettas in the mid-1950s. The former were luxuriously-finished two-seaters for road use, while the latter, also two-seaters, did away with the frills and were suitable for competition. These cars were called long-wheelbase Berlinettas until Potago won the 1956 Tour de France, whereupon they received the unofficial title of 'Tour de France'. Although built for competition, Berlinettas were practical as every-day transport, although the thin aluminium coachwork was easily damaged. With such a dual personality, the 250 GT 'Tour de France' has become one of the most collectable Ferraris.

l. **1973 MGB Roadster,** 1950cc, rebuilt engine with Stage 3 head, 100bhp, Sebring valances, headlamp covers, aluminium bonnet and strap, bucket seats and harnesses, FIA roll-bar, completely restored, excellent condition.
£10,500–12,000 *H&H*

MILITARY VEHICLES

1943 Austin 10hp Utility G/YG, 1230cc, 4 cylinders, 29.5bhp, sidevalve engine, 4-speed gearbox, driving rear wheels, Girling mechanical brakes, leaf spring suspension, tyre size 6.00-16, wheelbase 93.5in, overall dimensions 156 x 63 x 78 in, weight 2240lb.
£4,750–5,250 *PC*

Derived from 10hp saloon and produced in large numbers during WWII for British and Allied Forces.

r. **1941–44 White Scout Car 4x4 M3A1,** 6 cylinders, 87bhp, driving rear or all wheels, 4-speed gearbox, 2-speed transfer box, hydraulic brakes with vacuum servo, leaf spring suspension, weight 8,900lb, American.
£7,000–8,000 *RRM*

1940–42 Karrier K6 GS Truck, Humber 4086cc, 6 cylinders, 80hp, 3 ton, 4 x 4, fitted with winch.
£2,500–3,750 *MVT*

c1941 White Half-Track, 6 cylinders, 386 cu in, sidevalve liquid-cooled petrol engine, 127bhp at 3,000rpm, dry plate clutch, 4F1R gearbox, 2-speed transfer box with front axle declutch, hydraulic brakes with vacuum servo, rigid front axle with leaf springs, rear suspension with volute springs, weight 14,800lb, gross 19,800lb, American.
Unrestored £3,000–3,500
Restored   £10,000–12,000 *RRM*

r. **1943 International M5 A1 Half-Track Personnel Carrier,** 6 cylinders, 124bhp overhead valve, 451 cu in, 4 forward gears, one reverse with high/low transer box.
£14,000–16,000 *PC*

These vehicles were produced from 1941 onwards.

1942–44 VW Schwimmwagen Light 4x4 Amphibious Car, 1131cc engine, 25bhp flat four air-cooled, rear wheels driven via a 5-speed gearbox, front wheels driven an option, 2 self-locking diffs, water speed around 10km/h, very good condition.
£15,000–28,500 *MVT*

WWII Daimler Dingo MkII 4x4 Scout Car, 2520cc, 6 cylinders, 55bhp, mounted at the rear, all-wheel drive, 5-speed gearbox, and single speed transfer.
£3,500–7,500 *MVT*

1950s Creusot-Loire AMX13 Light Tank, 8260cc, overhead valve engine, 250bhp, 5-speed gearbox, and Cleveland-type controlled differential, torsion-bar suspension, mechanical brakes, French.
£8,000–10,000 *RRM*

c1960s White AML 90, French.
£6,000–7,000 *RRM*

r. **1967 Austin Mini Moke CL,** 1275cc, good original condition.
£4,000–4,500 *PC*

WWII NAAFI Truck, built on an Austin chassis.
£1,000–3,000 *MVT*
This vehicle is one of only two known in this country.

c1946 Scammel Explorer 10 Ton Recovery 6x6 FV 11301, 6 cylinders, 175bhp, 6-speed gearbox with 2-speed transfer.
£1,000–4,500 *MVT*

1955–68 Auto Union 'Munga' DKW F91 4x4, 897cc, 2-stroke, 3 cylinders, 38–40bhp, 4-speed gearbox and 2-speed auxiliary box, independent suspension.
£400–1,500 *MVT*
A total of 55,000 were built. From 1958 the engine output was increased to 44bhp with a 974cc engine.

AUTOMOBILE ART

Gamy, The Splitdorf Magneto – Grand Prix of America 1910, hand-coloured lithograph depicting a chain-driven racing Mercedes, published by Mabileau et Cie, dated '1910', 18 x 36in (45 x 91cm).
£700–750 *C*

Bryan de Grineau, Le Mans 1928, depicting the winning 4½-litre Bentley driven by Barnato and Rubin, watercolour on paper with wash and charcoal heightened with white, signed, mounted, framed and glazed, 14 x 20½in (36 x 52cm).
£2,650–2,850 *S*

Barnato and Rubin had completed 1,658.6 miles at an average speed of 69.108mph at the end of the 24 hours.

Tony Upson, mural of a Bugatti Type 35, acrylic on board, framed, 48 x 96in (122 x 244cm).
£375–425 *BKS*

Roy Nockolds, Bugatti Type 57CS Atlantic Coupé in the Alps, hand-coloured silkscreen print with inscribed title, 18 x 22in (45 x 56cm).
£115–130 *S*

Roy Nockolds, (1911–80), W. O. Bentley driving his 8-litre in the South of France, a view through the windscreen, hand-painted silkscreen print, proof with inscribed title, 18 x 26½in (45 x 67cm).
£140–160 *S*

Tony Upson, mural of a Maserati at speed, acrylic on board, framed, 48 x 96in (122 x 244cm).
£400–440 *BKS*

Tony Upson, mural of a Bentley at Le Mans, acrylic on board, framed, 48 x 96in (122 x 244cm).
£615–635 *BKS*

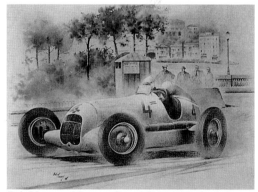

Bob Murray, Monaco Grand Prix 1935, depicting Rudolf Caracciola's winning Mercedes-Benz W25, watercolour and airbrush, signed, mounted, framed and glazed, 17 x 20in (43 x 51cm).
£230–260 *C*

Tony Upson, Ferrari 250GTO, acrylic on board, 48 x 96in (122 x 244cm).
£350–380 *COYS*

Tony Upson, Ferrari 250LM, acrylic on board, 48 x 96in (122 x 244cm).
£700–750 *COYS*

Roy Nockolds, Raymond Mays' ERA R4D at Shelsley Walsh, 1947, hand-painted, silkscreen print with inscribed title, 22 x 30in (56 x 76cm).
£115–130 *S*

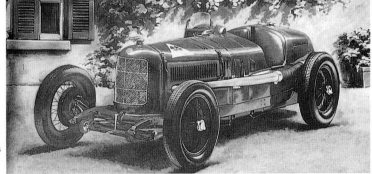

r. Tony Upson, mural of an Alfa Romeo, No. 26, acrylic on board, framed, 48 x 96in (122 x 244cm).
£630–660 *BKS*

Tony Upson, mural of a Birkin Bentley in the pits, acrylic on board, framed, 48 x 96in (122 x 244cm).
£640–680 *BKS*

r. Michael Wright, 1939 Gross Glockener, depicting H. P. Müller in the 6-litre V16 Auto Union, mixed media, signed and inscribed, mounted, framed and glazed, 29½ x 27½in (75 x 70cm).
£1,800–2,200 *BKS*

Posters

Crescent Bicycles, lithographic poster printed in Amsterdam c1905, good general condition, crease damage and some foxing, framed, glazed, 42 x 28in (106 x 71cm).
£350–380 *BKS*

Seneca, Coppa Della Perucina, lithographic poster, printed signature, linen-backed, c1920, 56 x 39¼in (142 x 100cm).
£3,000–3,300 *S*

Le Mans, Scorciatoia per L'inferno, an original film poster, large format, c1970.
£175–225 *C*

AUTOMOBILIA

l. A set of 6 porcelain cups and saucers, each featuring a picture of a Mercedes-Benz car, saucer 4¼in (10.7cm) diam.
£45–60 *LF*

A Michelin 20th Road Race plate, 1989, 17in (43cm) diam.
£10–12 *Tar*

A bowl, depicting a lady with a steering wheel, 9¼in (23.5cm) diam.
£85–95 *PC*

A Vauxhall presentation ashtray, 1932, 7in (17.8cm) diam.
£450–500 *PC*

A Ballot cigarette case, c1920.
£300–325 *PC*

A silver motor car interior vase, hallmarked, 1915.
£140–160 *BC*

A Mille Miglia competitor's commemorative printed cotton scarf, mounted, framed and glazed, 1953.
£750–800 *C*

r. The Thirst Extinguisher, a silver-plated novelty cocktail shaker by Asprey's, in the form of a fire extinguisher with decorative bayonet cap, the revolving base giving the recipes for 8 cocktails, 1932, 15in (38cm) high.
£1,900–2,300 *BKS*

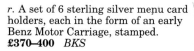

A foot warmer, excellent condition, c1920.
£30–40 *SW*

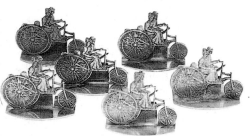

r. A set of 6 sterling silver menu card holders, each in the form of an early Benz Motor Carriage, stamped.
£370–400 *BKS*

Badges, Trophies & Rally Plates

A silver dollar, presented to G. Eyston and carried by him when he broke the land speed record at 357.5mph, on 16 September 1938.
£500–600 *PC*

A Club Mille Miglia driver's gold lapel badge, inscribed with name on reverse.
£550–600 *BC*

A collection of 29 motoring badges, including DDAC, British Field Sports Society, Royal Ocean Racing Club, AA and RAC, mounted on a badge bar and Mercedes-Benz radiator grille, with enamel badge and three-pointed star mascot, 30in (76cm) high overall.
£630–680 *S*

top. An RAC West Holland Tulpen Rallye plate, 1960, 12in (30.5cm) wide.
£50–60
bottom. A Rallye Monte-Carlo plate, 1964, 18in (45.7cm) wide.
£180–200 *LE*

r. An Eastbourne Rally award, on original marble base, and a folder of documents relating to the recipient, c1935.
£185–200 *BKS*

Two silver Brooklands trophies, 1933, 9½in (24cm) high.
£400–500 each *LE*

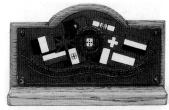

A Lisbon Rally finisher's award, 1953, 5½in (14cm) wide.
£100–120 *LE*

Components

A Heuer Super Autavia chronograph and stopwatch rally timer, the black dial with hours and minutes, centre seconds and permanent seconds dial, movable hour bezel, in a chromium case.
£1,000–1,200 *BKS*

> **Miller's is a price GUIDE not a price LIST**

A polished brass headlamp, with original swivel ball socket mounting and glass with Stephen Grebel etching, rear handle, c1911–25.
£475–525 *BKS*

r. A pair of Lucas R100L electric headlamps, with ribbed reflectors, RR bulb bars, the pillar-mounted chromed cases worn, 1937–39, lens 10¾in (27.5cm) diam.
£460–500 *S*

A pair of French brass oil sidelamps, by Bleriot, each with side flange mount, 'signed' doors, chimneys and reservoirs with seasoned cracking, one lens cracked, c1910, 15¼in (39cm) high.
£270–320 *S*

r. A pair of Lucas QK596 headlamps, designed for Jaguar SS100 cars, with mesh stone guards, restored, perfect condition, 1936–39.
£1,100–1,400 *BKS*

A pair of Lucas self-generating acetylene Lorilite commercial vehicle headlamps, No. CM54, each brass body with cross-body generator, mirror reflector and concave lens, worn, one lacking water reservoir cap, c1908, lenses 7in (17.5cm) diam.
£420–450 *S*

A pillar-mounted spotlamp, 16in (40.5cm) long.
£60–75 *DRJ*

l. & r. A pair of Lucidus headlamps, 11in (28cm) diam.
£575–625
centre. A small Lucidus spotlamp, 9in (23cm) diam.
£150–180 *DRJ*

r. A Halda Speedpilot, 5½in (14cm) wide.
£300–350 *DRJ*

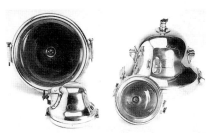

A pair of CAV Model F bell-shaped headlamps, and a pair of Model GS sidelamps, with bevel-edged front glass, nickel-silver reflectors, good condition, c1913.
£440–500 *BKS*

A pair of Lucas 640 series polished brass oil sidelamps, No. 644, correct front condenser lenses, star-cut square side glasses, quick-release oil fonts, opening rims, removable tops, c1910.
£780–830 *BKS*

An ammeter, by Royce Ltd, Manchester, mounted, 12in (30.5cm) high.
£90–100 *CGC*

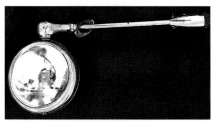

l. A Lamborghini museum display engine, No. 54255, 4 litre, V12, all alloy, double overhead camshafts, 6 Weber 40DCOE carburettors, no internals, c1972, on a stand.
£4,800–5,300 *C*

Mascots

A French pewter mascot, Boubou, by M. Le Verrier, illuminated when fitted, good condition, base of lantern needs replacing, signed, 1925, 5¾in (14.5cm) high.
£375–425 *PC*

A Franklin nickel-plated lion mascot, by Sterling Bronze Co, marked '1924 design G. Derujinsky', and 'Aura Vincit' (Air Conquers), very good condition, 1925–28, 4¼in (10.8cm) high.
£140–160 *PC*

A French silvered-bronze horse's head mascot, by E. Bregeon, signed, c1920, 3¾in (9.5cm) high, on a wooden display base.
£2,000–2,300 *S*

A French mascot, in the form of a monkey with a cooking pot, by M. Le Verrier, lid missing, good condition, c1920, 5½in (14cm) high.
£375–400 *PC*

A horse and jockey mascot, 4in (10cm) high.
£100–125 *CARS*

An Art Deco style leaping horse mascot, by Brau, retailed by Hermès in Paris, original design number 17608, signed, 1925, 4in (10cm) high.
£1,500–2,000 *BKS*

A French nickel-plated bronze Hispano-Suiza Cigogne mascot, by Frederick Bazin, signed, base stamped 'HS525', mounted on a wooden plinth, c1920, 8in (20.7cm) long.
£1,450–1,750 *S*

The Hispano-Suiza mascot is probably the most copied mascot ever produced. The design was originally used by WWI ace, Georges Guynemer, on his aircraft.

A silvered-bronze butterfly mascot, signed 'E. Famin', wingspan 6¼in (16cm).
£460–500 *BKS*

A glass mascot, in the form of a mouse, by Ernest Sabino, signed and inscribed, excellent condition, c1930.
£1,150–1,400 *BKS*

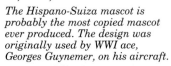

l. A chrome-plated bronze Bentley winged 'B' mascot, pre-1931, 7in (18cm) wide, mounted on a display base.
£750–850 *S*

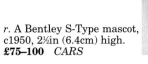

r. A Bentley S-Type mascot, c1950, 2½in (6.4cm) high.
£75–100 *CARS*

A Pontiac Chieftain mascot, chrome finish, c1950, 20in (50.8cm) long.
£200–225 PC

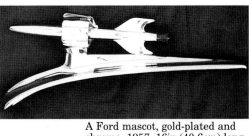

A Ford mascot, gold-plated and chrome, 1957, 16in (40.6cm) long, in original box.
£200–235 PC

A nickel-bronze golfing caddy mascot, with original flag, marked with design number to rear of base, c1910.
£700–800 BKS

A French footballer mascot, signed 'Gallot', c1915.
£425–450 BKS

A Lalique clear and frosted glass dragonfly mascot, marked 'R. Lalique' and etched on side of base, mounted on metal and turned black wooden display mount, c1930.
£550–600 BKS

An American silver-plated bronze mascot, entitled 'Speed', designed by Harriet Frishmuth, by Gorham Co, stamped with founder's mark, c1922, 12in (30.5cm) wide.
£6,300–7,000 C

This is one of only 2 designs for car mascots commissioned by Gorham in the 1920s by this well-known American sculptor.

A Speed Nymph mascot, 7½in (19cm) high.
£255–285 DRJ

A French silver-plated bronze St Christopher mascot, signed 'G. Poitvin', 1920s, 7½in (19cm) high.
£400–450 PC

A nickeled-bronze mascot, signed 'Edit. Granet', depicting a youth riding a winged phoenix, mounted on a radiator cap, c1920.
£1,700–2,000 BKS

A Brooklands Aero Club mascot, by Spencer, 6in (15cm) high.
£500–600 DRJ

l. A brass lifeboatman mascot, c1930.
£80–90
r. A Civil Service mascot, on a Bullnose Morris radiator cap, c1930.
£60–65 GAZE

A bronze mascot, in the form of an AA patrol-man, on marble plinth, 11in (27.9cm) high.
£110–120 *LF*

Mascot History

Lord Montagu's father is credited as being the first to commission a car mascot when, in 1899, he attached a St Christopher to his Daimler. Early manufacturers' and accessory mascots proliferated in a variety of themes, including Rolls-Royce's famous Spirit of Ecstasy mascot in 1911. Lalique glass mascots were produced from 1925 in over thirty designs. Mascots declined from the 1950s onwards as their pedestrian-piercing properties became a safety issue.

A frog dragging a snail mascot by Luchet, finely detailed, nickel-bronze, signed, mounted on early French radiator cap, turned wooden plinth.
£1,900–2,300 *BKS*

This mascot won the second prize in the 1923 Paris Concours.

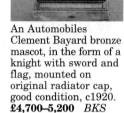

An Automobiles Clement Bayard bronze mascot, in the form of a knight with sword and flag, mounted on original radiator cap, good condition, c1920.
£4,700–5,200 *BKS*

Models

A model of a 1934 Lagonda M45, by Gerald Wingrove, signed, 1:20 scale, 1971, 8¾in (22cm) long.
£2,500–3,000 *S*

This is a model of the 1935 Le Mans winning car, and is the third of three built by Wingrove. The other two were presented to the owner of the actual car and the National Motor Museum.

A model of a Jaguar D-Type, by Rex Hays, with alloy wheels, Dunlop tyres, riveted panelwork, cockpit detail, leather seat and trim, finished in British Racing Green, mounted on a polished wooden base with bronze plaque and inscription.
£4,000–5,000 *C*

A silver model of a Porsche 356 coupé inscribed '50th Birthday – F. Porsche', with facsimile signature of Ferdinand Porsche.
£8,650–9,650 *C*

This model was presented to Dennis Drewitt on his 50th birthday by the directors of Porsche UK, in recognition of the assistance given by him to the Porsche racing department as racing fuels expert.

Don't Forget!

If in doubt please refer to the 'How to Use' section at the beginning of this book.

A bronze model of a Ferrari, by F. Reggiani, with plaque to the wooden base inscribed 'Evoluzione 50 years Scuderia Ferrari – Modena 30-11-1979'.
£2,250–2,500 *C*

The full-size version of this sculpture has been on display in Modena, Italy. It symbolises the evolution of Ferrari design.

A glass paperweight, depicting a Mercedes-Benz saloon, 1970s, 6½in (16.5cm) wide.
£10–15 *CARS*

A model of a 4½ litre Talbot-Lago GS in 1950 Le Mans specification, 16in (40cm) long.
£4,400–5,400 *C*

Petrol Pumps

A Shell Super National petrol pump, c1960, 89in (226cm) high.
£325–375 *PC*

A BP petrol pump, non-original globe, c1960, 77in (195.5cm) high.
£400–450 *PC*

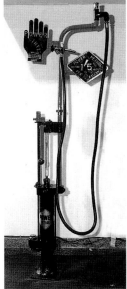

A Bowser hand-operated petrol pump, painted in Pratts colours, with alloy brand and price plates.
£250–300 *CGC*

A Wayne hand-operated petrol pump, painted in Shell colours, with alloy brand and price plates.
£250–300 *CGC*

An Avery Hardoll electric petrol pump, with Esso globe, c1960.
£300–400 *CRC*

l. A Burmah petrol pump, c1970, 74in (188cm) high.
£350–400 *PC*

r. An Anglo American oil cabinet, containing 2 hand-cranked oil pumps with glass cylinders, a large tin plate inside listing grade of oil for various cars and trucks, rebuilt and repainted with Pratts livery, 1920, 60in (152cm) high.
£400–500 *TPS*

Globes

A Fleetline glass petrol pump globe, c1960, 13in (33cm) high.
£150–175 *MSMP*

An International Petroleum Services glass petrol pump globe, c1950.
£225–275 *MSMP*

r. An Esso glass petrol pump globe, c1960, 17in (43cm) high.
£150–185 *MSMP*

A Shell glass petrol pump globe, lettered in red, dated '5.66', 17⅝in (45cm) high.
£130–150 *S*

A Mobilgas glass petrol pump globe, by Webb's Crystal, c1950, 16in (40.5cm) high.
£400–450 *MSMP*

r. An Empire Regent Spirit glass petrol pump globe, c1930, 17in (43cm) high.
£400–500 *MSMP*

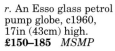

Photographs

A photograph of Malcolm
Campbell, signed, c1930.
£45–50 *PMB*

Picnic Sets, Vanity
Cases & Travel Goods

A James Dixon & Sons
travelling set, shaped leather
case, initialled 'E.R.G.',
fitted with plated metal flask
and sandwich box, both
bearing maker's mark,
5¼in (13cm) high, c1905.
£175–200 *S*

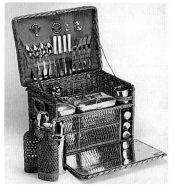

A Finnigans six-person fold-
fronted wicker picnic set,
with 3 Autotherm drinks flasks,
sandwich and storage boxes,
plates, preserve jars, foul
weather protective canvas,
original lock and keys,
original condition, c1905.
£1,700–2,000 *BKS*

A photograph of Stirling Moss
in his Mercedes W196, by George
Monkhouse, signed and titled
'Stirling Moss winner of the
British Grand Prix at Aintree
1955 for Mercedes-Benz', signed
dedication to Rivers Fletcher,
'To Rivers may I suggest that you
share this one with me! Stirling
23.4.57', mounted, framed and
glazed, 15¼ x 19¾in (40 x 50cm).
£460–520 *S*

A Finnigans four-person suitcase
picnic set, the fitted interior with
kettle and burner, sandwich box
with ceramic base, ceramic
preserve jar, stacking china
cups and saucers, enamel plates
in the lid, ceramic condiment
jars in original glass holders
inside wicker-covered stacking
glasses, pre-1914.
£700–800 *BKS*

A blue crocodile suitcase,
with brass catches and locks,
matching blue leather handle,
distressed silk-lined interior,
worn blue canvas cover, c1910,
22in (56cm) wide.
£300–350 *S*

l. An Asprey's lady's tan leather
overnight vanity case, the silk-
lined interior with 3 silver-topped
bottles and jars, hallmarked
London 1938, silver-gilt mounted
hair and clothes brushes and
comb, hand mirror, some
discolouration, 13¾in (35cm) wide.
£520–570 *S*

A photograph of Alfred
Neubauer, by Elisabeth Junek,
signed by her and Neubauer,
12 x 9½in (30 x 24cm).
£550–600 *C*

A Brexton four-person picnic
set, 1950.
£45–60 *PA*

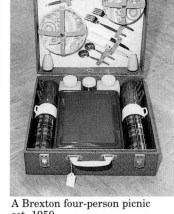

A Cartier lady's tan pigskin
overnight vanity case, the lid
with a mirror, the honey-coloured
leather interior with suede
detailing, the vanity set with
tortoiseshell accessories marked
with monogram 'E' surmounted
by a ducal coronet, case initialled
'E.S.', gilded-effect locks and
catches, some stitching worn,
leather scratched, c1927,
34in (86.5cm) wide.
£1,600–2,000 *S*

*This case was supplied by Cartier
in December 1938 to the Duke
and Duchess of Sutherland as
a special commission.*

Enamel Signs

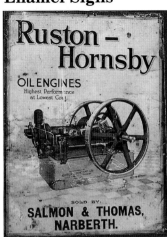

A printed tin Rushton Hornsby sign, poor condition, c1900, 24 x 18in (61 x 45.5cm).
£150–175 *MSMP*

An enamel Michelin advertising sign, 8in (20.5cm) diam.
£20–25 *CGC*

A tin Oldham Batteries sign, 12 x 18in (30.5 x 45.5cm).
£5–10 *LF*

A tin Redex advertising sign, 25 x 18in (63.5 x 45.5cm).
£30–35 *LF*

A single-sided enamel AA combined location and warning sign, good condition, c1905, 36in (91.5cm) diam.
£375–425 *MSMP*

An enamel Morris Trucks sign, c1920, 22 x 16in (56 x 40.5cm).
£300–350 *HOLL*

l. An enamel Castrol sign, 10 x 7½in (25.5 x 19cm).
£17–20 *CGC*

An enamel Shell Lubricating Oils sign, c1920, 48 x 36in (122 x 91.5cm).
£200–250 *JUN*

A glass Bianchi Cars showroom advertising sign, gold on black, central badge in gold, red and blue, minor flaking to edges, c1930, 24in (61cm) wide.
£1,700–2,000 *S*

Founded in 1899, Bianchi began by producing a single-cylinder voiturette. By 1914, a powerful 8-litre chain-driven sports car was available, but they refrained from entering the sporting arena, preferring to earn a reputation as producers of heavily-built, long-lasting family cars. This well-earned reputation lasted until production ceased in 1938.

Watches & Clocks

An 8-day clock, by O. S. Speedometer Co Ltd, 3½in (8.9cm) diam.
£60–65 *DRJ*

A Jaeger aluminium cased chronograph, with brushed silver dial, centre seconds and Total Minutes window, 8-day LeCoultre movement appears sound, dual wind and setting crowns intact and operable, good condition, 3in (7.6cm) diam.
£1,400–1,600 *BKS*

MOTOR RACING MEMORABILIA
Prints, Paintings & Original Artwork

Tony Upson, Ferrari, depicting a racing car and driver, acrylic on board, 48 x 96in (122 x 244cm).
£200–300 *BKS*

Roy Nockolds, Monaco Grand Prix 1937, hand-coloured print with inscribed title, 24 x 33in (61 x 84cm).
£110–130 *S*

The Mercedes of von Brauchitsch and Caracciola are shown rounding Station Hairpin on their way to a 1-2 victory.

l. Nicholas Watts, Paris-Dakar 1986, limited-edition print, signed by René Metge, 24¾ x 33in (63 x 84cm).
£70–75 *MPG*

The winning Porsche 959 of Metge and Lemoyne is shown in full flight during the Paris-Dakar event of 1986.

B. A. Willis, Ayrton Senna 1988 World Champion, artist's proof of a print, signed by Senna, 15¾ x 11¾in (40 x 30cm).
£630–700 *S*

l. Nicholas Watts, Mille Miglia 1951, limited-edition print, signed by Gigi Villoresi, 24¾ x 33in (63 x 84cm).
£90–95 *MPG*

This print depicts Gigi Villoresi in his damaged Ferrari 340 America heading for victory in the 1951 Mille Miglia.

Books

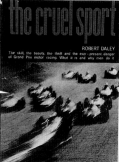

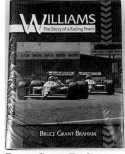

Bruce Grant-Braham, *Williams – The Story of a Racing Team*, 1990.
£20–25 *GPCC*

Robert Daley, *The Cruel Sport*, 1963.
£45–55 *GPCC*

r. S. C. H. Davis, *Atalanta – Women as Racing Drivers*, c1950.
£18–22 *PMB*

L. J. K. Setright, *The Grand Prix Car 1954/1966*, 1968.
£100–120 *PMB*

r. Peter Roberts, *The Shell Book of Epic Motor Races*, 1964.
£15–20 *GPCC*

Overalls

A set of Sparco K-Mart mechanic's overalls, signed by Nigel Mansell.
£450–550 *BKS*

A race suit worn by Martin Brundle, with his name and British flag embroidered on the belt, signed by Brundle.
£1,275–1,425 *BKS*

A Nomex Sparco/Benetton race suit worn by Michael Schumacher during the 1993 season, driver's name embroidered on the belt, good general condition.
£2,000–2,500 *BKS*

A TWR fire crew suit, 1989.
£150–200 *GPT*

l. A white Bell Helmets cap, signed by Gilles Villeneuve and 8 other personalities from the 1976 Players' Formula Atlantic Championship, mounted in display case.
£175–225 *BKS*

A set of racing overalls used by Derek Warwick while driving for Silk Cut Jaguar during 1986-87, certificate of authenticity from TWR Jaguar.
£230–280 *S*

A Jordan waterproof top, 1996.
£75–95 *GPT*

A white linen racing helmet and goggles worn by Paul Greifzu during the 1930s, with a signed photograph of the driver and a copy of his biography by Herbert Beyer, dated 1954.
£300–350 *BKS*

Components

r. A Les Leston steering wheel for a Mini Cooper, light alloy with pierced spokes, leather-covered rim, wreath and chequered flag boss, signed by Les Leston.
£90–100 *CARS*

A selection of Formula 1 Benetton wheel nuts, 3¼in (8.3cm) diam.
£10–20 each *GPT*

Two Lotus Honda 99T rear wing flaps from Ayrton Senna's 1987 Detroit Grand Prix race winning car, signed 'Ayrton Senna Detroit 87'.
£1,275–1,425 *BKS*

GLOSSARY

We have attempted to define some of the terms that you will come across in this book. If there are any terms or technicalities you would like explained or you feel should be included in future please let us know.

All-weather: A term used to describe a vehicle with a more sophisticated folding hood than the normal Cape hood fitted to a touring vehicle. The sides were fitted with metal frames and transparent material, in some cases glass.

Barchetta: Italian for 'little boat', an all-enveloping open sports bodywork.

Berline: Originally a 4 wheeler with hooded seat behind, more recently French usage for English term saloon (Berlina in Italian).

Boost: The amount of pressure applied by a supercharger or turbocharger.

Boxer: Engine configuration with horizontally opposed cylinders.

Brake Horsepower – bhp: This is the horse power of the combustion engine measured at the engine flywheel (See Horsepower).

Brake: A term dating from the days of horse drawn vehicles. Originally the seating was fore and aft, with the passengers facing inwards.

Cabriolet: The term Cabriolet applies to a vehicle with a hood which can be closed, folded half way, or folded right back. The Cabriolet can be distinguished from the Landaulette as the front of the hood reaches the top of the windscreen whereas the Landaulette only covers the rear quarter of the car.

Chain drive: A transmission system in which the wheels are attached to a sprocket, driven by a chain from an engine powered sprocket usually on the output side of a gearbox.

Chassis: A framework to which the car body, engine, gearbox, and axles are attached.

Chummy: An open top 2 door body style usually with 2 front seats and one at the rear.

Cloverleaf: A 3 seater open body style usually with a single door, 2 seats in the front and one at the rear.

Concours: *Concours d'Elegance* is a competition of cars of aesthetic qualities. *Concours d'Etat* is a competition of condition. Concours has become a byword for a vehicle in excellent condition.

Cone Clutch: One in which both driving and driven faces form a cone.

Connollising: Leather treatment produced by British firm Connolly to rejuvenate and restore suppleness to old and dry leather.

Convertible: A general term (post-war) for any car with a soft top.

Continental: This is a car specifically designed for high speed touring, usually on the Continent. Rolls-Royce and Bentley almost exclusively used this term during the 1930s and post-WWII.

Coupé: In the early Vintage and Edwardian period, it was only applied to what is now termed a Half Limousine or Doctor's Coupé which was a 2 door, 2 seater. The term is now usually prefixed by Drophead or Fixed Head.

Cubic Capacity: The volume of an engine obtained by multiplying the bore and the stroke.

De Ville: Almost all early coachwork had an exposed area for the driver to be in direct control of his horses, and so the motor car chauffeur was believed to be able to control the vehicle more easily if he was open to the elements. As the term only refers to part of the style of the car, i.e. the front, it is invariably used in connection with the words Coupé and Sedanca.

Dickey Seat: A passenger seat, usually for 2 people contained in the boot of the car without a folding hood (the boot lid forms the backrest). Known in America as a rumble seat.

Doctor's Coupé: A fixed or folding head coupé without a dickey seat and the passenger seat slightly staggered back from the driver's to accommodate the famous black bag.

Dog Cart: A horsedrawn dog cart was originally used to transport beaters and their dogs to a shoot (the dogs were contained in louvred boxes under the seats, the louvres were kept for decoration long after the dogs had gone).

Dos-à-dos: Literally back-to-back, i.e. the passenger seating arrangement.

Double duck: double layered fabric used in construction of soft tops.

Drophead Coupé: Originally a 2 door 2 seater with a folding roof, see Roadster.

Dry Sump: A method of lubricating engines, usually with 2 oil pumps, one of which removes oil from the sump to a reservoir away from the engine block.

Engine: Engine sizes are given in cubic centimetres (cc) in Europe and cubic inches (cu in) in the USA. 1 cubic inch equals 16.38cc (1 litre = 61.02cu in).

Fender: American usage for the English word wing.

Fixed Head Coupé: FHC, a coupé with a solid fixed roof.

Golfer's Coupé: Usually an open 2 seater with a square-doored locker behind the driver's seat to accommodate golf clubs.

Hansom: As with the famous horse drawn cab, an enclosed 2 seater with the driver out in the elements either behind or in front.

Homologation: To qualify for entry into some race series rules can require that a minimum number of road-going production versions of the race car are built. These are generally known as 'homologation specials'.

Hood: American usage for English term bonnet. English usage for a retracting soft top.

Horsepower: The unit of measurement of engine power. One horsepower represents the energy expended in raising 33,000lb by one foot in 60 seconds.

Landau: An open carriage with a folding hood at each end which would meet in the middle when erected.

Laudaulette: Also Landaulet, a horsedrawn Landaulette carried 2 people and was built much like a coupé. A Landau was a town carriage for 4 people. The full Landau was rarely built on a motor car chassis because the front folding hood took up so much room between the driver's seat and the rear compartment. The roof line of a Landaulette has always been angular, in contrast to the Cabriolet and the folding hood, and very often made of patent leather. A true Landaulette only opens over the rear compartment and not over the front seat at all.

Limousine: French in origin, always used to describe a closed car equipped with occasional seats and always having a division between the rear and driver's compartments. Suffixes and prefixes are often inappropriately used with the term Limousine and should be avoided.

Monobloc engine: An engine with all cylinders cast in a single block.

Monocoque: A type of construction of car bodies without a chassis as such, the strength being in the stressed panels. Most modern mass-produced cars are built this way.

Monoposto: Single seater (Italian).

Nitrided: Hardening of engine components, particularly crankshafts, to stand up to the stresses of racing.

OHC: Overhead camshaft, either single (SOHC) or double (DOHC).

OHV: Overhead valve engine.

Phæton: A term dating back to the the days of horsedrawn vehicles for an open body, sometimes with a Dickey or Rumble Seat for the groom at the rear. It was an owner/driver carriage and designed to be pulled by 4 horses. A term often misused during the Veteran period but remains in common use, particularly in the United States.

Post Vintage Thoroughbred (PVT): A British term drawn up by the Vintage Sports Car Club (VSCC) for selected models made in the vintage tradition between 1931 and 1942.

Roadster: A 2 seater sports car. The hood should be able to be removed totally rather than folded down as a drophead coupé.

Roi des Belges: A luxurious open touring car with elaborately contoured seat backs, named after King Leopold II of Belgium. The term is sometimes wrongly used for general touring cars.

Rotary engine: An engine in which the cylinder banks revolve around the crank, for example the Wankel engine with its rotating piston.

Rpm: Engine revolutions per minute.

Rumble Seat: A folding seat for 2 passengers, used to increase the carrying capacity of a standard 2 passenger car.

Runabout: A low powered light open 2 seater from the 1900s.

Saloon: A 2 or 4 door car with 4 or more seats and a fixed roof.

Sedan: See Saloon.

Sedanca de Ville: A limousine body with the driving compartment covered with a folding or sliding roof section, known in America as a Town Car.

Sociable: A cycle car term meaning that the passenger and driver sat side-by-side.

Spider/Spyder: An open 2 seater sports car, sometimes a 2+2 (2 small seats behind the 2 front seats).
Spider is generally the Italian usage, and Spyder the German spelling.

Stanhope: A term from the days of horsedrawn vehicles for a single seat 2 wheel carriage with a hood. Later, a 4 wheeled 2 seater, sometimes with an underfloor engine.

Station Wagon: See Brake.

Stroke: The distance a piston moves up-and-down within the cylinder. This distance is always measured in millimetres.

Supercharger: A device for forcing fuel/air into the cylinder for extra power.

Superleggera: Italian for 'super lightweight' method of construction devised by Touring of Milan, whereby a lightweight aluminium skin was attached to a framework of tubes to produce a light yet strong structure. One of the best known proponents of this method was Aston Martin who employed Superleggera construction in some of their DB series cars.

Surrey: An early 20thC open 4 seater with a fringed canopy. A term from the days of horse drawn vehicles.

Tandem: A cycle car term, the passengers sat in tandem, with the driver at the front or at the rear.

Targa: A coupé with a removable centre roof section.

Tonneau: A rear entrance tonneau is a 4 seater with access through a centrally placed door at the rear. A detachable tonneau meant that the rear seats could be removed to make a 2 seater. Tonneau nowadays usually means a waterproof cover over an open car used when the roof is detached.

Torpedo: An open tourer with an unbroken line from the bonnet to the rear of the body.

Tourer: An open 4 or 5 seater with 3 or 4 doors, folding hood, with or without sidescreens, generally replaced the term torpedo, with seats flush with the body sides. This body design began in about 1910, but by 1920 the word tourer was used instead – except in France, where 'torpédo' continued until the 1930s.

Unitary Construction: Vehicle with integral body and chassis – the chassis is no longer a separate item. See monocoque.

Veteran: All vehicles manufactured before 31st December 1918, only cars built before 31st March 1904 are eligible for the London to Brighton Commemorative Run.

Victoria: Generally an American term for a 2 or 4 seater with a very large folding hood. If a 4 seater, the hood would only cover the rear seats.

Vintage: Any vehicles manufactured between the end of the veteran period and 31st December 1930. See Post Vintage Thoroughbred.

Vis-à-Vis: Face-to-face, an open car where one or 2 passengers sit opposite each other.

Voiturette: A French term meaning a very light car, originally used by Léon Bollée.

Wagonette: A large car for 6 or more passengers, in which the rear seats faced each other. Entrance was at the rear, and the vehicles were usually open.

Waxoyled: Treatment of underside of car with Waxoyl, a proprietary oil and wax spray that protects against moisture and rust.

Weyman: A system of construction employing Rexine fabric panels over a Kapok filling to prevent noise and provide insulation.

Wheelbase: The distance between the centres of the front and rear wheels.

DIRECTORY OF CAR CLUBS

If you would like your Club to be included in next year's directory, or have a change of address or telephone number, please inform us by 31 May 1999. Entries will be repeated unless we are requested otherwise.

105E Anglia Owners Club Middlesex Group, 9 Evelyn Avenue, Ruislip, Middlesex HA4 8AR Tel: 01895 672251

1100 Club, Paul Vincent, 32 Medgbury Road, Swindon, Wiltshire SN1 2AS

2CVGB Deux Chevaux Club of GB, PO Box 602 Crick, Northampton, Northamptonshire NN6 7UW

750 Motor Club Ltd, Courthouse, St Winifreds Road, Biggin Hill, Kent TN16 3H Tel: 01959 575812

AC Owners Club, R A Morpeth, The Clovers, Mursley, Buckinghamshire MK17 0RT

A40 Farina Club, Membership Secretary, 2 Ivy Cottages, Fullers Vale, Headley Down, Bordon, Hants GU35 8NR

ABC Owners Club, D. A. Hales, The Hedgerows, Sutton St Nicholas, Hereford HR1 3BU Tel: 01432 880726

Alexis Racing and Trials Car Register, Duncan Rabagliati, 4 Wool Road, Wimbledon, London SW20 0HW

Alfa Romeo 1900 Register, Peter Marshall, Mariners, Courtlands Avenue, Esher, Surrey KT10 9HZ

Alfa Romeo Owners Club, Michael Lindsay, 97 High Street, Linton, Cambridgeshire CB1 6JT

Alfa Romeo Section (VSCC Ltd), Allan & Angela Cherrett, Old Forge, Quarr, Nr Gillingham, Dorset SP8 5PA

Allard Owners Club, Miss P Hulse, 1 Dalmeny Avenue, Tufnell Park, London N7

Alvis Owners Club, 1 Forge Cottages, Bayham Road, Little Bayham, Lamberhurst, Kent TN3 8BB

Alvis Register, Mr J. Willis, The Vinery, Wanborough Manor, Nr Guildford, Surrey GU3 2JR Tel: 01483 810308

American Auto Club UK, 11 Wych Elm, Colchester, Essex CO2 8PR Tel: 01206 564404

Amilcar Salmson Register, RAF King, Apple House, Wildmoor Lane, Sherfield on Lodden, Hampshire RG27 0HA

Armstrong Siddeley Owners Club Ltd, Peter Sheppard, 57 Berberry Close, Bourneville, Birmingham, West Midlands B30 1TB

Assoc of British Volkswagen Clubs, Dept PC, 66 Pinewood Green, Iver Heath, Buckinghamshire SL0 0QH

Association of Healey Owners, Don Griffiths, The White House, Hill Pound, Swanmore, Hampshire SO32 2PS Tel: 01489 895813

Association of Old Vehicle Clubs in Northern Ireland Ltd, Secretary Trevor Mitchell, 38 Ballymaconnell Road, Bangor, Co. Down, Northern Ireland BT20 5PS Tel: 01247 467886

Association of Singer Car Owners, Anne Page, 39 Oakfield, Rickmansworth, Hertfordshire WO3 2LR Tel: 01923 778575

Aston Martin Owners Club Ltd, Jim Whyman, AMOC Ltd, 1A High Street, Sutton Nr Ely, Cambridgeshire CB6 2RB Tel: 01353 777353

Atlas Register, 38 Ridgeway, Southwell, Nottinghamshire NG25 0DJ

Austin Atlantic Owners Club, 124, Holbrook Road, Stratford, London E15 3DZ Tel: 0181 534 2682 (home) 0171 833 7907 (work)

Austin Big 7 Register, R E Taylor, 101 Derby Road, Chellaston, Derbyshire DE73 1SB

Austin Cambridge/Westminster Car Club, Mr J Curtis, 4 Russell Close, East Budleigh, Budleigh Salterton, Devon EX 9 7EH Tel: 01395 446210

Austin Eight Register, Ian Pinniger, 3 La Grange Martin, St Martin, Jersey, Channel Islands JE3 6JB

Austin Gipsy Register 1958-1968, Mike Gilbert, 24 Green Close, Rixon, Sturminster Newton, Dorset DT10 1BJ

Austin Healey Club, 47 George Crescent, Muswell Hill, London N10 1AL Tel: 0181 444 0156

Austin Healey Club, Mike Ward, Midland Centre, 9 Stag Walk, Sutton Coldfield, West Midlands B76 1JZ Tel: 0121 382 3223

Austin J40 Car Club, BG Swann, 19 Lavender Avenue, Coudon, Coventry CV6 1DA

Austin Maxi Club, Mrs C J Jackson, 27 Queen Street, Bardney, Lincolnshire LN3 5XF

Austin Seven Mulliner Register, Mike Tebbett, Little Wyche, Walwyn Road, Upper Colwall, Nr Malvern, Worcestershire WR13 6PL

Austin Seven Owners Club (London), Mr and Mrs Simpkins, 5 Brook Cottages, Riding Lane, Hildenborough, Kent TN11 9QL

Austin Seven Sports Register, C. J. Taylor, 222 Prescot Road, Aughton, Ormskirk, Lancashire L39 5AQ

Austin Seven Van Register 1923-29, N. B. Baldry, 32 Wentworth Crescent, Maidenhead, Berkshire SL6 4RW

Austin Sheerline & Princess Club, Ian Coombes 44 Vermeer Crescent, Shoeburyness, Essex S53 9TJ

Austin Swallow Register, G. L. Walker, School House, Back Way, Great Haseley, Oxfordshire OX44 7JP

Austin Ten Drivers Club Ltd, Mrs Patricia East, Brambledene, 53 Oxted Green, Milford, Godalming, Surrey GU8 5DD

Battery Vehicle Society, Keith Roberts, 29 Ambergate Drive, North Pentwyn, Cardiff, Wales CF2 7AX

Bean Car Club, G Harris, Villa Rosa, Templewood Lane, Farnham Common, Buckinghamshire SL2 3H

Bentley Drivers Club, 16 Chearsley Road, Long Crendon, Aylesbury, Buckinghamshire HP18 9AW

Berkeley Enthusiasts Club, Paul Fitness, 9 Hellards Road, Stevenage, Hertfordshire SG1 3PN Tel: 01438 724164

Biggin Hill Car Club with XJ Register of JDC, Peter Adams, Jasmine House, Jasmine Grove, London SE20 8JY Tel: 0181 778 7531

BMW Car Club, PO BOX 328, Andover, Hampshire SP10 1YN Tel: & Fax 01264 337883

BMW Drivers Club, Sue Hicks, Bavaria House, PO Box 8, Dereham, Norfolk NR19 1TF Tel: 01362 694459

Bond Owners Club, Stan Cornock, 42 Beaufort Avenue, Hodge Hill, Birmingham, West Midlands B34 6AE

Borgward Drivers Club, Mr D. C. Farr, 19 Highfield Road, Kettering, Northamptonshire NN15 6HR Tel: 01536 510771

Brabham Register, Ed Walker, The Old Bull, 5 Woodmancote, Dursley, Gloucestershire GL11 4AF Tel: 01453 543243

Bristol Austin Seven Club, 1 Silsbury Hill Cottages, West Kennett, Marlborough, Wiltshire SN8 1QH

Bristol Microcar Club, 123 Queens Road, Bishopsworth, Bristol, Gloucestershire BS13 8QB Tel: 0117 964 2901

Bristol Owners Club, John Emery, Uesutor, Marringdean Road, Billingshurst, Sussex RH14 9HD

British Ambulance Preservation Society, Roger Leonard, 21 Victoria Road, Horley, Surrey RH6 9BN

British Automobile Racing Club, Thruxton Circuit, Andover, Hampshire SP11 8PN Tel: 01264 772607 & 772696/7

British Racing and Sports Car Club, Brands Hatch, Fawkham, Dartford, Kent DA3 8NG

British Saab Enthusiasts, Mr M. Hodges, 75 Upper Road, Poole, Dorset BH12 3EN

British Salmson Owners Club, John Maddison, 86 Broadway North, Walsall, West Midlands WS1 2QF Tel: 01922 29677

Brooklands Society Ltd, Reigate Lodge, Chartway, Reigate, Surrey RG2 0NZ

Brough Superior Club, P. Staughton, Secretary, 4 Summerfields, Northampton, Northants NN4 9YN

BSA Front Wheel Drive Club, Barry Baker, 164 Cottimore Lane, Walton-on-Thames, Surrey KT12 2BL

Buckler Car Register, Stan Hibberd, 52 Greenacres, Woolton Hill, Newbury, Berkshire RG15 9TA Tel: 01635 254162

Bugatti Owners Club Ltd, Sue Ward, Prescott Hill, Gotherington, Cheltenham, Gloucestershire GL52 4RD

Bullnose Morris Club, Richard Harris, PO Box 383, Hove, Sussex BN3 4FX

C A Bedford Owners Club, GW Seller, 7 Grasmere Road, Benfleet, Essex SS7 3HF

Cambridge-Oxford Owners Club, 32 Reservoir Road, Southgate, London N14 4BG

Capri Club International, Field House, Ipsley Church Lane, Redditch, Worcestershire B98 0AJ Tel: 01527 502066

Capri Club International North London Branch, 12 Chalton Road, Edmonton, London N9 8EG Tel: 0181 364 7845/0181 804 6326

Capri Drivers Association, Mrs Moira Farrelly (Secretary), 9 Lyndhurst Road, Coulsdon, Surrey CR5 3HT

Chiltern Vehicle Preservation Group, Chiltern House, Aylesbury, Buckinghamshire HP17 8BY Tel: 01296 651283

Citroen Car Club, P O Box 348, Bromley, Kent BR2 2QT

Citroen Traction Owners Club, Steve Reed,
1 Terwick Cottage, Rogate, Petersfield, Hants GU31 5EG

Clan Owners Club, Chris Clay, 48 Valley Road,
Littleover, Derbyshire DE23 6HS Tel: 01332 767410

Classic and Historic Motor Club Ltd,
Tricia Burridge, The Smithy, High Street, Ston Easton,
Bath, Somerset BA3 4DE

Classic Corvette Club (UK), Ashley Pickering,
The Gables, Christchurch Road, Tring, Hertfordshire
HP23 4EF

Classic Crossbred Club, Alan Easto, 7 Wills Hill,
Stanford Le Hope, Essex SS17 7AY
Tel: 01375 679943

Classic Hearse Register, Tel: 01268 472313

Classic Saloon Car Club, 7 Dunstable Road, Luton,
Bedfordshire LU1 1BB Tel: 01582 31642

Classic Z Register, Lynne Godber, Thistledown,
Old Stockbridge Road, Kentsboro, Wallop, Stockbridge,
Hampshire SO20 8LB Tel: 01264 781979

Club Alfa Romeo 2600/2000 International,
Roger Monk, Knighton, Church Close, West Runton,
Cromer, Norfolk NR27 9QY

Club Alpine Renault UK Ltd, 71 Bedford Avenue,
Barnet, Hertfordshire EN5 2ES

Club Lotus, Lotus Lodge, PO Box 8, Dereham, Norfolk
NR19 1TF Tel: 01362 694459

Club Marcos International, Mrs I. Chivers,
Membership Secretary, 8 Ludmead Road, Corsham,
Wiltshire SN13 9AS Tel: 01249 713769

Club Peugeot UK, Club Regs 504 Cab/Coupe,
Beacon View, Forester Road, Soberton Heath,
Southampton, Hampshire SO32 3QG
Tel: 01329 833029

Club Peugeot UK, (General Secretary), Pole Position,
2 Steeple Heights Drive, Biggin Hill, Westerham,
Kent TN16 3UN

Club Triumph, Derek Pollock, 86 Waggon Road, Hadley
Wood, Hertfordshire EN14 0PP Tel: 0181 440 9000

Club Triumph Eastern, Mr D. A. Davies,
72 Springwater Road, Eastwood, Leigh-on-Sea,
Essex SS9 5BJ

Clyno Club, Swallow Cottage, Langton Farm,
Elmesthorpe, Leicestershire LE9 7SE

Commercial Vehicle and Road Transport Club,
Steven Wimbush, 8 Tachbrook Road, Uxbridge,
Middlesex UB8 2QS

Connaught Register, Duncan Rabagliati, 4 Wool Road,
Wimbledon, London SW20 0HW

Cortina Mk II Register, Mark Blows, 78 Church
Avenue, Broomfield, Chelmsford, Essex CM1 7HA

Cougar Club of America, Barrie S Dixon, 11 Dean
Close, Partington, Greater Manchester M31 4BQ

Crayford Convertible Car Club, 58 Geriant Road,
Downham, Nr Bromley, Kent BR1 5DX
Tel: 0181 461 1805

Crossley Climax Register, Mr G. Harvey
7 Meadow Road, Basingstoke, Hampshire RG21 3LL

Crossley Register, Malcolm Jenner, Willow Cottage,
Lexham Road, Great Dunham, Kings Lynn,
Norfolk PE32 2LS

DAF Owners Club, SK Bidwell (Club Sec), 56 Ridgedale
Road, Bolsover, Chesterfield, Derbyshire S44 6TX

Daimler and Lanchester Owners Club, John Ridley,
Trewyn Manor, Pandy, Abergavenny, Gwent,
Wales NP7 7PG Tel: 01873 890737

De Tomaso Drivers Club, Chris Statham,
2-4 Bank Road, Bredbury, Stockport, Cheshire SK6 1DR
Tel: 0161 430 5052

Delage Section of the VSCC Ltd, Peter Jacobs
(Secretary) Clouds' Reach, The Scop, Almondsbury,
Bristol, Gloucestershire BS3 4DU

Delahaye Club GB, A F Harrison, 34 Marine Parade,
Hythe, Kent CT21 6AN Tel: 01303 261016

Dellow Register, Douglas Temple Design Group,
4 Roumelia Lane, Bournemouth, Dorset BH5 1EU
Tel: 01202 304641

Delorean Owners Club, Linehill House, Sapey Common,
Clifton-upon-Teme, Worcestershire WR6 6EP
Tel: 01886 853294

Diva Register, Steve Pethybridge, 8 Wait End Road,
Waterlooville, Hampshire PO7 7DD Tel: 01705 251485

DKW Owners Club, C P Nixon, Rose Cottage,
Rodford, Westerleigh, Bristol, Gloucestershire BS17

Droop Snoot Group, 41 Horsham Avenue, Finchley,
London N12 9BG Tel: 0181 368 1884

Dunsfold Land Rover Trust, Dunsfold, Surrey GU8
4NP Tel: 01483 200058

Dutton Owners Club, Rob Powell, 20 Burford Road,
Baswich, Stafford, Staffordshire ST17 0BT
Tel: 01785 56835

Early Ford V8 Club, 12 Fairholme Gardens, Cranham,
Upminster, Essex RM14 1HJ Tel: 01708 222729

Elva Owners Club, RA Dunbar, Maple Tree Lodge,
The Hawthorns, Smock Alley, West Alley,
West Chiltington, Sussex RH20 2QX

Enfield & District Veteran Vehicle Trust, Whitewebbs
Museum, Whitewebbs Road, Enfield, Middlesex EN2 9HW
Tel: 0181 367 1898

ERA Club, Guy Spollon, Arden Grange, Tanworth-in-
Arden, Warwickshire B94 5AE

F and FB Victor Owners Club, Wayne Parkhouse,
5 Farnell Road, Staines, Middlesex TW18 4HT

F-Victor Owners Club, Alan Victor Pope,
34 Hawkesbury Drive, Mill Lane, Calcot, Reading,
Berkshire RG3 5ZR Tel: 01635 43532

Facel Vega Owners Club, Roy Scandrett, Windrush,
16 Paddock Gardens, East Grinstead, Sussex RH19 4AE

Fairthorpe Sports Car Club, Tony Hill, 9 Lynhurst
Crescent, Uxbridge, Middlesex UB10 9EF

Ferrari Club of GB, Betty Mathias, 7 Swan Close,
Blake Down, Kidderminster, Worcestershire DY10 3JT
Tel: 01562 700009

Fiat 130 Owners Club, Michael Reid, 28 Warwick
Mansions, Cromwell Crescent, London SW5 9QR
Tel: 0171 373 9740

Fiat Dino Register, Mr Morris, 59 Sandown Park,
Tunbridge Wells, Kent TN2 4RT

Fiat Motor Club (GB), H. A. Collyer, Barnside,
Chilkwell Street, Glastonbury, Somerset BA6 8D
Tel: 01458 31443

Fiat Osca Register, Mr M Elliott, 36 Maypole Drive,
Chigwell, Essex IG7 6DE Tel: 0181 500 7127

Fiat Twin-Cam Register, 3 Anderson Place, Bagshot,
Surrey GU19 5LX

Fire Service Preservation Group, Andrew Scott,
50 Old Slade Lane, Iver, Buckinghamshire SL0 9DR

Five Hundred Owners Club Association, David
Docherty, 'Oakley', 68 Upton Park, Chester,
Cheshire CH2 1DQ Tel: 01244 382789

Ford 105E Owners Club, Sally Harris, 30 Gower Road,
Sedgley, Dudley, West Midlands DY3 3PN
Tel: 01902 671071

Ford Avo Owners Club, D. Hensley, 11 Sycamore Drive,
Patchway, Bristol, Gloucestershire BS12 5DH

Ford Capri Enthusiasts Register, Liz Barnes,
46 Manningtree Road, South Ruislip, Middlesex HA4 7LB
Tel: 0181 842 0102

Ford Corsair Owners Club, Mrs E Checkley,
7 Barnfield, New Malden, Surrey KT3 5RH

Ford Cortina 1600E Enthusiasts Club, D Wright ,
32 St Leonards Avenue, Hove, Sussex BN3 4QL

Ford Cortina 1600E Owners Club, Dave Marston,
23 Cumberland Road, Bilston, West Midlands WV14 6LT
Tel: 01902 405055

Ford Escort 1300E Owners Club, Robert Watt,
65 Lindley Road, Walton-on-Thames, Surrey KT12 3EZ

Ford Executive Owners Register, Jenny Whitehouse,
3 Shanklin Road, Stonehouse, Coventry, Warwickshire
CV3 4EE

Ford Granada MkI Owners Club, Paul Bussey,
Bay Tree House, 15 Thornbera Road, Bishops Stortford,
Hertfordshire CM23 3NJ

Ford GT Owners, c/o Riverside School, Ferry Road,
Hullbridge, Hockley Essex SS5 6ND

Ford MkII Independent O/C, 173 Sparrow Farm Drive,
Feltham, Middlesex TW14 0DG Tel: 0181 384 3559

Ford MkIII Zephyr & Zodiac Owners Club,
John Wilding, 10 Waltondale, Telford, Shropshire
TF7 5NQ Tel: 01952 580746

Ford Mk IV Zephyr & Zodiac Owners Club,
29 Ruskin Way, Worcester Park, Surrey KT4 8LG
Tel: 0181 649 0685

Ford Model 'T' Ford Register of GB, Mrs Julia Armer,
3 Strong Close, Keighley, Yorkshire BD21 4JT
Tel: 01535 607978

Ford RS Owners Club, PO Box 135, Newport, Gwent,
Wales NP6 2YU Tel: 01633 412626

Ford Sidevalve Owners Club, Membership Secretary,
30 Earls Close, Bishopstoke, Eastleigh, Hampshire
SO50 8HY

Frazer-Nash Section of the VSCC, Mrs J. Blake,
Daisy Head Farm, South Street, Caulcott, Bicester,
Oxfordshire OX6 3NE

Friends of The British Commercial Vehicle,
c/o BCVM, King Street, Leyland, Preston, Lancashire
PR5 1LE

Gentry Register, Frank Tuck, 1 Kinross Avenue,
South Ascot, Berkshire SL5 9EP Tel: 01990 24637

Gilbern Owners Club, P. C. Fawkes, 24 Mayfield,
Buckden, Huntingdon, Cambridgeshire PE18 9SZ
Tel: 01480 812066

Ginetta Owners Club, Dave Baker, 24 Wallace Mill Gardens, Mid Calder, Livingstone, West Lothian, Scotland EH53 0BD Tel: 01506 8883129

Gordon Keeble Owners Club, Ann Knott, Westminster Road, Helmdon, Brackley, Northamptonshire NN13 5QB Tel: 01280 702311

Granada Mk II and Mk III Enthusiasts' Club, 10 Alder Grove, Halesowen, West Midlands B62 9TL Tel: 0121 426 2346 (Mobile 0860 423126)

Grand Prix Contact Club, David Hayhoe, 43 New Barn Lane, Bridgeway, Uckfield, East Sussex TN22 5EL Tel: 01825 764918

Gwynne Register, H. K. Good, 9 Lancaster Avenue, Hadley Wood, Barnet, Hertfordshire EN4 0EP

Heinkel Trojan Owners and Enthusiasts Club, Y Luty, Carisbrooke, Wood End Lane, Fillongley, Coventry, Warwickshire CV7 8DF

Hillman Commer Karrier Club, A Freakes, Kingfisher Court, Bridge Road, East Molesey, Surrey KT8 9HL Tel: 0181 941 0604

Historic Commercial Vehicle Society HCVS, Iden Grange, Cranbrook Road, Staplehurst, Kent TN12 0ET

Historic Grand Prix Cars Association, 106 Gifford Street, London N1 0DF Tel: 0171 607 4887

Historic Lotus Register, Nyes Place, Newdigate, Surrey RH5 5BX Tel: 01737 767371/01293 871541

Historic Rally Car Register RAC, Martin Jubb, 38 Longfield Road, Bristol, Gloucestershire BS7 9AG

Historic Sports Car Club, Cold Harbour, Kington Langley, Wiltshire SN15 5LY

Historic Volkswagen Club, 11a Thornbury Lane Church Hill, Redditch, Worcestershire B98 7RP Tel: 01527 591883

Holden UK Register, GRC Hardy, Clun Felin, Woll's Castle, Haverfordwest, Pembrokshire, Dyfed, Wales SA62 5LR

Honda S800 Sports Car Club, Chris Wallwork, 23a High Street, Steeton, Yorkshire BD20 6NT Tel: 01535 653845

Hotchkiss Association GB, Michael Edwards, Wootton Tops, Sandy Lane, Boars Hill, Oxford, Oxfordshire OX1 5HN Tel: 01865 735180

HRG Association, I. J. Dussek, Little Allens Allens Lane, Plaxtol, Sevenoaks, Kent TN15 0QZ

Humber Register, R.N. Arman, Northbrook Cottage, 175 York Road, Broadstone, Dorset BH18 8ES

Imp Club, Michelle Ross, 71 Evesham Road, Stratford-upon-Avon, Warwickshire CV37 9BA Tel: 01789 204778

Invicta Military Vehicle Preservation Society, 58 Ladds Way, Swanley, Kent BR8 8HW Tel: 01322 408738

Isetta Owners Club, 19 Towcester Road, Old Stratford, Milton Keynes, Buckinghamshire MK19 6AH Tel: 01908 569103

Jaguar Car Club, R Pugh, 19 Eldorado Crescent, Cheltenham, Gloucestershire GL50 2PY

Jaguar Drivers Club, JDC Jaguar House, Stuart Street, Luton, Bedfordshire LU1 2SL Tel: 01582 419332

Jaguar Enthusiasts Club, 176 Whittington Way, Pinner, Middlesex HA5 5JY Tel: 0181 866 2073

Jaguar/Daimler Owners Club, 130/132 Bordesley Green, Birmingham, West Midlands B9 4SU

Jensen Owners Club, Caroline Clarke, 45 Station Road, Stoke Mandeville, Buckinghamshire HP22 5UE Tel: 01296 614072

Jensen Owners Club, Brian Morrey, Selwood, Howley, Nr Chard, Somerset Tel: 01460 64165

Jowett Car Club, Ian Preistly, Membership Secretary, 626 Huddersfield Road, Wyke, Bradford, Yorks BD12 8JR

Junior Zagato Register, Kenfield Hall, Petham, Nr Canterbury, Kent CT4 5RN Tel: 01227 700555

Jupiter Owners Auto Club, Steve Keil, 16 Empress Avenue, Woodford Green, Essex IG8 9EA Tel: 0181 505 2215

Karmann Ghia Owners Club, Astrid Kelly (Secretary), 7 Keble Road, Maidenhead, Berkshire SL6 6BB Tel: 01628 39185

Kieft Racing and Sports Car Club, Duncan Rabagliati, 4 Wool Road, Wimbledon, London SW20 0HW

Lagonda Club, Colin Bugler (Hon Secretary), Wintney House, London Road, Hartley Wintney, Hampshire RG27 8RN Tel: & Fax: 01252 845451

Lancia Motor Club, Dave Baker (Secretary), Mount Pleasant, Penrhos, Brymbo, Wrexham, Clwyd, Wales LL11 5LY

Land Rover Register (1947–51), Membership Secretary, High House, Ladbrooke, Leamington Spa, Warwickshire CV33 0BT

Land Rover Series One Club, David Bowyer, East Foldhay, Zeal Monachorum, Crediton, Devon.

Land Rover Series Two Club, PO Box 1609, Yatton, Bristol, Gloucestershire

Landcrab Owners Club International, Bill Frazer, PO Box 218, Cardiff, Wales

Landrover Series 3 Owners Club Ltd, 23 Deidre Avenue, Wickford, Essex SS12 0AX Tel: 01268 560818

Lea Francis Owners Club, R. Sawers, French's, High Street, Long Wittenham, Abingdon, Oxon OX14 4QQ

Les Amis de Panhard et Levassor GB, Denise Polley, 11 Arterial Avenue, Rainham, Essex RM13 9PD

Lincoln-Zephyr Owners Club, Colin Spong, 22 New North Road, Hainault, Ilford, Essex IG6 2XG

London Bus Preservation Trust, Cobham Bus Museum, Redhill Road, Cobham, Surrey KT11 1EF

London Vintage Taxi Association, Steve Dimmock, 51 Ferndale Crescent, Cowley, Uxbridge, UB8 2AY

Lotus Cortina Register, Fernleigh, Hornash Lane, Shadoxhurst, Ashford, Kent TN26 1HX

Lotus Drivers Club, Lee Barton, 15 Pleasant Way, Leamington Spa, Warks CV32 5XA Tel: 01926 313514

Lotus Seven Owners Club, David Miryless 18 St James, Beaminster, Dorset DT8 3PW

Malaysia & Singapore Vintage Car Register, 2 Asimont Lane, Singapore 1130

Manta A Series Register, Mark Kinnon, 112 Northwood Avenue, Purley, Surrey CR8 2EQ

Marcos Owners Club, 62 Culverley Road, Catford, London SE6 2LA Tel: 0181 697 2988

Marendaz Special Car Register, John Shaw, 107 Old Bath Road, Cheltenham, Gloucestershire GL53 7DA Tel: 01242 526310

Marina/Ital Drivers Club, Mr J. G. Lawson, 12 Nithsdale Road, Liverpool, Merseyside L15 5AX

Marlin Owners Club, Mrs J. Cordrey, 14 Farthings Went, Capel St Mary, Ipswich, Suffolk IP9 2UJ

Maserati Club, Michael Miles, The Paddock, Old Salisbury Road, Abbotts Ann, Andover, Hampshire SP11 7N Tel: 01264 710312

Masters Club, Barry Knight, 2 Ranmore Avenue, East Croydon, Surrey CR0 5QA

Matra Enthusiasts Club, MEC, 19 Abbotsbury, Orton Goldhay, Peterborough, Cambridgeshire PE2 5PS Tel: 01733 234555

Mercedes-Benz Club Ltd, P. Bellamy, 75 Theydon Grove, Epping, Essex CM16 4PE Tel: 01992 573304

Messerschmitt Enthusiasts Club, Mrs Brenda Anstey, 10 Litchaton Way, Plymouth, Devon PL7 4RD Tel: 01752 339022

Messerschmitt Owners Club, Mrs Eileen Hallam, Birches, Ashmores Lane, Rusper, Sussex RH12 4PS Tel: 01293 871417

Metropolitan Owners Club, Nick Savage, The Old Pump House, Nutbourne Common, Pulborough, Sussex RH20 2HB Tel: 01798 813713

MG Car Club, 7 Chequer Lane, Ash, Canterbury, Kent CT3 2ET Tel: 01304 240380/01304 813863

MG Octagon Car Club, Unit 19, Hollins Business Centre, Rowley Street, Stafford, Staffordshire ST16 2RH Tel: 01785 251014

MG Owners Club, Octagon House, Swavesey, Cambridgeshire CB4 5QZ Tel: 01954 231125

MG 'Y' Type Register, Mr J. G. Lawson, 12 Nithsdale Road, Liverpool, Merseyside L15 5AX

Midget & Sprite Club, Nigel Williams, 15 Foxcote, Kingswood, Bristol, Gloucestershire BS15 2TX

Military Vehicle Trust, 7 Carter Fold, Mellor, Lancs BB2 7ER Tel: 01254 812894

Mini Cooper Club, Joyce Holman, 1 Weavers Cottages, Church Hill, West Hoathly, Sussex RH19 4PW

Mini Cooper Register, 141 Church Lane, Cheshunt, Hertfordshire EN8 0DX Tel: 01992 627863

Mini Marcos Owners Club, Roger Garland, 28 Meadow Road, Worcester WR3 7PP Tel: 01905 58533

Mini Moke Club, Paul Beard, 13 Ashdene Close, Hartlebury, Worcestershire DY11 7TN

Mini Owners Club, 15 Birchwood Road, Lichfield, Staffordshire WS14 9UN

MKI Consul, Zephyr & Zodiac Club, 180 Gypsy Road, Welling, Kent DA16 1JQ Tel: 0181 301 3709

MkI Cortina Owners Club, R. J. Raisey, 51 Studley Rise, Trowbridge, Wiltshire BA14 0PD

MkII Consul, Zephyr & Zodiac Club, 170 Conisborough Crescent, Catford, London SE6 2SH

MkII Granada Owners Club, 58 Jevington Way, Lee, London SE12 9NQ Tel: 0181 857 4356

Model A Ford Club of Great Britain, Mr S. J. Shepherd, 32 Portland Street, Clifton, Bristol, Gloucestershire BS8 4JB Tel: 0117 973 9355

Morgan Sports Car Club Ltd, Mrs Christine Healey (Registrar), 41 Cordwell Close, Castle Donington, Derby, Derbyshire DE74 2JL

Morgan Three-Wheeler Club Ltd, Membership Secretary Dennis Plater, Holbrooks, Thoby Lane, Mountnessing, Brentwood, Essex CM15 0TA Tel: 01277 352867

Morris 12 Club, D. Hedge, Crossways, Potton Road, Hilton, Huntingdon, Cambridgeshire PE18 9NG

Morris Cowley and Oxford Club, Derek Andrews, 202 Chantry Gardens, Southwick, Trowbridge, Wiltshire BA14 9QX

Morris Marina Owners Club, Nigel Butler, Llys-Aled, 63 Junction Road, Stourbridge, West Midlands DY8 4YJ

Morris Minor Owners Club, Jane White, 127-129 Green Lane, Derby, Derbyshire DE1 1RZ

Morris Register, Greenstones, 205 Main Road, Great Leighs, Chelmsford, Essex CM3 1NS Tel: 01245 361517

Moss Owners Club, David Pegler, Pinewood, Weston Lane, Bath, Somerset BA1 4AG Tel: 01225 331509

Naylor Car Club, John W. Taylor (Secretary), c/o Naylor Brothers Restoration, Airedale Garage, Hollins Hill, Shipley, Yorkshire BD17 7QN

Norfolk Military Vehicle Group, Fakenham Road Stanhoe, King's Lynn, Norfolk PE31 8PX Tel: 01485 518052

North East Club for Pre-War Austins, Tom Gatenby, 9 Townsend Cres, Morpeth, Northumberland NE61 2XW

North London MG Club, 2 Duckett Road, Harringey, London N4 1BN Tel: 0181 366 6655/0181 341 7436

North Thames Military Vehicle Preservation Society, 22 Victoria Avenue, Grays, Essex RM16 2RP

Nova Owners Club, Ray Nicholls, 19 Bute Avenue, Hathershaw, Oldham, Lancashire OL8 2AQ

NSU Owners Club, Rosemarie Crowley, 58 Tadorne Road, Tadworth, Surrey KT20 5TF Tel: 01737 812412

Ogle Register, Chris Gow, 108 Potters Lane, Burgess Hill, Sussex RH15 9JN Tel: 01444 248439

Old Bean Society, P. P. Cole, 165 Denbigh Drive, Hately Heath, West Bromwich, West Midlands B71 2SP

Opel GT UK Owners Club, Dean Hayes, 11 Thrale Way, Parkwood, Rainham, Kent ME8 9LX Tel: 01634 379065

Opel Manta Owners Club, 14 Rockstowes Way, Bristol, Gloucestershire BS10 6JE

Opel Vauxhall Drivers Club, The Old Mill, Dereham, Norfolk NR20 5RT

Panther Car Club, George Newell (Secretary), 91 Fleet Road, Farnborough, Hampshire GU14 9RE Tel: 01252 540217

Pedal Car Collectors Club (P.C.C.C.), c/o A. P. Gayler, 4/4a Chapel Terrace Mews, Kemp Town, Brighton, Sussex BN2 1HU Tel: 01273 601960

Piper (Sports and Racing Car) Club, Clive Davies, Pipers Oak, Lopham Rd, East Harling, Norfolk NR16 2PE Tel: 01953 717813

Porsche Club Great Britain, Robin Walker, c/o Cornbury House, Cotswold Business Village, London Road, Moreton-in-Marsh, Gloucestershire GL56 0JQ Tel: 01608 652911/01296 688760

Post Office Vehicle Club, 7 Bignal Rand Close, Wells, Somerset BA5 2EE

Post-War Thoroughbred Car Club, 87 London Street, Chertsey, Surrey KT16 8AN

Post-Vintage Humber Car Club, 32 Walsh Crescent, New Addington, Croydon, Surrey CR0 0BX Tel: 01689 849851

Potteries Vintage and Classic Car Club, B. Theobald, 78 Reeves Avenue, Cross Heath, Newcastle, Staffordshire ST5 9LA

Pre-1940 Triumph Owners Club, Jon Quiney, 2 Duncroft Close, Reigate, Surrey RH2 9DE

Pre-'67 Ford Owners Club, Mrs A Miller, 100 Main Street, Cairneyhill, Dumfermline, Scotland KY12 8QU

Pre-War Austin Seven Club Ltd, Mr J. Tatum, 90 Dovedale Avenue, Long Eaton, Nottingham NG10 3HU Tel: 0115 972 7626

Pre-'50 American Auto Club, Alan Murphy, 41 Eastham Rake, Wirral, Merseyside L62 9AN Tel: 0151 327 1392

Radford Register, Chris Gow, 108 Potters Lane, Burgess Hill, Sussex RH15 9JN Tel: 01444 248439

Range Rover Register, Chris Tomley, Cwm/Cochen, Bettws, Newtown, Powys, Wales SY16 3LQ

Rapier Register, DCH Williams, Smithy, Tregynon, Newtown, Powys, Wales SY16 3EH Tel: 01686 650396

Rear Engine Renault Club, R. Woodall, 346 Crewe Road, Cresty, Crewe, Cheshire CW2 5AD

Register of Unusual Micro-Cars, Jean Hammond, School House Farm, Hawkenbury, Staplehurst, Kent TN12 0EB

Reliant Owners Club, Graham Close, 19 Smithey Close, High Green, Sheffield, Yorkshire S30 4FQ

Reliant Sabre and Scimitar Owners Club, PO Box 67, Teddington, Middlesex TW11 8QR Tel: 0181 977 6625

Renault Frères, J. G. Kemsley, Yew Tree House, Jubliee Road, Chelsfield, Kent BR6 7QZ

Renault Owners Club, C. Marsden, Chevin House, Main Street, Burley-in-Wharfedale, Ilkley, Yorkshire LS29 7DT Tel: 01943 862700

Riley Motor Club, 37 Gibbon Road, Acton, London W3 7AF Tel: 0181 743 9585

Riley Register, J. A. Clarke, 56 Cheltenham Road, Bishops Cleeve, Cheltenham, Gloucestershire GL52 4LY

Riley RM Club, Mrs Jacque Manders, Y Fachell, Ruthin Road, Gwernymynydd, Mold, Clwyd, Wales CH7 5LQ

Ro80 Club GB, Simon Kremer, Mill Stone Cottage, Woodside Road, Winkfield, Windsor, Berkshire SL4 2DP Tel: 01344 890411

Rochdale Owners Club, Brian Tomlinson, 57 West Avenue, Birmingham, West Midlands B20 2LU

Rolls-Royce Enthusiasts' Club, Peter Baines, The Hunt House, Paulerspury, Northamptonshire NN12 7NA

Ronart Car Club, Simon Sutton (Membership Secretary), Orchard Cottage, Allan Lane, Fritchley, Derbyshire DE56 2FX Tel: 01773 856901

Ronart Drivers Club, Chalk Dell House, Batchworth Hill, London Road, Rickmansworth, Hertfordshire WD3 1JP Tel: 0171 722 1212/01923 779966

Rootes Easidrive Register, M Molley, 35 Glenesk Road, London SE9 1AG

Rover P4 Drivers Guild, 54 Ingaway, Lee Chapel South, Basildon, Essex SS16 5QR Tel: 01268 413395

Rover P5 Owners Club, G. Moorshead, 13 Glen Avenue, Ashford, Middlesex TW15 2JE Tel: 01784 258166

Rover P6 Owners Club, PO Box 11, Heanor, Derbyshire DE75 7YG

Rover SD1 Club, PO Box 12, Owlsmoor, Sandhurst, Berkshire GU47 4WZ Tel: 01344 761791

Rover Sports Register, Cliff Evans, 8 Hilary Close, Great Boughton, Chester, Cheshire CH3 5QP

Saab Enthusiasts Club, PO Box 96, Harrow, Middlesex HA3 7DW Tel: 01249 815792

Saab Owners Club of GB Ltd, Mrs K. E. Piper, 16 Denewood Close, Watford, Hertfordshire WD1 3SZ Tel: 01923 229945

Salmons Tickford Enthusiasts Club, Keith Griggs, 40 Duffins Orchard, Ottershaw, Surrey KT16 0LP

Savage Register, Trevor Smith, Hillcrest, Top Road, Little Cawthorpe, Louth, Lincolnshire LN11 8NB

Scimitar Drivers Club, c/o Mick Frost, Pegasus, Main Road, Woodham Ferrers, Essex CM3 8RN Tel: 01245 320734

Scootacar Register, Stephen Boyd, Pamanste, 18 Holman Close, Aylsham, Norwich, Norfolk NR11 6DD Tel: 01263 733861

Simca Owners Register, David Chapman, 18 Cavendish Gardens, Redhill, Surrey RH1 4AQ

Singer Owners Club, 3 Riverhill, Watton-at-Stone, Hertfordshire SG14 3SD Tel: 01920 830517

Small Ford Club, 115 Woodland Gardens, Isleworth, Middlesex TW7 6LU Tel: 0181 568 3227

Solent Austin Seven Club Ltd, F Claxton, 185 Warsash Road, Warsash, Hampshire SO31 9JE

South Devon Commercial Vehicle Club, Bob Gale, Avonwick Station, Diptford, Totnes, Devon TQ9 7LU Tel: 01364 73130

South Hants Model Auto Club, C. Derbyshire, 21 Aintree Road, Calmore, Southampton, Hants SO40 2TL

South Wales Austin Seven Club, Mr and Mrs J. Neill, 302 Peniel Green Road, Peniel Green, Swansea, Wales SA7 9BW

Spartan Owners Club, Steve Andrews, 28 Ashford Drive, Ravenhead, Nottinghamshire NG15 9DE Tel: 01623 793742

Sporting Escort Owners Club, 26 Huntingdon Crescent, Off Madresfield Drive, Halesowen, West Midlands B63 3DJ

Stag Owners Club, 4 Channel Close, Folkestone, Kent CT19 6QN Tel: 01303 241090/01303 252941

Standard Motor Club, 12 Majors Close, Chedburgh, Bury St Edmunds, Suffolk IP29 4UN Tel: 01284 850896

Star, Starling, Stuart and Briton Register, D. E. A. Evans, New Wood Lodge, 2A Hyperion Rd, Stourton, Stourbridge, West Midlands DY7 6SB

Sunbeam Alpine Owners Club, Pauline Leese, 53 Wood Street, Mow Cop, Stoke-on-Trent, Staffordshire ST7 3PF Tel: 01782 519865

Sunbeam Rapier Owners Club, Peter Meech, 12 Greenacres, Downtown, Salisbury, Wiltshire SP5 3NG Tel: 01725 21140

Sunbeam Talbot Alpine Register, Derek Cook, Memebership Secretary, 47 Crescent Wood Road, Sydenham, London SE26 6SA

Sunbeam Talbot Darracq Register, R. Lawson, West Emlett Cottage, Black Dog, Crediton, Devon EX17 4QB

Sunbeam Tiger Owners Club, Brian Postle, Beechwood, 8 Villa Real Estate, Consett, Co Durham DH8 6BJ Tel: 01207 508296

Surrey Classic Vehicle Club, 55a Ditton Road, Surbiton, Surrey KT6 6RF Tel: 0181 390 3570

Swift Club and Swift Register, John Harrison, 70 Eastwick Drive, Bookham, Leatherhead, Surrey KT23 3NX Tel: 01372 452120

Tame Valley Vintage and Classic Car Club, Mrs S. Ogden, 13 Valley New Road, Royton, Oldham, Lancashire OL2 6BP

Tornado Register, Dave Malins, 48 St Monica's Avenue, Luton, Bedfordshire LU3 1PN Tel: 01582 37641

Toyota Enthusiasts Club, c/o Billy Wells, 28 Park Road, Feltham, Middx TW13 6PW Tel: 0181 898 0740

TR Drivers Club, Bryan Harber, 19 Irene Road, Orpington, Kent BR6 0HA

TR Register, 1B Hawksworth, Southmead Industrial Park, Didcot, Oxfordshire OX10 7HR Tel: 01235 818866

Traction Enthusiasts Club, Preston House Studio, Preston, Canterbury, Kent CT3 1HH

Traction Owners Club, Peter Riggs, 2 Appleby Gardens, Dunstable , Bedfordshire LU6 3DB

Trident Car Club, Ken Morgan, Rose Cottage, 45 Newtown Rd, Verwood, Dorset BH31 6EG Tel: 01202 822697

Triumph 2000/2500/2.5 Register, M. Aldous, 42 Hall Orchards, Middleton, King's Lynn, Norfolk PE32 1RY Tel: 01553 841700

Triumph Dolomite Club, 39 Mill Lane, Upper Arncott, Bicester, Oxfordshire OX6 0PB Tel: 01869 242847

Triumph Mayflower Club, T. Gordon, 12 Manor Close, Hoghton, Preston, Lancashire PR5 0EN

Triumph Razoredge Owners Club, Stewart Langton, 62 Seaward Avenue, Barton-on-Sea, Hants BH25 7HP Tel: 01425 618074

Triumph Roadster Club, Paul Hawkins, 186 Mawnay Road, Romford, Essex RM7 8BU Tel: 01708 760745

Triumph Spitfire Club, Mr Cor Gent, Anemoon 41, 7483 AC Haaksbergen, The Netherlands

Triumph Sporting Owners Club, G. R. King, 16 Windsor Road, Hazel Grove, Stockport, Cheshire SK7 4SW

Triumph Sports Six Club Ltd, 121B St Mary's Road, Market Harborough, Leicestershire LE16 7DT

Trojan Owners Club, Derrick Graham, Troylands, St Johns, Earlswood Common, Redhill, Surrey RH1 6QF Tel: 01737 763643

Turner Register, Dave Scott, 21 Ellsworth Road, High Wycombe, Buckinghamshire HP11 2TU

TVR Car Club, c/o David Gerald, TVR Sports Cars Tel: 01386 793239

UK Buick Club, Alf Gascoine, 47 Higham Road, Woodford Green, Essex IG8 9JN Tel: 0181 505 7347

United States Army Vehicle Club, Dave Boocock, 31 Valley View Close, Bogthorn, Oakworth Rd, Keighley, Yorkshire BD22 7LZ

Vanden Plas Owners Club, Old School House, Sutterton Drove, Amber Hill, Boston, Lincolnshire PE20 3RQ Tel: 01205 290436

Vanguard 1&2 Owners Club, R. Jones, The Villa, The Down, Alviston, Gloucestershire BS12 2TQ Tel: 01454 419232**Vauxhall Cavalier Convertible Club**, Ron Goddard, 47 Brooklands Close, Luton, Bedfordshire LU4 9EH

Vauxhall Owners Club, Roy Childers (Membership Secretary), 31 Greenbanks, Melbourn, Nr Royston, Cambridgeshire SG8 6AS

Vauxhall PA/PB/PC/E Owners Club, G. Lonsdale, 77 Pilling Lane, Preesall, Lancashire FY6 0HB Tel: 01253 810866

Vauxhall VX4/90 Drivers Club, c/o 43 Stroudwater Pk, Weybridge, Surrey KT13 0DT

Vectis Historic Vehicle Club, 10 Paddock Drive, Bembridge, Isle of Wight PO35 5TL

Victor 101 FC (1964-1967), 12 Cliff Crescent, Ellerdine, Telford, Shropshire TF6 6QS

Vintage Austin Register, Frank Smith, The Briars, Four Lane Ends, Oakerthorpe, Alfreton, Derbyshire DE5 7LN Tel: 0773 831646

Vintage Sports Car Club Ltd, The Secretary, 121 Russell Road, Newbury, Berkshire RG14 5JX Tel: 01635 44411

Viva Owners Club, Adrian Miller, The Thatches, Snetterton North End, Snetterton, Norwich, Norfolk NR16 2LD

Volkswagen '50-67' Transporter Club, Peter Nicholson, 11 Lowton Road, Lytham St Annes, Lancashire FY8 3JD Tel: 01253 720023

Volkswagen Cabriolet Owners Club (GB), Emma Palfreyman (Sec), Dishley Mill, Derby Road, Loughborough, Leicestershire LE11 0SF

Volkswagen Owners Caravan Club (GB), Mrs Shirley Oxley, 18 Willow Walk, Hockley, Essex SS5 5DQ

Volkswagen Owners Club (GB), PO Box 7, Burntwood, Walsall, West Midlands WS7 8SB

Volkswagen Split Screen Van Club, Brian Hobson, 12 Kirkfield Crescent, Thorner, Leeds, Yorks LS14 3EN

Volvo Enthusiasts Club, Kevin Price, 4 Goonbell, St Agnes, Cornwall TR5 0PH

Volvo Owners Club, North View, Broadmoor Road, Carbrooke, Thetford, Norfolk IP25 6SZ Tel: 01953 885591

Vulcan Register, D Hales, The Hedgerows, Sutton St Nicholas, Herefordshire HR1 3BU Tel: 01432 880726

VW Type 3 and 4 Club, Jane Terry, Pear Tree Bungalow, Exted, Elham, Canterbury, Kent CT4 6YG

Wanderers (Pre-War Austin Sevens), D. Tedham, Newhouse Farm, Baveney Wood, Cleobury, Mortimer, Kidderminster, Worcestershire DY14 8JB

Wartburg Owners Club, Bernard Trevena, 55 Spiceall Estate, Compton, Guildford, Surrey GU3 1 Tel: 01483 810493

Wolseley 6/80 and Morris Oxford Club, John Billinger, 67 Fleetgate, Barton-on-Humber, Lincolnshire DN18 5QD Tel: 01652 635138

Wolseley Hornet Special Club, Kylemor, Crown Gardens, Fleet, Hampshire GU13 9PD Tel: 01252 622411

Wolseley Register, M. Stanley (Chairman), 1 Flashgate, Higher Ramsgreave Road, Ramsgreave, Nr Blackburn, Lancashire BB1 9DH

X/19 Owners Club, Sally Shearman, 86 Mill Lane, Dorridge, Solihull, West Midlands B93 8NU

XR Owners Club, Paul Townend, 50 Wood Street, Castleford, Yorkshire WF10 1LJ

XR Owners Club, 20a Swithland Lane, Rothley, Leicestershire LE7 7SE

Yankee Jeep Club, 8 Chew Brook Drive, Greenfield, Saddleworth, Lancashire OL3 7PD

Yorkshire Thoroughbred Car Club, Bob Whalley, 31 Greenside, Walton, Wakefield, Yorkshire WF2 6NN

Zephyr and Zodiac MkIV Owners Club, Richard Cordle, 29 Ruskin Drive, Worcester Park, Surrey KT4 8LG Tel: 0181 330 2159

DIRECTORY OF AUCTIONEERS

Academy Auctioneers & Valuers, Northcote House, Northcote Avenue, Ealing, London W5 3UR Tel: 0181 579 7466

Aylesbury Motor Auctions, Pembroke Road, Stocklake, Aylesbury, Bucks HP20 1DB Tel: 01296 339150

C. Boisgirard, 2 Rue de Provence, Paris, France 75009 Tel: 00 33 147708136

Bonhams, 65-69 Lots Road, Chelsea, London SW10 0RN Tel: 0171 393 3900

British Car Auctions Ltd, Classic & Historic Automobile Division, Auction Centre, Blackbushe Airport, Blackwater, Camberley, Surrey GU17 9LG Tel: 01252 878555

Brooks (Auctioneers), 81 Westside, London SW4 9AY Tel: 0171 228 8000

Carey, Mervyn, Twysden Cottage, Benenden, Cranbrook, Kent TN17 4LD Tel: 01580 240283

Central Motor Auctions Plc, Central House, Pontefract Road, Rothwell, Leeds, Yorkshire LS26 0JE Tel: 0113 282 0707

Chapman, Moore & Mugford, 9 High Street, Shaftesbury, Dorset SP7 8JB Tel: 01747 852400

H. C. Chapman & Son, The Auction Mart, North Street, Scarborough, Yorkshire YO11 1DL Tel: 01723 372424

Christie Manson & Wood International Inc., 502 Park Avenue, (including Christie's East), New York, NY 10022 USA Tel: (212) 546 1000

Christie Manson & Wood Ltd, 8 King Street, St James's, London SW1Y 6QT Tel: 0171 839 9060

Christie's (Monaco), S.A.M., Park Palace, Monte Carlo 98000 Tel: 00 337 9325 1933

Christie's Pty Ltd, 1 Darling Street, South Yarra, Melbourne, Victoria, Australia 3141 Tel: 010 613 820 4311

Christie's South Kensington Ltd, 85 Old Brompton Road, London SW7 3LD Tel: 0171 581 7611

Coys of Kensington, 2/4 Queen's Gate Mews, London SW7 5QJ Tel: 0171 584 7444

Dickinson Davy and Markham, Wrawby Street, Brigg, Humberside DN20 8JJ Tel: 01652 653666

David Dockree, Cheadle Hulme Business Centre, Clemence House, Mellor Road, Cheadle Hulme, Cheshire SK7 1BD Tel: 0161 485 1258

Dreweatt Neate Holloways, 49 Parsons Street, Banbury, Oxon OX16 8PF Tel: 01295 253197

Evans & Partridge, Agriculture House, High Street, Stockbridge, Hampshire SO20 6HF Tel: 01264 810702

Thomas Wm Gaze & Son, 10 Market Hill, Diss, Norfolk IP22 3JZ Tel: 01379 651931

Greens (UK) Ltd, Worcestershire WR14 2AY Tel: 01684 575902

H & H Classic Auctions Ltd, Whitegate Farm, Hatton Lane, Hatton, Warrington, Cheshire WA4 4BZ Tel: 01925 730630

Halls Fine Art Auctions, Welsh Bridge, Shrewsbury, Shropshire SY3 8LA Tel: 01743 231212

Hamptons Antique & Fine Art Auctioneers, 93 High Street, Godalming, Surrey GU7 1AL Tel: 01483 423567

Andrew Hartley, Victoria Hall Salerooms, Little Lane, Ilkley, Yorkshire LS29 8EA Tel: 01943 816363

Kidson Trigg, Estate Office, Friars Farm, Sevenhampton, Highworth, Swindon, Wiltshire SN6 7PZ Tel: 01793 861000

Kruse International, PO Box 190, 5400 County Road 11A, Auburn, Indiana, 46706 USA Tel: 219 925 5600

Lambert & Foster, 77 Commercial Rd, Paddock Wood, Kent TN12 6DR Tel: 01892 832325

Lawrences Auctioneers, Norfolk House, 80 High Street, Bletchingley, Surrey RH1 4PA Tel: 01883 743323

Thomas Mawer & Son, The Lincoln Saleroom, 63 Monks Road, Lincoln, Lincolnshire LN2 5HP Tel: 01522 524984

Morphets of Harrogate, 6 Albert Street, Harrogate, Yorkshire HG1 1JL Tel: 01423 530030

Neales, 192-194 Mansfield Road, Nottingham, Nottinghamshire NG1 3HU Tel: 0115 962 4141

John Nicholson, The Auction Rooms, Longfield, Midhurst Road, Fernhurst, Surrey GU27 3HA Tel: 01428 653727

Onslow's, The Depot, 2 Michael Road, London SW6 2AD Tel: 0171 371 0505

Palm Springs Exotic Car Auctions, 602 East Sunny Dunes Road Palm Springs, California, 92264 USA Tel: 760 320 3290

Palmer Snell, 65 Cheap Street, Sherborne, Dorset DT9 3BA Tel: 01935 812218

Parkes Auctions Ltd, 2/4 Station Road, Swavesey, Cambridgeshire CB4 5QJ Tel: 01954 232332

J. R. Parkinson Son & Hamer Auctions, The Auction Rooms, Rochdale Road (Kershaw Street), Bury, Lancashire BL9 7HH Tel: 0161 761 1612/7372

Phillips, Blenstock House, 101 New Bond Street, London W1Y 0AS Tel: 0171 629 6602

Phillips, 20 The Square, Retford, Nottinghamshire DN22 6BX Tel: 01777 708633

Phillips Scotland, 207 Bath Street, Glasgow, Scotland G2 4HD Tel: 0141 221 8377

Rogers Jones & Co, The Saleroom, 33 Abergele Road, Colwyn Bay, Wales LL29 7RU Tel: 01492 532176

Martyn Rowe, The Truro Auction Centre, Calenick Street, Truro, Cornwall TR1 2SG Tel: 01892 260020

RTS Auctions Ltd, 35 Primula Drive, Eaton, Norwich, Norfolk NR4 7LZ Tel: 01603 505718

Sotheby's, 34-35 New Bond St, London W1A 2AA Tel: 0171 293 5000

Sotheby's, 1334 York Avenue, New York, NY 10021 USA Tel: 212 606 7000

Sotheby's, B.P. 45, Le Sporting d'Hiver, Place du Casino, Monaco/Cedex MC 98001 Tel: 0101 3393 30 88 80

Sotheby's Sussex, Summers Place, Billingshurst, Sussex RH14 9AD Tel: 01403 833500

Sotheby's Zurich, Bleicherweg 20, Zurich, Switzerland CH-8022 Tel: 41 (1) 202 0011

Specialised Postcard Auctions, 25 Gloucester Street, Cirencester, Gloucestershire GL7 2DJ Tel: 01285 659057

G. E. Sworder & Sons, 14 Cambridge Road, Stansted Mountfitchet, Essex CM24 8BZ Tel: 01279 817778

Thimbleby & Shorland, 31 Great Knollys St, Reading, Berkshire RG1 7HU Tel: 01734 508611

Walker, Barnett & Hill, 3/5 Waterloo Road Salerooms, Clarence Street, Wolverhampton, West Midlands WV1 4JE Tel: 01902 773531

Wellers Auctioneers, The Saleroom, Moorfield Road, Slyfield Green, Guildford, Surrey GU1 1SG Tel: 01483 447447

Welsh Bridge Salerooms, Welsh Bridge, Shrewsbury, Shropshire SY3 8LH Tel: 01743 231212

Wintertons Ltd, Lichfield Auction Centre, Wood End Lane, Fradley, Lichfield, Staffordshire WS13 8NF Tel: 01543 263256

World Classic Auction & Exposition Co, 3600 Blackhawk Plaza Circle, Danville, California 94506, USA

DIRECTORY OF MUSEUMS

BEDFORDSHIRE

Shuttleworth Collection,
Old Warden Aerodrome,
Nr Biggleswade SG18 9EP
Tel: 01767 627288

BUCKINGHAMSHIRE

West Wycombe Motor Museum,
Cockshoot Farm, Chorley Road,
High Wycombe, West Wycombe HP14 3AR

CHESHIRE

Mouldsworth Motor Museum,
Smithy Lane, Mouldsworth,
Chester CH3 8AR
Tel: 01928 731781

CO. DURHAM

North of England Open Air Museum,
Beamish, Stanley DH9 0RG

CORNWALL

Automobilia Motor Museum,
The Old Mill, Terras Road,
St Stephen,
St Austell PL26 7RX

CUMBRIA

Cars of the Stars Motor Museum,
Standish Street, Keswick CA12 5LS
Tel: 01768 73757

Lakeland Motor Museum,
Holker Hall, Cark-in-Cartmel,
Nr Grange-over-Sands LA11 7SS
Tel: 01448 53314

DERBYSHIRE

The Donnington Collection,
Donnington Park,
Castle Donnington DE74 2RP
Tel: 01332 810048

DEVON

Totnes Motor Museum,
Steamer Quay, Totnes TT9 5AL
Tel: 01803 862777

ESSEX

Ford Historic Car Collection,
Ford Motor Co, Eagle Way,
Brentwood CM13 3BW

GLOUCESTERSHIRE

Bristol Industrial Museum,
Princes Wharf, City Docks,
Bristol BS1 4RN
Tel: 0117 925 1470

The Bugatti Trust, Prescott Hill,
Gotherington, Cheltenham GL52 4RD
Tel: 01242 677201

Cotswold Motor Museum,
Sherbourne Street,
Bourton-on-the-Water,
Nr Cheltenham GL54 2BY
Tel: 01451 821255

GREATER MANCHESTER

Manchester Museum of Transport,
Boyle Street M8 8UW

HAMPSHIRE

Gangbridge Collection,
Gangbridge House, St Mary Bourne,
Andover SP11 6EP

National Motor Museum,
Brockenhurst, Beaulieu SO42 7ZN
Tel: 01590 612123/612345

HUMBERSIDE

Bradford Industrial Museum,
Moorside Mills, Moorside Road,
Bradford BD2 3HP
Tel: 01274 631756

Hull Transport Museum,
36 High Street, Hull HU1 1NQ

Museum of Army Transport,
Flemingate, Beverley HU17 0NG
Tel: 01482 860445

Peter Black Collection,
Lawkholme Lane, Keighley BD21 3BB

Sandtoft Transport Centre,
Sandtoft, Nr Doncaster DN8 5SX

NORTHERN IRELAND

Ulster Folk and Transport Museum,
Cultra Manor, Holywood, Co. Down
Tel: 01232 428428

SOUTHERN IRELAND

Kilgarven Motor Museum,
Kilgarven, Co. Kerry
Tel: 00 353 64 85346

National Museum of Irish Transport,
Scotts Garden, Killarney, Co. Kerry

ISLE OF MAN

Manx Motor Museum,
Crosby
Tel: 01624 851236

Port Erin Motor Museum,
High Street, Port Erin
Tel: 01624 832964

JERSEY

Jersey Motor Museum,
St Peter's Village

KENT

Dover Transport Museum,
Old Park, Whitfield,
Dover CT16 2HL

**Historic Vehicles Collection of
C. M. Booth,**
Falstaff Antiques, 63-67 High Street,
Rolvenden TN17 4LP
Tel: 01580 241234

The Motor Museum,
Dargate, Nr Faversham ME13 9EP

Ramsgate Motor Museum,
West Cliff Hall, Ramsgate CT11 9JX
Tel: 01843 581948

LANCASHIRE

British Commercial Vehicles Museum,
King Street, Leyland, Preston PR5 1LE
Tel: 01772 451011

Bury Transport Museum,
Castlecroft Road, off Bolton Street, Bury

Tameside Transport Collection,
Warlow Brook, Friezland Lane, Greenfield,
Oldham OL3 7EU

LONDON

Science Museum,
Exhibition Road, South Kensington SW7 2DD
Tel: 0171 589 3456

MIDDLESEX

British Motor Industry,
Heritage Trust, Syon Park, Brentford

Enfield & District Veteran Vehicle Trust,
Whitewebbs Museum, Whitewebbs Road,
Enfield EN2 9HW
Tel: 0181 367 1898

NORFOLK

Caister Castle Car Collection,
Caister-on-Sea, Nr Great Yarmouth

NOTTINGHAMSHIRE

Nottingham Industrial Museum,
Courtyard Buildings, Wallaton Park

SCOTLAND

Doune Motor Museum,
Carse of Cambus, Doune, Perthshire FK16 6HG

Grampian Transport Museum,
Main Street, Alford, Aberdeen AB33 8AD
Tel: 019755 62292

Highland Motor Heritage,
Bankford, Perthshire

Melrose Motor Museum,
Annay Road, Melrose TD6 9LW
Tel: 01896 822 2624

Moray Motor Museum,
Bridge Street, Elgin IV30 2DE
Tel: 01343 544933

Museum of Transport,
Kelvin Hall, 1 Bunhouse Road,
Glasgow G3 8DP
Tel: 0141 357 3929

Myreton Motor Museum,
Aberlady, Longniddry,
East Lothian EH32 0PZ
Tel: 018757 288

Royal Museum of Scotland,
Chambers Street, Edinburgh EH1 1JF
Tel: 0131 225 7534

SHROPSHIRE

Midland Motor Museum,
Stanmore Hall, Stourbridge Road,
Bridgnorth WV15 6DT
Tel: 01746 762992

SOMERSET

Haynes Sparkford Motor Museum,
Sparkford, Yeovil BA22 7LH
Tel: 01963 440804

SURREY

Brooklands Museum,
The Clubhouse, Brooklands Road,
Weybridge KT13 0QN
Tel: 01932 857381

Dunsfold Land Rover Museum,
Dunsfold GU8 4NP Tel: 01483 200567

SUSSEX

Bentley Motor Museum,
Bentley Wild Fowl Trust, Harvey's Lane,
Ringmer, Lewes BN8 5AF

Foulkes-Halbard of Filching,
Filching Manor, Filching, Wannock,
Polegate BN26 5QA
Tel: 01323 487838

TYNE & WEAR

Newburn Hall Motor Museum,
35 Townfield Garden, Newburn NE15 8PY

USA

Behring Automotive Museum,
3700 Blackhawk Plaza Circle, Danville,
California CA 94506
Tel: (510) 736 2280

WALES

Conway Valley Railway Museum Ltd,
Ffordd Hen Eglwys, Betws-y-Coed,
Gwynedd LL24 0AL
Tel: 01690 710568

WARWICKSHIRE

Heritage Motor Centre,
Banbury Road,
Gaydon CV35 0YT
Tel: 01926 645040

Museum of British Road Transport,
St. Agnes Lane, Hales Street,
Coventry CV1 1PN
Tel: 01203 832425

WEST MIDLANDS

Birmingham Museum of Science & Industry,
136 Newhall Street,
Birmingham B3 1RZ
Tel: 0121 235 1651

Black Country Museum,
Tipton Road,
Dudley DY1 4SQ

WILTSHIRE

Science Museum,
Red Barn Gate, Wroughton,
Swindon SN4 9NS
Tel: 01793 814466

YORKSHIRE

Automobilia Transport Museum,
Huddersfield
Tel: 01484 559086

INDEX TO ADVERTISERS

BIBLIOGRAPHY

Baldwin, Nick; Georgano, G. N.; Sedgwick, Michael; and Laban, Brian; The World Guide to Automobiles, Guild Publishing, London, 1987.

Colin Chapman Lotus Engineering, Osprey, 1993.

Flammang, James M; Standard Catalog of Imported Cars, Krause Publications Inc, 1992.

Georgano, G. N.; ed: Encyclopedia of Sports Cars, Bison Books, 1985.

Georgano, Nick; Military Vehicles of World War II, Osprey 1994.

Harding, Anthony; Allport, Warren; Hodges, David; Davenport, John; The Guinness Book of the Car, Guinness Superlatives Ltd, 1987.

Hay, Michael; Bentley Factory Cars, Osprey, 1993.

Hough, Richard; A History of the World's Sports Cars, Allen & Unwin, 1961.

Isaac, Rowan; Morgan, Osprey, 1994.

McComb, F. Wilson; MG by McComb, Osprey, 1978.

Nye, Doug; Autocourse History of the Grand Prix Car 1966–1991, Hazleton Publishing, 1992.

Posthumus, Cyril, and Hodges, David; Classic Sportscars, Ivy Leaf, 1991.

Robson, Graham; Classic and Sportscar A–Z of Cars of the 1970s, Bay View Books, 1990.

Sedgwick, Michael; Gillies, Mark; Classic and Sportscar A–Z of Cars of the 1930s, Bay View Books, 1989.

Sedgwick, Michael, Gillies, Mark; Classic and Sportscar A–Z of Cars 1945–70, Bay View Books, 1990.

Sieff, Theo; Mercedes Benz, Gallery Books, 1989.

Vanderveen, Bart; Historic Military Vehicles Directory, After the Battle Publications, 1989.

Willson, Quentin; Selby, David; The Ultimate Classic Car Book, Dorling Kindersley, 1995.

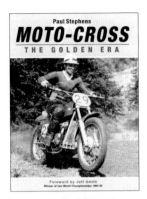
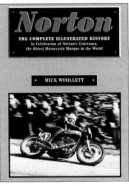
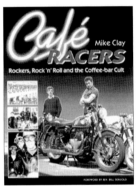
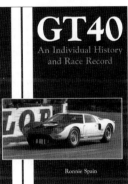

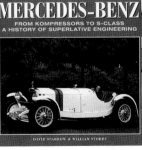

INDEX

Italic page numbers denote colour pages; **bold** numbers refer to information and pointer boxes